FIRST EDITION

INTRODUCTION TO VIBRATION IN ENGINEERING

BY SUNG W. LEE AND NORMAN M. WERELEY
UNIVERSITY OF MARYLAND

Bassim Hamadeh, CEO and Publisher
Kassie Graves, Director of Acquisitions
Jamie Giganti, Senior Managing Editor
Miguel Macias, Senior Graphic Designer
Amy Stone, Field Acquisitions Editor
Sean Adams, Project Editor
Luiz Ferreira, Senior Licensing Specialist
Allie Kiekhofer, Associate Editor

Printed in the United States of America

ISBN: 978-1-63487-994-1 (pbk) / 978-1-63487-995-8 (br)

TABLE OF CONTENTS

CHAPTER 8

FINITE ELEMENT MODELING 151

APPENDICES 189

PREFACE

This book is written as a textbook for undergraduate and first-year graduate students who are interested primarily in aerospace engineering. We have had the privilege of teaching a course in aerospace vibration, including aeroelasticity, for a number of years. The challenge in developing a course of this type is that many of the existing textbooks focus on vibrations from a perspective different from that of an aerospace engineer.

The challenges faced by an aerospace engineer in studying vibrations are that vibrations are often caused by aerodynamic or motion-dependent forces. In addition, the aerospace system or structure undergoing vibration can be complex, with distributed mass and stiffness. For example, a wing or fuselage structure contains a stressed skin surrounding a multitude of spars and ribs that seem to defy simple analyses. Yet, the physical insights that are developed from a careful study of a single-degree-of-freedom system described by a simple, ordinary differential equation—that is, a mass and spring and possibly a damper—are profound, and in limited cases, can describe the bending vibration of such a wing. For systems with multi-degrees of freedom, the notion of a mode as a single-degree-of-freedom system described by an ordinary differential equation is manifested in the concept of the normal mode equations.

Therefore, a key objective of this book is to develop a solid foundation and understanding of single-degree-of-freedom systems that can be used as building blocks to tackle more difficult and general multi-degree-of-freedom systems. A second goal of this book is to introduce the Lagrange equation approach, which can be used to construct equations of motion for complex systems. Subsequently, simple models with two degrees of freedom are used to discuss the subject of dynamic instability, which can occur for such systems as a slender body under a follower force or an aircraft wing in flight. Interactions between the flexible structure and the follower force, including aerodynamic loads and inertia, can lead to dynamic instabilities. Another key goal of this book is to develop and illustrate the tools by which a structural body can be transformed via the finite element method into an equation of motion of finite degrees of freedom. This is done by using a slender body undergoing longitudinal, torsional, or bending motions as examples.

But perhaps the most important purpose of this book is to provide an approachable textbook for the student. For each topic covered, concepts are illustrated through examples and short explanations. Moreover, the goal is to show how to compute solutions, whether analytical or numerical, and to illustrate how the vibrations of complex aerospace structural vibrations can be reduced in complexity using a set of tools that are easily programmed in software such as MATLAB. Ultimately, the aerospace engineer seeks to develop analytical models, compute results, make assessments, and then decide what should be done to improve the performance of the aerospace structure. Therefore, the focus is on practical application of techniques, with the goal of computing solutions to enable the aerospace engineering design iteration.

The material in this book serves as the textbook for our senior-level one-semester class in Aerospace Vibrations. We have concurrently taught both a regular and an honors version of the class based on these materials each year. Some of the advanced topics can be easily omitted to slow the pace and pressure of the class.

As with any project of this kind, many colleagues and students have contributed to the overall content. We thank all of our students who have taken the class, our teaching assistants, and our graduate students and postdoctoral staff, all of whom have contributed to the various aspects of this book. In particular, we thank Dr. Soonwook Kwon, who provided tremendous help in editing the manuscript for this book.

Prof. Sung W. Lee
Prof. Norman M. Wereley
Department of Aerospace Engineering
University of Maryland
College Park, Maryland

1 DYNAMIC RESPONSE OF SDOF SYSTEMS

Many physical systems undergoing dynamic motion can be modeled as a single-degree-of-freedom (SDOF) system with a mass, a spring, and a damper. A degree of freedom (DOF) is a linear displacement or an angular displacement that describes the motion of a system. Once a physical system is modeled as a collection of a mass, a spring, and a damper, one can construct an equation of motion via Newton's second law of motion or an energy approach. The equation motion appears as an ordinary differential equation (ODE) to which one can apply mathematical techniques to determine the system response.

In this chapter, we will construct an equation of motion for SDOF systems by applying Newton's second law of motion. We will then consider "free" vibration, in which a system undergoes vibrational motion with no (or free of) externally applied load. The free vibration starts with the "initial conditions" in terms of a displacement and a velocity specified at the start of the motion. We will find that free vibration occurs at a frequency and amplitude determined by the system parameters (such as mass, spring constant, and damping constant) and the initial conditions. The discussion on free vibration will then be followed by the study of forced vibration under externally applied loads such as step function load or impulse. Subsequently, we will introduce a numerical method that can be used for numerical integration of equation of motion in time to determine the response of SDOF systems subjected to any types of applied loads. The topics to be covered in this chapter are summarized as follows:

1.1 Equation of motion
1.2 Free vibration of undamped SDOF systems
1.3 Free vibration of damped SDOF systems
1.4 Forced vibration: step function load and impulse
1.5 Numerical methods to determine system response

In this chapter and the following chapters, we will adopt both the SI system of units and the English engineering system of units still used in the United States. The basic units in the SI system relevant to dynamics are kilogram (*kg*) for mass, meter (*m*) for length and second (sec or s) for time while the basic units in the English engineering system are *slug* for mass, foot (*ft*) for length and second (sec or s) for time. In the SI system a force of newton (*N*) is defined as $1\ \mathrm{N} = 1\ kg \times 1\ m/\sec^2$. In the English engineering system a force of pound (*lb*) is defined as $1\ lb = 1\ slug \times 1\ ft/\sec^2$.

1.1 Equation of Motion

The equation of motion for a SDOF system with a mass, a spring, and a dashpot damper can be derived using Newton's second law.

Example 1.1.1 Spring-mass-damper system

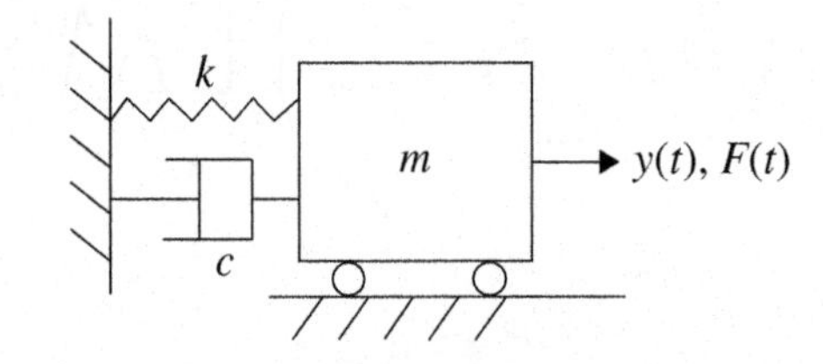

Figure 1.1 Mass-spring-dashpot damper system.

In Figure 1.1, concentrated mass m, spring constant k, and damping constant c represent the effective mass, stiffness, and energy-dissipating properties of the system, while y is the displacement or DOF or the system, and F is the applied load. Velocity and acceleration of the system are expressed as follows:

$$\dot{y} = \frac{dy}{dt}\text{: velocity,} \qquad \ddot{y} = \frac{d^2y}{dt^2}\text{: acceleration}$$

To apply Newton's second law, we isolate the mass and draw a free-body diagram (FBD) as shown below.

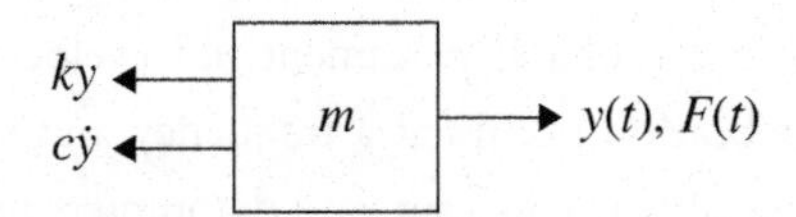

Figure 1.2 Free-body diagram.

In the FBD, ky is the restoring spring force, and $c\dot{y}$ is the restoring damping force. According to Newton's second law,

$$m\ddot{y} = F - ky - c\dot{y}$$

or

$$m\ddot{y} + c\dot{y} + ky = F \tag{1.1.1}$$

Example 1.1.2 Effect of gravity

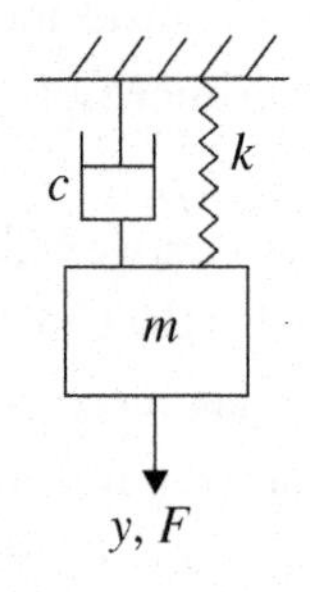

Figure 1.3 SDOF system under gravity effect.

Equation of motion is

$$m\ddot{y} + c\dot{y} + ky = mg + F \tag{1.1.2}$$

where g is the gravity constant and y is the displacement measured from the original length of the spring. For a mass at static equilibrium under gravity,

$$ky_s = mg \tag{1.1.3}$$

Displacement y can be expressed as

$$y = y_s + \hat{y} \tag{1.1.4}$$

where y_s: static displacement measured from the original length of the spring
$\hat{y}$: displacement measured from the static equilibrium position

Placing equation (1.1.4) into equation (1.1.2),

$$m(\ddot{y}_s + \ddot{\hat{y}}) + c(\dot{y}_s + \dot{\hat{y}}) + k(y_s + \hat{y}) = mg + F \tag{1.1.5}$$

Using equation (1.1.3) and noting that $\ddot{y}_s = \dot{y}_s = 0$

$$m\ddot{\hat{y}} + c\dot{\hat{y}} + k\hat{y} = F \tag{1.1.6}$$

Accordingly, when the displacement is measured from the static equilibrium position, the gravity term disappears from the equation of motion.

Example 1.1.3 Consider an instrument package of mass m installed in the nose cone of a rocket with a cushion against vibration. The cushion is represented by a spring k and a damper c. The rocket is fired vertically from rest with a given acceleration $\ddot{d}$. For this case, one can use a model of a SDOF system with a moving base as shown in Figure 1.4.

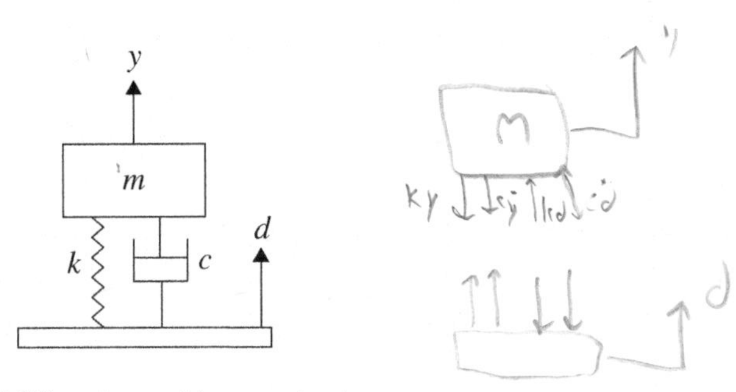

Figure 1.4 SDOF system with a moving base.

Isolating the mass (instrument) to draw a free-body diagram, taking into account the spring forces and damping forces acting on the mass, and applying Newton's second law,

$$m\ddot{y} = -ky + kd - c\dot{y} + c\dot{d} = -k(y - d) - c(\dot{y} - \dot{d}) \tag{1.1.7}$$

Introducing $y_R = y - d$,

$$m(\ddot{y}_R + \ddot{d}) = -ky_R - c\dot{y}_R \tag{1.1.8}$$

$$m\ddot{y}_R + c\dot{y}_R + ky_R = -m\ddot{d} \tag{1.1.9}$$

Equation (1.1.9) represents a SDOF system with displacement y_R under applied load $F = -m\ddot{d}$ in which the bottom end of the spring is fixed to the base.

1.2 Free Vibration of Undamped SDOF Systems

When a system vibrates with no external force (F = 0), the system is then said to undergo **free vibration.** For free vibration, the system starts the motion with given initial displacement and initial velocity, called **initial conditions.**

Let's consider free vibration of an undamped ($c = 0$) system.

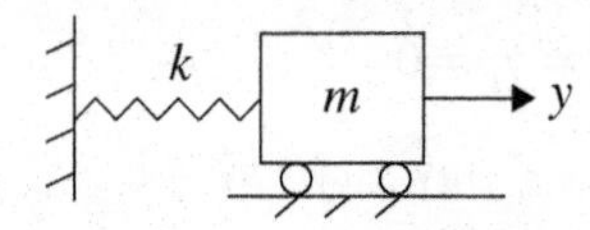

Figure 1.5 SDOF system with no damping.

Equation of motion: $m\ddot{y} + ky = 0$ (1.2.1)

Initial conditions:

initial displacement: $y(0) = y_0$

initial velocity: $\dot{y}(0) = \dot{y}_0$

Note:

1) y_0 and $\dot{y}_0$ represent given values.
2) The initial displacement corresponds to the initial strain energy stored in the spring $\left(= \frac{1}{2}ky_0^2\right)$.
3) The initial velocity corresponds to the initial kinetic energy of the mass $\left(= \frac{1}{2}m\dot{y}_0^2\right)$.

With no damping, total energy (= kinetic energy + strain energy) is conserved during free vibration. There is exchange of energy between the kinetic energy and the strain energy during vibration.

Equation (1.2.1) is a second-order (in time), homogeneous ordinary differential equation (ODE) with a solution of the following form:

$$y = Ae^{pt} \tag{1.2.2}$$

Placing equation (1.2.2) to equation (1.2.1),

$$(mp^2 + k)Ae^{pt} = 0$$

$\omega_d = \omega_n\sqrt{1-\xi}$

For nontrivial y (i.e., nonzero A),

$$mp^2 + k = 0 \tag{1.2.3}$$

Introducing

$$\omega_n = \sqrt{\frac{k}{m}} \tag{1.2.4}$$

Equation (1.2.3) can be expressed as

$$p^2 + \omega_n^2 = 0 \tag{1.2.5}$$

From equation (1.2.5),

$$p = \pm i\omega_n \rightarrow p_1 = i\omega_n \text{ and } p_2 = -i\omega_n \tag{1.2.6}$$

The general solution to equation (1.2.1) is then expressed as a linear combination of the two solutions corresponding to p_1 and p_2 in equation (1.2.6) as follows:

$$y = A_1 e^{p_1 t} + A_2 e^{p_2 t} = A_1 e^{i\omega_n t} + A_2 e^{-i\omega_n t} \tag{1.2.7}$$

Recall the following Euler's formula:

$$\begin{aligned} e^{iB} &= \cos B + i \sin B \\ e^{-iB} &= \cos B - i \sin B \end{aligned} \tag{1.2.8}$$

Using equation (1.2.8), equation (1.2.7) can be expressed as

$$y(t) = C_1 \cos\omega_n t + C_2 \sin\omega_n t \tag{1.2.9}$$

where C_1 and C_2 are a new set of constants. From equation (1.2.9),

$$\dot{y}(t) = -C_1\omega_n \sin\omega_n t + C_2\omega_n \cos\omega_n t \tag{1.2.10}$$

Constants C_1 and C_2 are determined by applying the initial conditions as follows:

At time $t = 0$, initial displacement: $y(0) = y_0$, and from equation (1.2.9),

$$C_1 = y_0 \tag{1.2.11}$$

Initial velocity is $\dot{y}(0) = \dot{y}_0$, and from equation (1.2.10),

$$C_2\omega_n = \dot{y}_0 \rightarrow C_2 = \frac{\dot{y}_0}{\omega_n} \tag{1.2.12}$$

Alternately, equation (1.2.9) can be expressed as a single sinusoidal function in time, such that

$$y(t) = C\sin(\omega_n t + \phi) \tag{1.2.13}$$

where C: amplitude

ϕ : phase angle

ω_n : angle covered in one second, called *natural frequency* (rad/sec)

Amplitude and phase angle are related to the initial conditions as follows. Using one of the trigonometric formulas, equation (1.2.13) can be expressed as

$$y(t) = C(\sin\omega_n t\cos\phi + \cos\omega_n t\sin\phi) \tag{1.2.14}$$

Comparing equation (1.2.14) with equation (1.2.9),

$$\begin{aligned} C_1 &= C\sin\phi \\ C_2 &= C\cos\phi \end{aligned} \tag{1.2.15}$$

From equation (1.2.15) and also from the sketch,

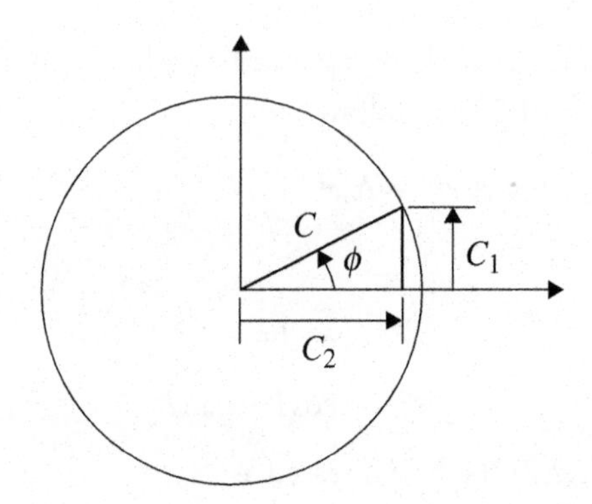

$$\begin{aligned} &C = \sqrt{C_1^2 + C_2^2} = \sqrt{y_0^2 + \left(\frac{\dot{y}_0}{\omega_n}\right)^2} \\ &\tan\phi = \frac{C_1}{C_2} = \frac{y_0}{(\frac{\dot{y}_0}{\omega_n})} \quad \rightarrow \quad \phi = \tan^{-1}\frac{C_1}{C_2} \end{aligned} \tag{1.2.16}$$

Note:

1) An undamped SDOF system undergoes free vibration with natural frequency

$$\omega_n\left(=\sqrt{\frac{k}{m}}\right) \text{ rad/sec}$$

2) T: period and

$$\omega_n T = 2\pi \rightarrow T = \frac{2\pi}{\omega_n} \tag{1.2.17}$$

3) Natural frequency f in cycles or Hertz (Hz) is defined as follows:

$$f = \frac{1}{T} = \frac{\omega_n}{2\pi} \tag{1.2.18}$$

Example 1.2.1 Consider a spacecraft on the ground. For vertical motion, the spacecraft is modeled as a SDOF system with mass M and spring k. The spring represents the vertical stiffness of the landing gear. Under the deadweight of the spacecraft, the spring displaces vertically by 7.62 cm.

(a) Determine the natural frequency of free vibration in the vertical direction.
(b) Determine the natural frequency when the stiffness of the spring is doubled.

(a)

$$Mg = ky_{static} \rightarrow \frac{k}{M} = \frac{g}{y_{static}}$$

$$\omega_n = \sqrt{\frac{k}{M}} = \sqrt{\frac{g}{y_{static}}} = \sqrt{\frac{9.81}{0.0762}} = 11.35 \text{ rad/sec}$$

$$f = \frac{\omega_n}{2\pi} = 1.806 \text{ Hz}$$

(b) For constant mass, $\omega_n \sim \sqrt{k}$ or $f \sim \sqrt{k}$

$$f = \sqrt{2} \times 1.806 = 2.554 \text{ Hz}$$

1.3 Free Vibration of Damped SDOF Systems

Consider a system that consists of a mass, a spring, and a damper.

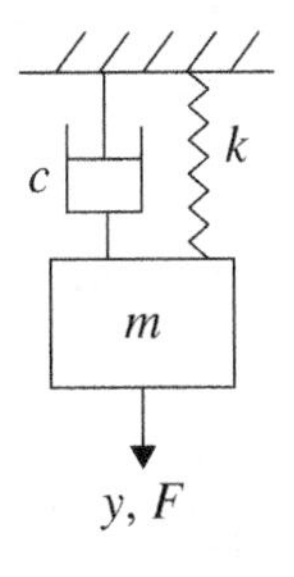

Figure 1.6 A damped SDOF system.

The dashpot with damping constant c represents an energy-dissipating mechanism. Newton's second law applied to the isolated mass:

$$m\ddot{y} = F - ky - c\dot{y}$$

$$m\ddot{y} + c\dot{y} + ky = F \tag{1.3.1}$$

$$\ddot{y} + \frac{c}{m}\dot{y} + \frac{k}{m}y = \frac{F}{m}$$

Let's now introduce a nondimensional damping ratio ζ as follows:

$$\frac{c}{m} = 2\varsigma\omega_n$$

Then,

$$\varsigma = \frac{c}{2m\omega_n} \tag{1.3.2}$$

The last of equation (1.3.1) can be rewritten as

$$\ddot{y} + 2\varsigma\omega_n\dot{y} + \omega_n^2 y = \frac{F}{m} \tag{1.3.3}$$

where

$$\omega_n^2 = \frac{k}{m}$$

For free vibration ($F = 0$),

equation of motion: $$\ddot{y} + 2\varsigma\omega_n\dot{y} + \omega_n^2 y = 0 \tag{1.3.4}$$

initial conditions: $$y(0) = y_0 \text{ and } \dot{y}(0) = \dot{y}_o \tag{1.3.5}$$

Note:
In the presence of damping, free vibration will die out eventually.

A solution to equation (1.3.4), which is homogeneous, is of the following form:

$$y(t) = Ae^{pt} \tag{1.3.6}$$

Then,

$$\dot{y}(t) = pAe^{pt}, \quad \ddot{y}(t) = p^2 Ae^{pt} \tag{1.3.7}$$

Placing equations (1.3.6) and (1.3.7) into equation (1.3.4),

$$(p^2 + 2\varsigma\omega_n p + \omega_n^2)Ae^{pt} = 0 \tag{1.3.8}$$

For nontrivial y (i.e., nonzero A),

$$p^2 + 2\varsigma\omega_n p + \omega_n^2 = 0 \tag{1.3.9}$$

Then, from equation (1.3.9),

$$\begin{aligned} (p+\varsigma\omega_n)^2 - (\varsigma\omega_n)^2 + \omega_n^2 &= 0 \\ (p+\varsigma\omega_n)^2 &= \omega_n^2(\varsigma^2 - 1) \\ p+\varsigma\omega_n &= \pm\omega_n\sqrt{\varsigma^2 - 1} \\ p &= -\varsigma\omega_n \pm \omega_n\sqrt{\varsigma^2 - 1} \end{aligned} \tag{1.3.10}$$

Depending on the magnitude of the damping ratio, one can consider the following three cases:

1) Overdamped case ($\varsigma > 1$)

$$p_1 = -\varsigma\omega_n + \omega_n\sqrt{\varsigma^2 - 1}$$
$$p_2 = -\varsigma\omega_n - \omega_n\sqrt{\varsigma^2 - 1} \tag{1.3.11}$$

For $\varsigma > 1$, both p_1 and p_2 are negative real numbers. The solution to the equation of motion in (1.3.4) is expressed as follows:

$$y(t) = c_1 e^{p_1 t} + c_2 e^{p_2 t} \tag{1.3.12}$$

Constants c_1 and c_2 are determined from the initial conditions. Note that, as time elapses, y drops to zero with no oscillation.

2) Critically damped case ($\varsigma = 1$)
For $\varsigma = 1$,

$$p_1 = p_2 = -\omega_n \tag{1.3.13}$$

The solution to the equation of motion in (1.3.4) is expressed as follows:

$$y(t) = c_1 e^{-\omega_n t} + c_2 t e^{-\omega_n t} \tag{1.3.14}$$

Constants c_1 and c_2 are determined from the initial conditions. Note that, as time elapses, y drops to zero with no oscillation.

3) Underdamped case ($\varsigma < 1$)
For $\zeta < 1$,

$$p_1 = -\varsigma\omega_n + i\omega_n\sqrt{1 - \varsigma^2} = -\varsigma\omega_n + i\omega_d$$
$$p_2 = -\varsigma\omega_n - i\omega_n\sqrt{1 - \varsigma^2} = -\varsigma\omega_n - i\omega_d \tag{1.3.15}$$

where

$$\omega_d = \omega_n\sqrt{1 - \varsigma^2} \tag{1.3.16}$$

The solution to equation (1.3.4) is then expressed as follows:

$$y(t) = A_1 e^{p_1 t} + A_2 e^{p_2 t} = A_1 e^{(-\varsigma\omega_n + i\omega_d)t} + A_2 e^{(-\varsigma\omega_n - i\omega_d)t}$$
$$= e^{-\varsigma\omega_n t}(A_1 e^{i\omega_d t} + A_2 e^{-i\omega_d t}) \tag{1.3.17}$$

or

$$y(t) = e^{-\varsigma\omega_n t}(C_1 \cos\omega_d t + C_2 \sin\omega_d t) \tag{1.3.18}$$

From equation (1.3.18) for $y(t)$,

$$\dot{y}(t) = -\varsigma\omega_n e^{-\varsigma\omega_n t}(C_1 \cos\omega_d t + C_2 \sin\omega_d t) + e^{-\varsigma\omega_n t}(-C_1\omega_d \sin\omega_d t + C_2\omega_d \cos\omega_d t) \tag{1.3.19}$$

Applying the initial conditions, i.e., equation (1.3.5) to equations (1.3.18) and (1.3.19),

$$y(0) = C_1 = y_0$$
$$\dot{y}(0) = -\varsigma\omega_n C_1 + C_2\omega_d = \dot{y}_0 \tag{1.3.20}$$
$$\rightarrow C_2 = \frac{\dot{y}_0 + \varsigma\omega_n y_0}{\omega_d}$$

Response $y(t)$ in equation (1.3.18) can be rewritten into a single sinusoidal function of time, such that

$$y(t) = e^{-\varsigma\omega_n t} C \sin(\omega_d t + \phi) \tag{1.3.21}$$

where $e^{-\varsigma\omega_n t} C$: amplitude that decays exponentially

ϕ : phase angle

Using one of the trigonometric formulas, equation (1.3.21) can be expressed as

$$y(t) = e^{-\varsigma\omega_n t} C(\sin\omega_d t \cos\phi + \cos\omega_d t \sin\phi) \tag{1.3.22}$$

Comparing equation (1.3.22) with equation (1.3.18),

$$C_1 = C\sin\phi, \quad C_2 = C\cos\phi \tag{1.3.23}$$

From equation (1.3.23) and also from the sketch,

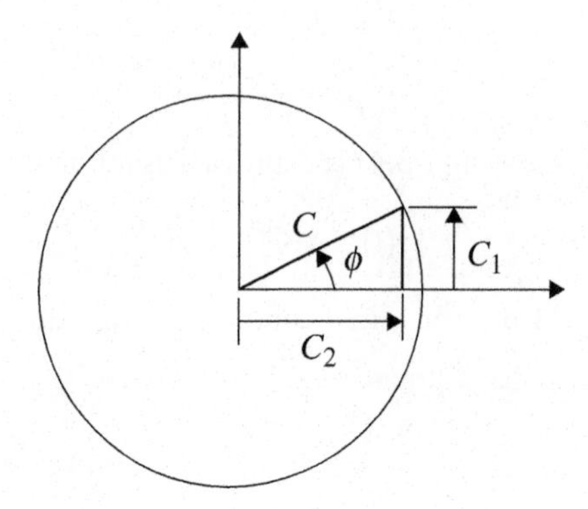

$$C = \sqrt{C_1^2 + C_2^2}$$
$$\tan\phi = \frac{C_1}{C_2} \rightarrow \phi = \tan^{-1}\frac{C_1}{C_2} \tag{1.3.24}$$

Recall:

$$C_1 = y_0, \quad C_2 = \frac{\dot{y}_0 + \varsigma\omega_n y_0}{\omega_d} \tag{1.3.25}$$

<u>Note:</u>

1) As time elapses, y approaches zero, i.e., free vibration dies out.
2) For $\zeta = 0$, the above solution reduces to that for free vibration of an undamped system.
3) $\omega_d = \omega_n\sqrt{1-\varsigma^2}$: frequency of damped free vibration

   When ς^2 is very small compared with 1, $\omega_d \approx \omega_n$.
   For example, for $\zeta = 0.1$, $\omega_d = 0.995\omega_n$.
4) $\omega_d T = 2\pi$ where T is the period.

Equation (1.3.21) can be expressed as

$$y(t) = Y_0 \sin(\omega_d t + \phi) \tag{1.3.26}$$

where $Y_0 = e^{-\varsigma\omega_n t} C$ is the amplitude that decays exponentially in time.

Then,

$$\ln Y_0 = -\varsigma\omega_n t + \ln C \tag{1.3.27}$$

At two different times, t_1 and t_2, equation (1.3.27) can be expressed as

$$\begin{aligned} \ln Y_1 &= -\varsigma\omega_n t_1 + \ln C \\ \ln Y_2 &= -\varsigma\omega_n t_2 + \ln C \end{aligned} \tag{1.3.28}$$

where

$$Y_1 = (Y_0)_{t=t_1}, \quad Y_2 = (Y_0)_{t=t_2} \tag{1.3.29}$$

From equation (1.3.28),

$$\ln Y_1 - \ln Y_2 = \varsigma\omega_n (t_2 - t_1) \tag{1.3.30}$$

$$\rightarrow \ln\frac{Y_1}{Y_2} = \varsigma\omega_n (t_2 - t_1) \tag{1.3.31}$$

or

$$\ln\frac{Y_1}{Y_2} = \frac{\varsigma}{\sqrt{1-\varsigma^2}}\omega_d (t_2 - t_1) \tag{1.3.32}$$

From equation (1.3.32),

$$\varsigma = \frac{\delta}{\sqrt{(2\pi n)^2 + \delta^2}} \tag{1.3.33}$$

where

$$\delta = \ln\frac{Y_1}{Y_2} \tag{1.3.34}$$

and n is the number of cycles between t_1 and t_2 (i.e. $t_2 - t_1 = nT$). For $n = 1$, δ is called "logarithmic decrement". Equation (1.3.33) can be used to determine damping ratio ζ as shown in the following example.

Example 1.3.1 Consider an assembly of a sting balance with a model of a flight vehicle placed on a vibration test rig. One end of the sting balance is attached to the rig, while the other end is free. The vibration of the assembly in the vertical direction is modeled as a SDOF system.

In order to determine effective static and dynamic properties of the model, initially a static force is applied vertically at the free tip of the assembly by hanging a weight. It turns out that the static tip displacement of the assembly is 0.2 in. for a weight of 60 lbs. The cable connecting the weight to the assembly is then cut to initiate a free vibration. The records of ensuing free vibration of the tip show that, after three cycles, the elapsed time is 1.5 sec and the amplitude is 0.1 in. Determine the following for the sting balance.

- **(a)** Effective spring constant k (lb/ft).
- **(b)** Effective damping ratio ς.
- **(c)** Undamped natural frequency (rad/sec and Hz).
- **(d)** Effective mass m (slugs).
- **(e)** Effective damping coefficient c (lb-sec/ft).
- **(f)** Energy loss (in percentage) of the system at the end of three cycles.

(a) $k = \dfrac{60\ lb}{0.2/12\ ft} = 3{,}600$ lb/ft

(b) $\delta = \ln\dfrac{Y_1}{Y_2} = \ln\dfrac{0.2}{0.1} = \ln 2$ and $n = 3$,

$$\varsigma = \frac{\delta}{\sqrt{(2\pi n)^2 + \delta^2}} = \frac{\delta}{\sqrt{(6\pi)^2 + \delta^2}} = \quad 0.0367$$

(c) $T = \dfrac{1.5}{3} = 0.5\,\text{sec}, \quad \omega_d = \dfrac{2\pi}{T} = 12.566$ rad/sec

$$\omega_n = \frac{\omega_d}{\sqrt{1-\varsigma^2}} = 12.567 \text{ rad/sec}$$

(d) $\omega_n = \sqrt{\dfrac{k}{m}} \rightarrow m = \dfrac{k}{\omega_n^2} = \dfrac{3{,}600}{(12.567)^2} = 22.795$ slug

(e) $c = m(2\varsigma\omega_n) = 21.03$ lb-sec/ft

(f) $\dfrac{\Delta E}{E_1} = \dfrac{E_1 - E_2}{E_1} = 1 - \left(\dfrac{Y_2}{Y_1}\right)^2 = 1 - \left(\dfrac{0.1}{0.2}\right)^2 = 0.75 \rightarrow 75\%$

1.4 Forced Vibration

Now, consider SDOF systems that are subjected to external load.

Equation of motion:

$$m\ddot{y} + c\dot{y} + ky = F \tag{1.4.1}$$

We can express $y(t)$ as follows:

$$y = y_H + y_p \tag{1.4.2}$$

where y_H is the solution to the following homogeneous equation:

$$m\ddot{y} + c\dot{y} + ky = 0 \tag{1.4.3}$$

and y_p is the particular solution to equation (1.4.1).

Then, for $\varsigma < 1$,

$$y(t) = e^{-\varsigma\omega_n t}(C_1 \cos\omega_d t + C_2 \sin\omega_d t) + y_p \tag{1.4.4}$$

where C_1 and C_2 are determined from the initial conditions.

1.4.1 A SDOF System Subjected to a Step Load

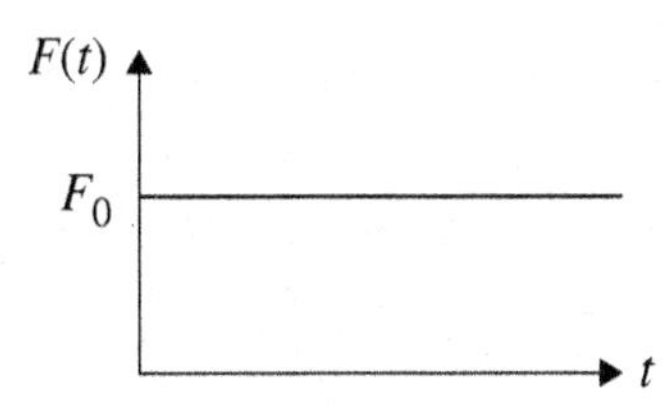

Figure 1.7 A step load of $F(t) = F_0$ constant in time.

The system is initially at rest. Assuming no damping, the equation of motion is

$$m\ddot{y} + ky = F_0 \tag{1.4.5}$$

and the initial conditions at $t = 0$ are

$$\begin{aligned} y(0) &= 0 \\ \dot{y}(0) &= 0 \end{aligned} \tag{1.4.6}$$

The homogeneous solution and a particular solution are as follows:

$$\begin{aligned} y_H &= C_1 \cos\omega_n t + C_2 \sin\omega_n t \\ y_P &= \frac{F_0}{k} \end{aligned} \tag{1.4.7}$$

Accordingly,

$$y = C_1 \cos\omega_n t + C_2 \sin\omega_n t + \frac{F_0}{k} \tag{1.4.8}$$

and

$$\dot{y} = \omega_n(-C_1 \sin\omega_n t + C_2 \cos\omega_n t) \tag{1.4.9}$$

Applying initial conditions to equations (1.4.8) and (1.4.9),

$$\text{equation (1.4.8)}: C_1 + \frac{F_0}{k} = 0 \rightarrow C_1 = -\frac{F_0}{k} \tag{1.4.10}$$

$$\text{equation (1.4.9)}: C_2 = 0 \tag{1.4.11}$$

Placing equations (1.4.10) and (1.4.11) into equation (1.4.8),

$$y = \frac{F_0}{k}(1 - \cos\omega_n t) \tag{1.4.12}$$

Now consider the case in which the same SDOF system is subjected to a static load of F_0. Then, the response is static, and

$$\begin{aligned} &ky_{STATIC} = F_0 \\ &\rightarrow y_{STATIC} = \frac{F_0}{k} \end{aligned} \tag{1.4.13}$$

Equation (1.4.12) can then be expressed as

$$y = y_{STATIC}(1 - \cos\omega_n t) \tag{1.4.14}$$

From equation (1.4.14), one can see that under the dynamic condition

$$\max |y|_{DYNAMIC} = 2y_{STATIC} \tag{1.4.15}$$

Also, under dynamic condition,

$$\max.(\text{spring force})_{DYNAMIC} = k(\max |y|_{DYNAMIC}) = k(2y_{STATIC}) = 2F_0 \tag{1.4.16}$$

So,

$$\text{dynamic overload} = 2F_0 - F_0 = F_0 \tag{1.4.17}$$

This simple example illustrates the importance of dynamic effect.

Example 1.4.1 Consider a spacecraft rotating to a specified angular orientation using an applied control moment. The spacecraft is initially at rest. For a rigid spacecraft under applied moment T,

$$I\ddot{\theta} = T$$

where I is the moment of inertia of the spacecraft. The control moment is expressed as

$$T = -K(\theta - \theta_F) - C\dot{\theta}$$

where θ_F is the desired final angle, and K and C are control gains. Then, the equation of motion is

$$I\ddot{\theta} + C\dot{\theta} + K\theta = K\theta_F$$

The solution to the above equation of motion can be expressed as

$$\theta(t) = e^{-\varsigma\omega_n t}(C_1 \cos\omega_d t + C_2 \sin\omega_d t) + \theta_F$$

Applying the initial conditions, one can find that

$$C_1 = -\theta_F, \quad C_2 = -\left(\frac{\varsigma}{\sqrt{1-\varsigma^2}}\right)\theta_F$$

Alternatively,

$$\theta = e^{-\varsigma\omega_n t}\hat{C}\sin(\omega_d t + \phi) + \theta_F$$

where

$$\hat{C} = \sqrt{C_1^2 + C_2^2}, \quad \phi = \tan^{-1}\frac{C_1}{C_2}$$

1.4.2 A Step Load of Finite Duration

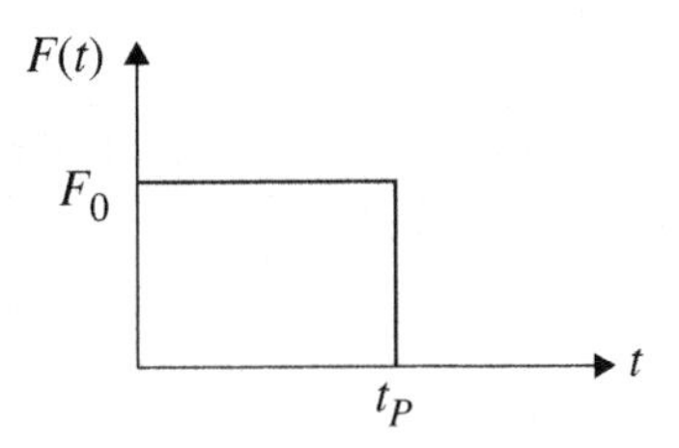

Figure 1.8 A step load of finite duration.

$$F(t) = F_0 \quad 0 \le t \le t_p$$
$$= 0 \quad t > t_p \tag{1.4.18}$$

For $0 \le t \le t_P$, equation (1.4.12) of Section 1.4.1 still holds.
Applied force disappears when $t > t_P$. Accordingly, for $t > t_P$, the system undergoes free vibration with the "initial" conditions at $t = t_P$.

From equation (1.4.12) of Section 1.4.1, at $t = t_P$,

$$y(t_P) = \frac{F_0}{k}(1 - \cos \omega_n t_P)$$
$$\dot{y}(t_P) = \frac{F_0}{k}\omega_n \sin \omega_n t_P \tag{1.4.19}$$

For undamped free vibration, the equation of motion is

$$m\ddot{y} + ky = 0 \tag{1.4.20}$$

Recall that the solution to the above homogeneous equation is

$$y = C_1 \cos \omega_n t + C_2 \sin \omega_n t \tag{1.4.21}$$

and

$$\dot{y} = \omega_n(-C_1 \sin \omega_n t + C_2 \cos \omega_n t) \tag{1.4.22}$$

Applying the initial conditions (for free vibration) at $t = t_P$ given in equation (1.4.19), one can show that

$$C_1 = \frac{F_0}{k}(\cos \omega_n t_P - 1)$$
$$C_2 = \frac{F_0}{k}\sin \omega_n t_P \tag{1.4.23}$$

1.4.3 Impulse Loading

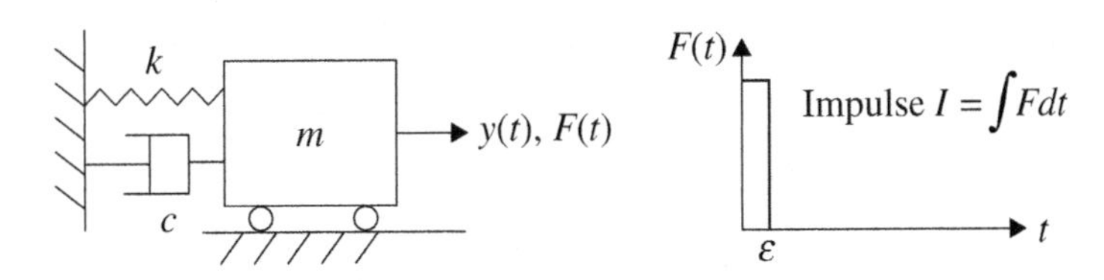

The system is initially at rest, and the force is applied over $0 \le t \le \varepsilon$. Let's consider the case in which $\varepsilon \to 0$ while I is held constant.

Equation of motion:
$$m\ddot{y} + c\dot{y} + ky = F \tag{1.4.24}$$

Integrating the above equation from $t = 0$ to $t = \varepsilon$,

$$m\int_{t=0}^{t=\varepsilon} \ddot{y}\,dt + c\int_{t=0}^{t=\varepsilon} \dot{y}dt + k\int_{t=0}^{t=\varepsilon} ydt = \int_{t=0}^{t=\varepsilon} Fdt \tag{1.4.25}$$

For the right-hand side of equation (1.4.25),

$$\int_{t=0}^{t=\varepsilon} Fdt = I \tag{1.4.26}$$

For the integrals on the left,

$$k\int_{t=0}^{t=\varepsilon} ydt = 0 \tag{1.4.27}$$

$$c\int_{t=0}^{t=\varepsilon} \dot{y}dt = c[y(\varepsilon) - y(0)] = c[0-0] = 0 \tag{1.4.28}$$

because the mass has no time to move. For the first integral

$$m\int_{t=0}^{t=\varepsilon} \ddot{y}\,dt = m[\dot{y}(\varepsilon) - \dot{y}(0)] = m[\dot{y}(\varepsilon) - 0] = m\dot{y}(\varepsilon) \tag{1.4.29}$$

Then, equation (1.4.25) becomes

$$m\dot{y}(\varepsilon) = I \tag{1.4.30}$$

or

$$\dot{y}(\varepsilon) = \frac{I}{m} \tag{1.4.31}$$

So, the mass has not moved, but it has acquired initial velocity at $t = \varepsilon$. Accordingly, noting that $\varepsilon \to 0$, the system response after the impulse can be treated as a vibration problem with a "new" set of initial conditions as

$$y(0) = 0,\ \dot{y}(0) = \frac{I}{m} \tag{1.4.32}$$

Note that we can come to the same conclusion using equation (1.4.19) as follows: Let time t_p approach zero while keeping $I = F_0 t_p$ constant.

Example 1.4.2 A small spacecraft is dropped from a tower for a landing test. The vertical motion of the spacecraft after landing impact is modeled as a SDOF system subject to a given impulse I. Assume that the spacecraft does not topple after landing. The equation of motion is

$$m\ddot{y} + c\dot{y} + ky = mg$$

where m is the spacecraft mass, and c and k represent the damping constant and the spring constant of the landing gear. The vertical displacement y is defined positive downward. The solution to the above equation is

$$y(t)=e^{-\varsigma\omega_n t}(C_1\cos\omega_d t+C_2\sin\omega_d t)+\frac{mg}{k}$$

Then,

$$\dot{y}(t)=-\varsigma\omega_n e^{-\varsigma\omega_n t}(C_1\cos\omega_d t+C_2\sin\omega_d t)+e^{-\varsigma\omega_n t}(-C_1\omega_d\sin\omega_d t+C_2\omega_d\cos\omega_d t)$$

At touchdown $(t=0)$, one can apply the initial conditions given as in equation (1.4.32),

$$0=C_1+\frac{mg}{k},\ \frac{I}{m}=-\varsigma\omega_n C_1+C_2\omega_d$$

from which one can obtain

$$C_1=-\frac{mg}{k},\ C_2=\frac{1}{\omega_d}\left(\frac{I}{m}-\varsigma\omega_n\frac{mg}{k}\right)$$

The static equilibrium position after the vibration dies out is

$$y_{static}=\frac{mg}{k}$$

1.5 Numerical Methods to Determine System Response

Consider a SDOF system represented by

equation of motion: $$m\ddot{y}+f(\dot{y},y)=F \tag{1.5.1}$$

initial conditions: $$y(0)=y_0,\ \dot{y}(0)=\dot{y}_0 \tag{1.5.2}$$

Note that

$$f(\dot{y},y)=c\dot{y}+ky \tag{1.5.3}$$

for the damping force and the spring force proportional to $\dot{y}$ and y respectively. The system response under arbitrary load $F(t)$ can be determined by numerical methods. For this, one may transform the above equation into a system of two first-order equations by introducing a new variable v, defined as follows:

$$\dot{y}=v \tag{1.5.4}$$

Then, equation (1.5.1) can be expressed as

$$m\dot{v}+f(v,y)=F \tag{1.5.5}$$

or

$$\dot{v}=\frac{1}{m}\left(F-f(v,y)\right) \tag{1.5.6}$$

Equations (1.5.4) and (1.5.6) can be combined in to a single matrix equation as follows:

$$\begin{Bmatrix} \dot{y} \\ \dot{v} \end{Bmatrix} = \begin{Bmatrix} v \\ \dfrac{1}{m}(F - f(v,y)) \end{Bmatrix} \tag{1.5.7}$$

or

$$\dot{\mathbf{x}} = \hat{\mathbf{f}}(\mathbf{x}, F) \tag{1.5.8}$$

where

$$\mathbf{x} = \begin{Bmatrix} y \\ v \end{Bmatrix}, \quad \dot{\mathbf{x}} = \begin{Bmatrix} \dot{y} \\ \dot{v} \end{Bmatrix} \tag{1.5.9}$$

$$\hat{\mathbf{f}}(\mathbf{x}, F) = \begin{Bmatrix} v \\ \dfrac{1}{m}(F - f(v,y)) \end{Bmatrix} \tag{1.5.10}$$

Note that equation (1.5.7) or (1.5.8) is a first-order equation. The "initial" condition for $\mathbf{x}$ is as follows:

$$\mathbf{x}(0) = \begin{Bmatrix} y(0) \\ v(0) = \dot{y}(0) \end{Bmatrix} = \begin{Bmatrix} y_0 \\ \dot{y}_0 \end{Bmatrix} \tag{1.5.11}$$

There are many numerical schemes that can be used to determine $\mathbf{x}$ as a function of time. We will consider now the simplest scheme called the **Euler method**.

Notations:

$\mathbf{x}_n = \mathbf{x}(t_n)$: $\mathbf{x}$ at time t_n, $\quad \dot{\mathbf{x}}_n = \dot{\mathbf{x}}(t_n)$: $\dot{\mathbf{x}}$ at time t_n,

$t_{n+1} = t_n + \Delta t$, Δt: time increment

$\mathbf{x}_{n+1} = \mathbf{x}(t_{n+1})$: $\mathbf{x}$ at time t_{n+1}

For the Taylor expansion around time t_n,

$$\mathbf{x}_{n+1} = \mathbf{x}_n + \dot{\mathbf{x}}_n \Delta t + \frac{1}{2}\ddot{\mathbf{x}}_n (\Delta t)^2 + \cdots\cdots \tag{1.5.12}$$

The Euler method assumes that

$$\mathbf{x}_{n+1} = \mathbf{x}_n + \dot{\mathbf{x}}_n \Delta t \tag{1.5.13}$$

where

$$\dot{\mathbf{x}}_n = \hat{\mathbf{f}}(\mathbf{x}_n, F_n) = \begin{Bmatrix} v_n \\ \dfrac{1}{m_n}(F_n - f(v_n, y_n)) \end{Bmatrix} \tag{1.5.14}$$

Given Δt, one can use equation (1.5.13) with equation (1.5.14) to determine $\mathbf{x}_{n+1}$. The entire process works as follows:

Choose a small Δt.
Set $n = 0$ and use equation (1.5.13) to determine $\mathbf{x}_1$ at $t_1 = \Delta t$.
Set $n = 1$ and use equation (1.5.13) to determine $\mathbf{x}_2$ at $t_2 = t_1 + \Delta t$.
Set $n = 2$ and use equation (1.5.13) to determine $\mathbf{x}_3$ at $t_3 = t_2 + \Delta t$.
Continue marching in time by increasing n until you obtain the solutions over the time span of your interest.

Note:
Higher order methods such as the fourth-order Runge-Kutta (RK4) method provide improved accuracy.

Chapter 1 Problem Sets

1.1 For the SDOF system shown below, draw a free-body diagram and set up the equation of motion for y. Identify the applied force term in the equation of motion. Note that A is a given displacement.

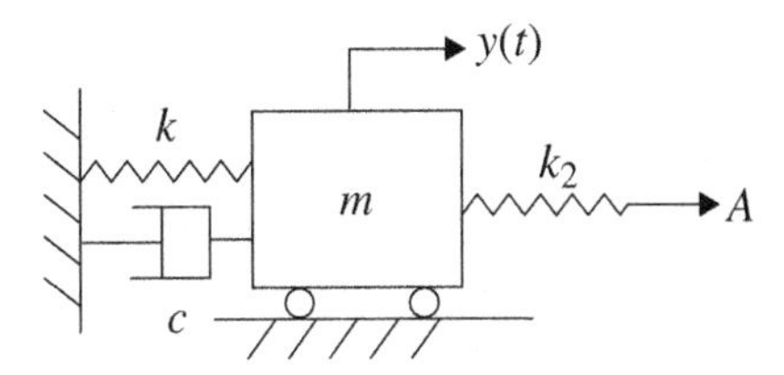

1.2 Consider a spacecraft undergoing vibration test on the ground. For vertical vibration, the spacecraft is modeled as a SDOF system. The landing gear consists of gas balloons. The natural frequency of the free vibration is measured at a given pressure. Subsequently, the gas pressure is reduced, and the natural frequency is measured. It turns out that the new frequency is reduced to 80% of the original frequency.

(a) Estimate the reduction in the stiffness of the system by determining a nondimensional quantity R defined as follows:

$$R = \frac{k_{old} - k_{new}}{k_{old}}$$

(b) Estimate the increase (in percent) in the static displacement.

1.3 The wingtip bending vibration of an aircraft is modeled as a single DOF system with a spring and a mass. The wing is fixed at the root. The natural frequency of the wing is measured to be 6.1 Hz. When a fuel tank weighing 5,400 N is added at the wingtip, the natural frequency reduces to 5.2 Hz. Neglect damping effect.

(a) Determine the effective mass m_1 (not including the fuel tank) of the model.
(b) Determine the effective stiffness k of the model.

$y(t)$: vertical displacement of wingtip
m_1: effective mass of the wing, m_F: fuel tank mass
$m_2 = m_1 + m_F$

(c) Determine the natural frequency (in rad/sec and Hz) when the fuel tank weight is reduced to 3,500 N. due to fuel consumption.

1.4 Consider free vibration test of an aircraft engine mounted to the rear fuselage. The engine weighs 1,300 lb. The measured frequency of free vibration is 50 Hz, and the displacement amplitude of free vibration reduces to 50% of the initial value in four cycles. Ignore the weight of the engine mount and do the following:

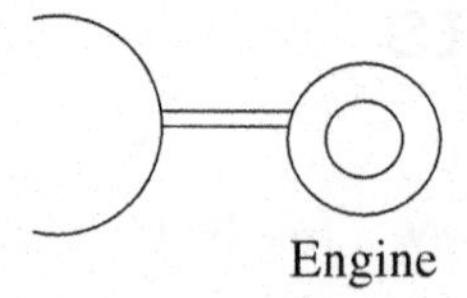

(a) Estimate the effective damping ratio ζ.
(b) Estimate the effective stiffness k (lb/ft) of the engine mount.
(c) Suppose the engine is replaced with a new engine weighing 1,000 lb. Estimate the new measured frequency of free vibration. Also, determine the new damping ratio and estimate the reduction in the displacement amplitude of free vibration after 4 cycles.

1.5 Consider a SDOF model for dynamics of pilot ejection. The head is modeled as a single mass of m. The spinal column supporting the head is modeled as a spring with k. Damping is neglected. The time history of the ejection seat acceleration $\ddot{d}$ is approximated as shown in the figure.

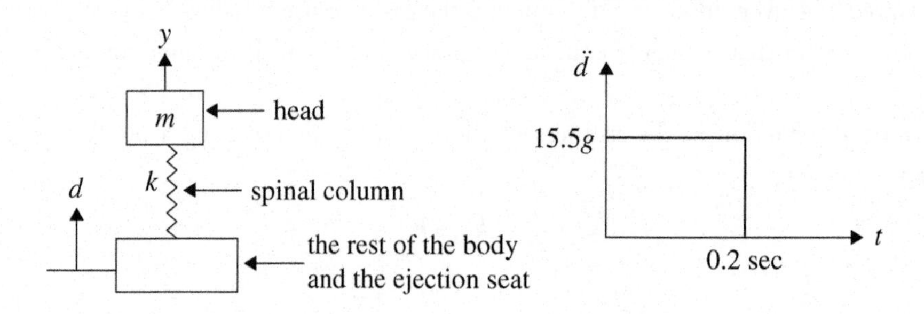

(a) Write the equation of motion in terms of the relative displacement $y_R = y - d$.
(b) Determine y_R of the head for $t < 0.2$ sec.
(c) Determine the absolute acceleration $\ddot{y}$ of the head. What is the peak value?
(d) Determine the force on the spinal column. What is the peak value?

1.6 A small UAV on takeoff run may hit a bump, and ensuing free vibration in the vertical direction can be modeled using a SDOF system of a mass, a spring, and a damper. The spring and the damper represent the landing gear. It is desired that the period of damped free vibration is 2.5 sec. and the amplitude of vertical

displacement reduces to one-fourth in one cycle. The mass of the UAV is 1,300 kg. Determine the following for the landing gear.
(**a**) damping ratio ζ, (**b**) damping constant c, (**c**) spring constant k.

1.7 A single block of mass, 100 kg is attached to movable points A and B through springs as shown below. The displacements of points A and B are controlled externally and are denoted by u and w, respectively. Mass, m, itself has a displacement y. k_1 = 20000 N/m, k_2 = 30000 N/m

a) Draw the free-body diagram and determine the dynamic equation of motion of the mass. How must the points A and B move in order for the mass to remain in static equilibrium at all times? State the condition in terms of u and w.
b) If the points A and B are fixed, i.e., $u = w = 0$, what is the natural frequency of vibration of the mass, m?
c) Points A and B are fixed, and the mass is hit with an impulse, I, at time t = 0. If both springs have a load limit of 1000 N, what is the maximum value of I for the springs to remain intact? If I is slightly increased above this value, which spring will break first?

1.8 A helicopter has a gross mass of 8000 kg. The main landing gear with a mass of 200 kg is connected to the mid-fuselage by a spring and a damper. A simple model is sketched below.

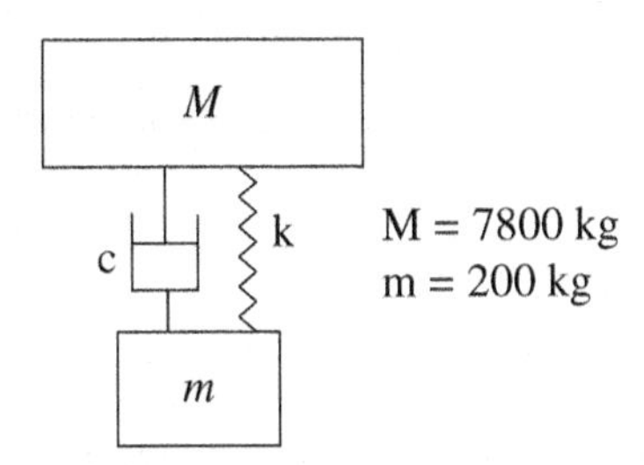

Prior to takeoff, the landing gear is in contact with the ground, and the static deflection of the spring is 25 cm.
a) What is the value of the spring constant, k?
b) What is the natural frequency of the helicopter on its landing gear in units of Hz? Neglect damping.

During steady flight, the helicopter is flying at a constant altitude.
c) What is the extension of the spring under static equilibrium?
d) What is the natural frequency, in Hz, of the landing gear attached to the helicopter during steady flight? Neglect damping.

During landing, the helicopter is descending at a constant rate of 1m/s. Assume that the tires remain in contact with the ground after touchdown. Let $t = 0$ at the point of touchdown.

- **e)** Draw the free-body diagram of the helicopter, and obtain the dynamic equation of motion of the helicopter in terms of parameters *M*, *k*, and *c*. (Hint: This is a forced vibration problem with a constant external force due to gravity.)
- **f)** What are the initial conditions for the helicopter? (Note: Be wary of signs.) Compute the displacement and the velocity of the helicopter as a function of time, t. Neglect damping.
- **g)** Repeat (h) for the value of damping coefficient, $\zeta = 0.2$.
- **h)** Plot the trajectory of the helicopter on a graph of displacement versus velocity for both (h) and (i). What do you observe? What can you say about the total energy of the system in both cases?

1.9 Consider a system of a concentrated mass *M*, a torsional spring with constant K and a rigid bar as shown in the sketch. The sketch shows an initially horizontalbar of length *L* in the rotated position with angle θ. Applied force *P* remains always horizontal. The rigid bar is assumed massless. Ignore the gravity effect for simplicity. One may consider this system as a crude model of a launch vehicle on a test stand, with *P* and K representing thrust and torsional spring bending stiffness respectively.

- **(a)** Derive the equation of motion for θ.
- **(b)** Assume small θ and simplify the equation of motion to $I\ddot{\theta} + k_{eff}\theta = 0$ where k_{eff} is the effective spring constant. Show that $K_{eff} = K - PL$.
- **(c)** Show that the natural frequency of the system decreases as force P increases.

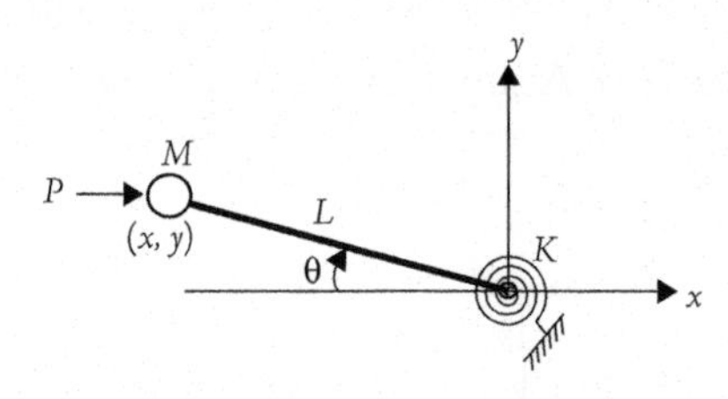

1.10 Consider ground vibration test of a small spacecraft weighing 5,300 *N*. For vertical vibration, the spacecraft is modeled as a SDOF system. The test results show that the period of damped free vibration is 1.2 *sec* and the amplitude of vertical displacement reduces to one-half in two cycles. Determine damping ratio ζ, damping constant *c* and spring constant *k* of the landing gear.

1.11 A seat with an occupant during crash landing is modeled as SDOF system undergoing vertical motion. The seat has a damper with adjustable damping. At a given damping ratio, the amplitude decays to 50% in one cycle. Determine the amplitude decay (in percentage) in one cycle if the damping ratio is doubled.

1.12 The sketch shows a mass M connected to a massless rigid bar of length L rotating about the z-axisat a constant speed of Ω rad/sec. The mass is also undergoing angular motion in the x-z plane. A rotational spring of constant K attached at the pivot point represents the bending stiffness of aslender body. The forces acting on the mass are the centrifugal force and the gravity force.

(a) Derive the equation of motion for θ.

(b) Assume small θ and simplify the equation of motion to $I\ddot{\theta}+k_{eff}\theta=0$ where k_{eff} is the effective spring constant.

(c) Show how the centrifugal force term contributes to the effective stiffness of the system.

(d) Does the natural frequency increases as the rotating speed increases?

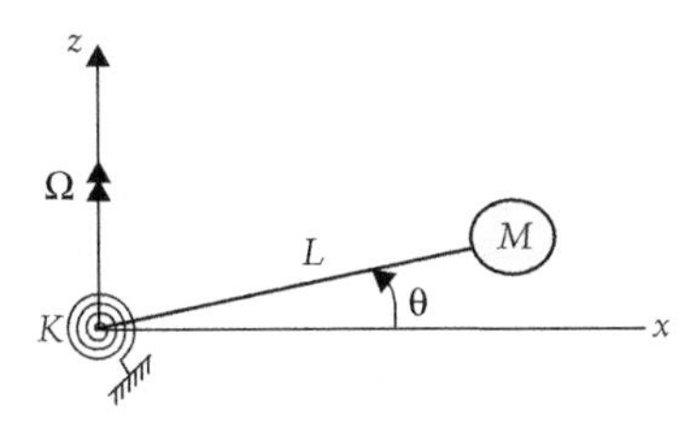

1.13 A force is applied to a lightly damped SDOF system which was initially at rest. The recorded acceleration of ensuing motion is found to fit $\ddot{y}=A\cos\omega_n t$ where $A=1000\ m/\sec^2$ Neglect damping and determine the following:

(a) velocity and displacement as a function of time.

(b) applied force for mass $m=100\ kg$.

1.14 The elastic force on the landing gear after touchdown may exhibit a nonlinear stiffening behavior as a function of aircraft vertical displacement. In this case, the SDOF equation of motion for vertical displacement of the aircraft may be expressed as

$$m\ddot{y}+c\dot{y}+F_s(y)=mg$$

with y defined positive downward. $F_s(y)$ is a nonlinear spring force. Use a numerical integration technique such as the Euler method or the RK4 method to determine vertical displacement of an aircraft with the following information:

Aircraft weight: 1,200 lb.
Damping constant: 200 lb-s/in.
Sink velocity at touchdown: 15 ft/sec.
Spring force: $F_s(y)=Ky\left(1+0.25\hat{y}^2\right)$, where K = 725 lb/in and $\hat{y}=0$ if $|y|$ measured in inches is less than 3 inches; otherwise, $\hat{y}=|y|-3$.

2 STEADY-STATE RESPONSE OF SDOF SYSTEMS

In this chapter, we will consider damped SDOF systems subject to harmonic or sinusoidal loading that is applied over an extended time span. Examples are vibration of systems with a rotating component, in which unbalanced mass provides the source of harmonic loading and an instrument placed on a base that is oscillating at given frequency. Of particular interest is the *steady-state* response, which is the system response after the transient response at the start of the dynamic motion has died down. The steady-state response can be determined by considering the particular solution of the SDOF systems expressed as an ordinary differential equation, with a sinusoidal forcing function on the right-hand side. Using this solution, one can then examine the effect of the ratio between the forcing frequency and the natural frequency, as well as the damping ratio on the system response. Specific topics to be covered are as follows:

2.1 Response of damped SDOF system to harmonic loading
2.2 Force transmitted to the base
2.3 Rotating systems with mass unbalance
2.4 SDOF systems with base motion

2.1 Response of Damped SDOF Systems to Harmonic Loading

Consider a SDOF system under a harmonic loading expressed as

$$F(t) = F_0 \sin \Omega t \tag{2.1.1}$$

where F_0 : amplitude of the applied force
Ω : frequency of the applied force

The equation of motion is then

$$m\ddot{y} + c\dot{y} + ky = F_o \sin \Omega t \tag{2.1.2}$$

or

$$\ddot{y} + 2\varsigma\omega_n \dot{y} + \omega_n^2 y = \frac{F_0}{m} \sin \Omega t \tag{2.1.3}$$

Recall that

$$\varsigma = \frac{c}{2m\omega_n}, \quad \omega_n = \sqrt{\frac{k}{m}} \tag{2.1.4}$$

The solution to equation (2.1.3) can be expressed as

$$y = y_H + y_P \tag{2.1.5}$$

where y_H is the solution to the homogeneous equation

$$\ddot{y} + 2\varsigma\omega_n \dot{y} + \omega_n^2 y = 0 \tag{2.1.6}$$

and y_P is a particular solution to equation (2.1.3).
Recall that, for $\varsigma < 1$,

$$y_H = e^{-\varsigma\omega_n t}(C_1 \cos \omega_d t + C_2 \sin \omega_d t) \tag{2.1.7}$$

The homogeneous part of the response decays with time and eventually dies out. Then,

$$y \approx y_P \tag{2.1.8}$$

So, particular solution y_P represents the response of the system after the homogeneous part, called the **transient response**, dies out. The particular solution y_P is called the **steady-state response.**

Determination of the Steady-State Response

For the particular solution to equation (2.1.3), we can try

$$y_P = A \sin \Omega t + B \cos \Omega t \tag{2.1.9}$$

From equation (2.1.9),

$$\begin{aligned}\dot{y}_P &= \Omega(A\cos\Omega t - B\sin\Omega t)\\ \ddot{y}_P &= -\Omega^2(A\sin\Omega t + B\cos\Omega t)\end{aligned} \tag{2.1.10}$$

Placing equations (2.1.9) and (2.1.10) into equation (2.1.3),

$$-\Omega^2(A\sin\Omega t + B\cos\Omega t) + 2\varsigma\omega_n\Omega(A\cos\Omega t - B\sin\Omega t) + \omega_n^2(A\sin\Omega t + B\cos\Omega t) = \frac{F_0}{m}\sin\Omega t \tag{2.1.11}$$

Collecting $\sin\Omega t$ terms and $\cos\Omega t$ terms of equation (2.1.11),

$$\begin{aligned}\sin\Omega t:&\ (\omega_n^2 - \Omega^2)A - (2\varsigma\omega_n\Omega)B = \frac{F_0}{m}\\ \cos\Omega t:&\ (\omega_n^2 - \Omega^2)B + (2\varsigma\omega_n\Omega)A = 0\end{aligned} \tag{2.1.12}$$

From the second of equation (2.1.12),

$$B = -\frac{2\varsigma\omega_n\Omega}{\omega_n^2 - \Omega^2}A \tag{2.1.13}$$

Placing equation (2.1.13) into the first of equation (2.1.12)

$$(\omega_n^2 - \Omega^2)A + \frac{(2\varsigma\omega_n\Omega)^2}{\omega_n^2 - \Omega^2}A = \frac{F_0}{m}$$

$$\rightarrow\ A\left[\frac{(\omega_n^2 - \Omega^2)^2 + (2\varsigma\omega_n\Omega)^2}{\omega_n^2 - \Omega^2}\right] = \frac{F_0}{m}$$

$$\rightarrow\ A = \left(\frac{F_0}{m}\right)\frac{\omega_n^2 - \Omega^2}{(\omega_n^2 - \Omega^2)^2 + (2\varsigma\omega_n\Omega)^2} \tag{2.1.14}$$

Placing equation (2.1.14) into equation (2.1.13),

$$B = -\left(\frac{F_0}{m}\right)\frac{2\varsigma\omega_n\Omega}{(\omega_n^2 - \Omega^2)^2 + (2\varsigma\omega_n\Omega)^2} \tag{2.1.15}$$

Alternately, the steady-state response y_P can be expressed as

$$y_P = Y_0\sin(\Omega t - \phi) \tag{2.1.16}$$

Using one of the trigonometric formulas, equation (2.1.16) can be written as

$$y_P = Y_0(\sin\Omega t\cos\phi - \cos\Omega t\sin\phi) \tag{2.1.17}$$

Comparing equation (2.1.17) with equation (2.1.9),

$$\begin{aligned}Y_0\cos\phi &= A\\ Y_0\sin\phi &= -B\end{aligned} \tag{2.1.18}$$

Then, from equation (2.1.18) and also from the sketch,

$$Y_0 = \sqrt{A^2 + (-B)^2} \tag{2.1.19}$$

$$\tan\phi = \frac{-B}{A} \tag{2.1.20}$$

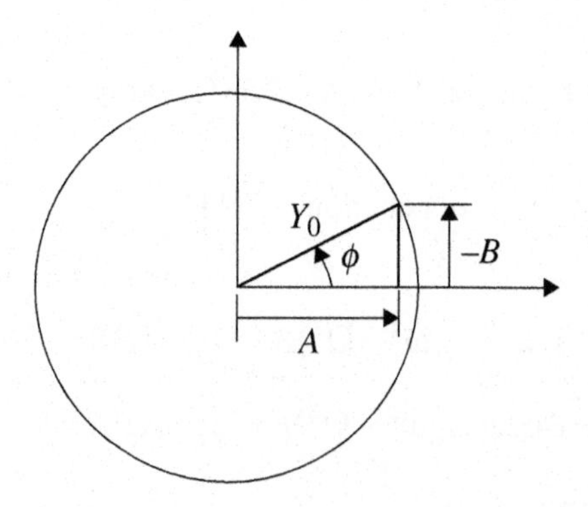

Placing equations (2.1.14) and (2.1.15) into equation (2.1.19),

$$Y_0 = \left(\frac{F_0}{m}\right)\frac{1}{\sqrt{(\omega_n^2 - \Omega^2)^2 + (2\varsigma\omega_n\Omega)^2}}$$

$$\rightarrow Y_0 = \left(\frac{F_0}{m\omega_n^2}\right)\frac{1}{\sqrt{\left[1-\left(\frac{\Omega}{\omega_n}\right)^2\right]^2 + \left(2\varsigma\frac{\Omega}{\omega_n}\right)^2}} \tag{2.1.21}$$

Recalling that $\omega_n^2 = \frac{k}{m}$,

Ω = driving frequency

$$Y_0 = \left(\frac{F_0}{k}\right)\frac{1}{\sqrt{[1-\left(\frac{\Omega}{\omega_n}\right)^2]^2 + \left(2\varsigma\frac{\Omega}{\omega_n}\right)^2}} \tag{2.1.22}$$

$$Y_0 = \left(\frac{F_0}{k}\right)\frac{1}{\sqrt{(1-R^2)^2 + (2\varsigma R)^2}} \tag{2.1.23}$$

where

$$R = \frac{\Omega}{\omega_n} \text{ : frequency ratio} \tag{2.1.24}$$

Placing equations (2.1.14) and (2.1.15) into equation (2.1.20),

$$\tan\phi = \frac{2\varsigma R}{1-R^2} \rightarrow \phi = \tan^{-1}\frac{2\varsigma R}{1-R^2} \tag{2.1.25}$$

....

In summary, y_P can be expressed as follows:

$$y_P = Y_0 \sin(\Omega t - \phi) \tag{2.1.26}$$

where amplitude Y_0 and phase angle ϕ are expressed as follows:

$$Y_0 = \frac{F_0}{k} \frac{1}{\sqrt{(1-R^2)^2 + (2\varsigma R)^2}} \tag{2.1.27}$$

$$\phi = \tan^{-1} \frac{2\varsigma R}{1-R^2} \tag{2.1.28}$$

Note:

1) For small ς, resonance occurs at $R \approx 1$.

2) $\dfrac{F_0}{k} = y_{STATIC}$: displacement under static load of F_0.

3) $\left|\dfrac{Y_0}{F_0/k}\right|$: magnification factor (MF). From equation (2.1.27),

$$MF = \frac{1}{\sqrt{(1-R^2)^2 + (2\varsigma R)^2}} \tag{2.1.29}$$

4) Consider three special cases as follows:

(i) $R \to 0$. Then $MF \to 1$ and $\phi \to 0$: The response is static.

(ii) $R = 1$. Then $MF = \dfrac{1}{2\varsigma}$ and $\phi = \dfrac{\pi}{2}$

(iii) $R \to \infty$. Then $MF \to 0$ and $\phi \to \pi$.

Resonance

For a lightly damped system, a large response occurs when the forcing frequency Ω is close to the natural frequency ω_n. This phenomenon is called *resonance*. The natural frequencies are also called the *resonance frequencies*.

(1) For system safety, avoid resonance.

(2) Resonance can be used to experimentally determine the natural frequency ω_n of a system. For this, apply $F \sim \sin \Omega t$ with variable Ω, and look for Ω, at which resonance occurs. If resonance occurs at $\Omega = \Omega_R$, then $\omega_n \sim \Omega_R$.

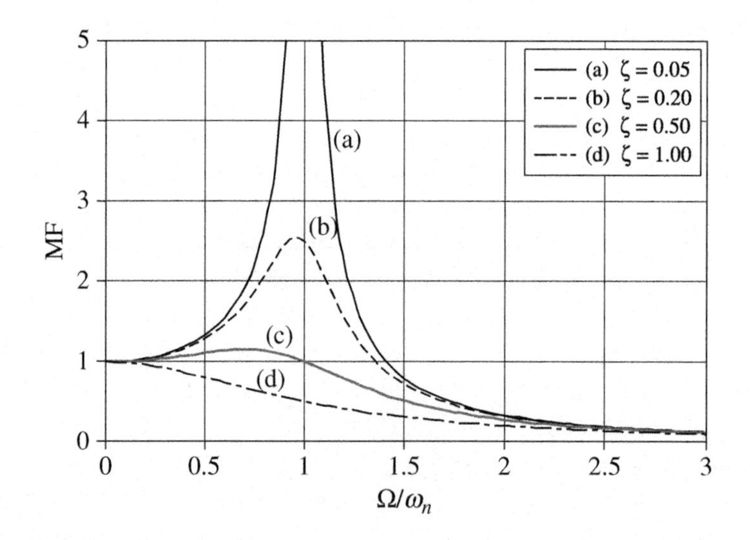

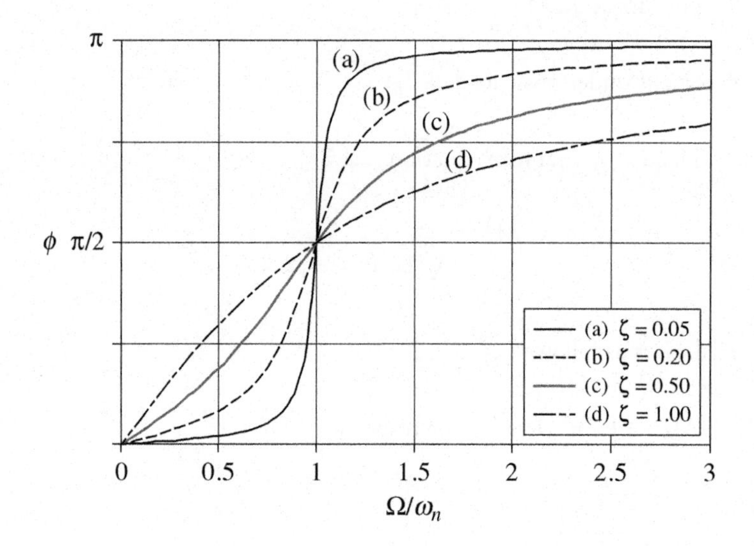

Figure 2.1 Magnification factor and phase angle.

Note:

It can be shown that for

$$F = F_0 \cos \Omega t, \tag{2.1.30}$$

$$y_P = Y_0 \cos(\Omega t - \phi) \tag{2.1.31}$$

where Y_0 is given in equation (2.1.27) and ϕ in equation (2.1.28).

2.2 Force Transmitted to the Base

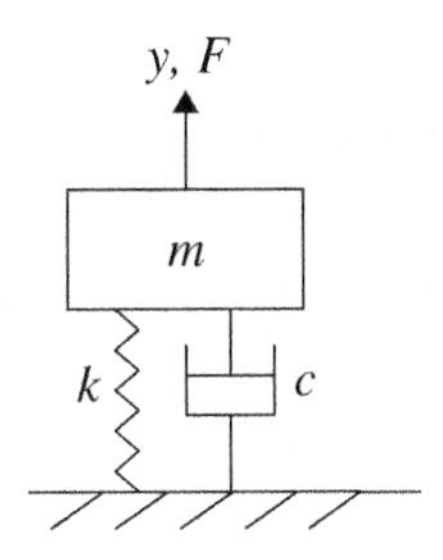

Figure 2.2 SDOF system on a rigid foundation.

F_T : force transmitted to the base

$$F_T = ky + c\dot{y} \tag{2.2.1}$$

For $F = F_0 \sin \Omega t$, recall that the steady-state response is

$$y = Y_0 \sin(\Omega t - \phi) \tag{2.2.2}$$

and

$$\dot{y} = Y_0 \Omega \cos(\Omega t - \phi) \tag{2.2.3}$$

Placing equations (2.2.2) and (2.2.3) to equation (2.2.1),

$$F_T = kY_0 \sin(\Omega t - \phi) + cY_0 \Omega \cos(\Omega t - \phi) \tag{2.2.4}$$

Equation (2.2.4) represents the force transmitted to the base corresponding to the steady-state response. The right-hand side of equation (2.2.4) can be expressed in a single sine function of time as follows:

$$F_T = \hat{F} \sin(\Omega t - \phi + \gamma) \tag{2.2.5}$$

where

$$\hat{F} = \sqrt{(kY_0)^2 + (cY_0\Omega)^2} \tag{2.2.6}$$

$$\gamma = \tan^{-1} \frac{cY_0\Omega}{kY_0} = \tan^{-1} 2\varsigma R \tag{2.2.7}$$

From equations (2.2.5) and (2.2.6),

$$\max |F_T| = \hat{F} = \sqrt{(kY_0)^2 + (cY_0\Omega)^2} = kY_0\sqrt{1 + (\frac{c\Omega}{k})^2} = kY_0\sqrt{1 + (2\varsigma R)^2} \tag{2.2.8}$$

As a nondimensional measure of force transmitted to the base, one may introduce **force transmissibility *TR***, defined as follows:

$$TR = \frac{\max |F_T|}{F_0} \tag{2.2.9}$$

Placing equation (2.2.8) into equation (2.2.9),

$$TR = \frac{kY_0}{F_0}\sqrt{1+(2\varsigma R)^2} = \frac{Y_0}{(\frac{F_0}{k})}\sqrt{1+(2\varsigma R)^2} = MF\sqrt{1+(2\varsigma R)^2} \tag{2.2.10}$$

where

$$MF = \frac{1}{\sqrt{(1-R^2)^2+(2\varsigma R)^2}} \tag{2.2.11}$$

Accordingly,

$$TR = \frac{\sqrt{1+(2\varsigma R)^2}}{\sqrt{(1-R^2)^2+(2\varsigma R)^2}} \tag{2.2.12}$$

Note:

1) For $R=1,\ TR=\frac{\sqrt{1+(2\varsigma)^2}}{2\varsigma}$

2) $TR=1$ for $R=\sqrt{2}$

3) For $R>\sqrt{2}$, TR increases as ς increases. So, decrease damping to decrease TR.

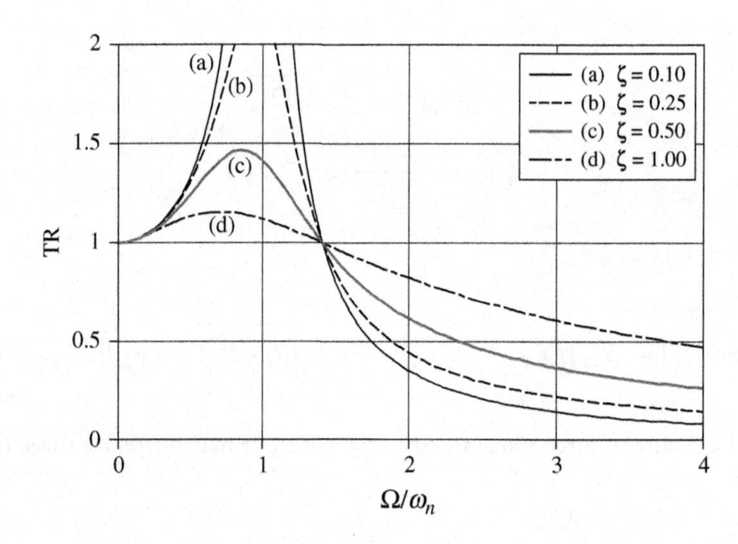

Figure 2.3 Force transmissibility versus frequency ratio.

2.3 Rotating Systems with Mass Unbalance

Examples: gas turbines, propellers, power transmission shafts, fans, laundry machines, automobile or aircraft landing gear, wheels, etc.

An engine with mass unbalance attached to a wing or fuselage, a helicopter tail rotor system attached to a tail boom, or a rotating tire wheel with mass unbalance can be modeled as a SDOF system.

A SDOF System Undergoing Vertical Motion

For a SDOF system undergoing vertical motion, mass unbalance can be represented by a single mass m_o with offset distance e from the axis of rotation as shown in the sketch.

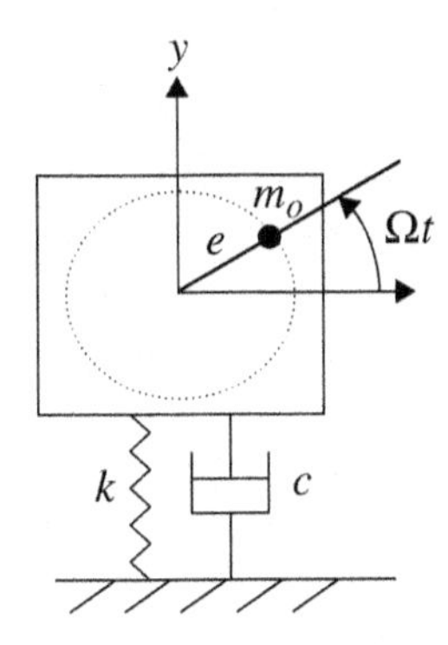

Figure 2.4 Rotating system with mass unbalance.

Equation of motion can be derived via Newton's second law as follows:

$$(m-m_o)\ddot{y}+m_o\frac{d^2}{dt^2}(y+e\sin\Omega t)=-c\dot{y}-ky \tag{2.3.1}$$

where m is the total mass.

$$(m-m_o)\ddot{y}+m_o\ddot{y}+m_o e(-\Omega^2\sin\Omega t)=-c\dot{y}-ky$$

$$m\ddot{y}+c\dot{y}+ky=m_o e\Omega^2\sin\Omega t=F_o\sin\Omega t \tag{2.3.2}$$

where

$$F_o=m_o e\Omega^2 \tag{2.3.3}$$

The right side of equation (2.3.2) represents the vertical component of the centrifugal force. The steady-state response corresponding to equation (2.3.2) is

$$y=Y_0\sin(\Omega t-\phi) \tag{2.3.4}$$

where

$$Y_0 = \frac{m_0 e\Omega^2}{k}\frac{1}{\sqrt{\left(1-R^2\right)^2+(2\varsigma R)^2}} = \frac{m_0 e}{m}\frac{R^2}{\sqrt{\left(1-R^2\right)^2+(2\varsigma R)^2}} \tag{2.3.5}$$

$$\varphi = \tan^{-1}\frac{2\varsigma R}{1-R^2} \tag{2.3.6}$$

Example 2.3.1 Consider a gas turbine engine mounted on an aircraft rear fuselage. The engine weighs 5,300 N and the natural frequency of the engine and mount assembly is 56.75 rad/sec. The gas turbine is out of balance and the unbalance is represented by em_0g = 38.82 N-mm where m_0 is the unbalanced mass and e is the offset distance. Determine the maximum force transmitted to the aircraft when the turbine operates at 6,500 rpm. Assume $\zeta = 0.1$.

Solution:

$$Y_0 = \frac{m_0 e\Omega^2}{k}\frac{1}{\sqrt{(1-R^2)^2+(2\varsigma R)^2}}$$

$$em_0 = \frac{38.82\times10^{-3}}{9.81} = 3.957\times10^{-3} \text{ kg-m}$$

$$k = m\omega_n^2 = \frac{5300}{9.81}(56.75)^2 = 1.74\times10^6 \text{ N/m}$$

$$\Omega = \frac{6500\times2\times\pi}{60\,\text{sec}} = 680.34 \text{ rad/sec}, \qquad R = \frac{680.34}{56.75} = 11.988$$

Accordingly, $Y_0 = 7.368\times10^{-6}$ m

Maximum force transmitted to the fuselage $= kY_0\sqrt{1+(2\varsigma R)^2} = 33.3$ N

2.4 SDOF Systems with Base Motion

Consider an instrument package mounted on a flight vehicle.

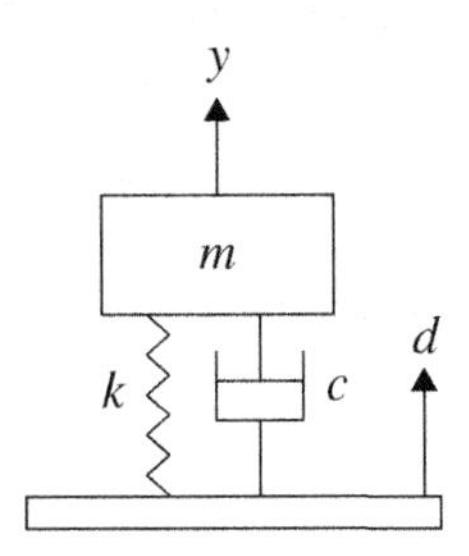

Figure 2.5 SDOF system with a moving base.

m: mass of the instrument package
c: damping constant of the mounting
k: spring constant of the mounting
y: displacement of the instrument
d: displacement of the base

Isolating the mass and considering the forces acting over it,

$$m\ddot{y} = -k(y-d) - c(\dot{y}-\dot{d}) \tag{2.4.1}$$

Relative displacement:
Introducing the relative displacement:

$$y_R = y - d \tag{2.4.2}$$

to equation (2.4.1),

$$m(\ddot{y}_R + \ddot{d}) = -ky_R - c\dot{y}_R \tag{2.4.3}$$

$$m\ddot{y}_R + c\dot{y}_R + ky_R = -m\ddot{d} \tag{2.4.4}$$

If the base is oscillating with frequency Ω and amplitude A such that

$$d = A\sin\Omega t \tag{2.4.5}$$

Then,

$$\ddot{d} = -A\Omega^2 \sin\Omega t \tag{2.4.6}$$

and equation (2.4.4) becomes

$$m\ddot{y}_R + c\dot{y}_R + ky_R = mA\Omega^2 \sin\Omega t = F_o \sin\Omega t \tag{2.4.7}$$

where $F_o = mA\Omega^2$

Equation (2.4.7) can be expressed as

$$\ddot{y}_R + 2\zeta\omega_n\dot{y}_R + \omega_n^2 y_R = A\Omega^2 \sin\Omega t \tag{2.4.8}$$

The steady-state response corresponding to equation (2.4.7) or (2.4.8) is

$$y_R = Y_0 \sin(\Omega t - \phi) \tag{2.4.9}$$

where

$$Y_0 = (\frac{F_o}{k})\frac{1}{\sqrt{(1-R^2)^2 + (2\varsigma R)^2}} = \frac{mA\Omega^2}{k}\frac{1}{\sqrt{(1-R^2)^2 + (2\varsigma R)^2}} \tag{2.4.10}$$

$$\phi = \tan^{-1}\frac{2\varsigma R}{1-R^2} \tag{2.4.11}$$

<u>Force transmitted to the base:</u>

$$F_T = ky_R + c\dot{y}_R \tag{2.4.12}$$

$$\max|F_T| = \hat{F} = \sqrt{(kY_0)^2 + (cY_0\Omega)^2} = kY_0\sqrt{1+(\frac{c\Omega}{k})^2} = kY_0\sqrt{1+(2\varsigma R)^2} \tag{2.4.13}$$

<u>Maximum absolute acceleration:</u>

From equation (2.4.1)

$$m\ddot{y} = -k(y-d) - c(\dot{y}-\dot{d}) = -ky_R - c\dot{y}_R \tag{2.4.14}$$

and

$$\max m|\ddot{y}| = \max|F_T| \tag{2.4.15}$$

From equation (2.4.13)

$$\max|\ddot{y}| = \frac{1}{m}kY_0\sqrt{1+(2\varsigma R)^2} \tag{2.4.16}$$

Also,

$$\max|\ddot{d}| = A\Omega^2 \tag{2.4.17}$$

Then, using equation (2.4.10)

$$\frac{\max|\ddot{y}|}{\max|\ddot{d}|} = \frac{\sqrt{1+(2\varsigma R)^2}}{\sqrt{(1-R^2)^2 + (2\varsigma R)^2}} \tag{2.4.18}$$

Equation (2.4.18) is identical to the equation for TR in (2.2.12).

Absolute displacement:
From equation (2.4.1)

$$m\ddot{y} + c\dot{y} + ky = kd + c\dot{d} \tag{2.4.19}$$

or

$$m\ddot{y} + c\dot{y} + ky = kA\sin\Omega t + cA\Omega\cos\Omega t \tag{2.4.20}$$

Then, for steady-state response

$$y = \frac{kA}{k}\frac{1}{\sqrt{(1-R^2)^2 + (2\varsigma R)^2}}\sin(\Omega t - \phi) + \frac{cA\Omega}{k}\frac{1}{\sqrt{(1-R^2)^2 + (2\varsigma R)^2}}\cos(\Omega t - \phi) \tag{2.4.21}$$

or

$$y = A\frac{\sqrt{1 + \left(\frac{c\Omega}{k}\right)^2}}{\sqrt{(1-R^2)^2 + (2\varsigma R)^2}}\sin(\Omega t - \phi + \gamma) \tag{2.4.22}$$

or

$$y = A\frac{\sqrt{1 + (2\varsigma R)^2}}{\sqrt{(1-R^2)^2 + (2\varsigma R)^2}}\sin(\Omega t - \phi + \gamma) \tag{2.4.23}$$

$$\frac{\max|y|}{\max|d|} = \frac{\sqrt{1 + (2\varsigma R)^2}}{\sqrt{(1-R^2)^2 + (2\varsigma R)^2}} \tag{2.4.24}$$

From equation (2.4.22)

$$\ddot{y} = -A\Omega^2\frac{\sqrt{1 + (2\varsigma R)^2}}{\sqrt{(1-R^2)^2 + (2\varsigma R)^2}}\sin(\Omega t - \phi + \gamma) \tag{2.4.25}$$

$$\max|\ddot{d}| = A\Omega^2 \tag{2.4.26}$$

Then,

$$\frac{\max|\ddot{y}|}{\max|\ddot{d}|}=\frac{\sqrt{1+(2\varsigma R)^2}}{\sqrt{(1-R^2)^2+(2\varsigma R)^2}} \tag{2.4.27}$$

Example 2.4.1 An instrument package weighing 890 N is to be mounted on a flight vehicle. An elastic mounting is used to protect the package from vibration of the base. The base is vibrating with a frequency of 18 *Hz*.

Under the steady-state condition, the maximum acceleration allowed for the package is 10% of the maximum acceleration of the base. Determine the upper bound to the effective spring constant of the mounting.

Solution:

$$\frac{\max|\ddot{y}|}{\max|\ddot{d}|}=\frac{\sqrt{1+(2\varsigma R)^2}}{\sqrt{(1-R^2)^2+(2\varsigma R)^2}}\leq 0.1$$

Assuming a small damping ratio,

$$\frac{\max|\ddot{y}|}{\max|\ddot{d}|}\approx\frac{1}{\sqrt{(1-R^2)^2}}\leq 0.1$$

Squaring the above equation and inverting,

$$(1-R^2)^2\geq 100 \quad \rightarrow \quad R^4-2R^2-99\geq 0$$

For equation $R^4-2R^2-99=0$, the solutions are as follows:

$$R^2=1\pm 10$$

Choosing the physically feasible solution,

$$R^2=11$$

To satisfy the inequality,

$$R^2\geq 11$$

$$\Omega^2\geq 11\omega_n^2 \rightarrow \omega_n^2\leq\frac{1}{11}\Omega^2 \rightarrow \frac{k}{m}\leq\frac{1}{11}\Omega^2 \rightarrow k\leq\frac{1}{11}m\Omega^2$$

Accordingly,

$$k \le \frac{1}{11}\left(\frac{890}{9.81}\right)(18\times 2\pi)^2 \rightarrow k \le 1.055\times 10^5\, N/m$$

which provides the upper bound to k.

Chapter 2 Problem Sets

2.1 An engine on elastic mounting is modeled as a SDOF system. The unbalanced engine weighs 2,500 N. It is required that the force transmitted to the fuselage bulkhead (assumed as a fixed base) be isolated such that TR is less than 0.1 or 10 %. Consider a design with negligible damping and determine the following.

(a) Lower bound of the frequency ratio.
(b) Spring constant of the mounting for an engine rpm of 5,000.

2.2 An instrument weighing 1,250 N is mounted on a base inside a spacecraft. For the mounting, the spring constant is k = 1,170 N/cm. and the damping ratio is $\varsigma = 0.018$. Measurements show that the instrument package vibrates at a steady-state frequency of 20 Hz with the maximum relative displacement of 4.0 mm. Determine the following:

(a) Displacement amplitude of the base.
(b) Maximum acceleration of the base.
(c) Maximum absolute acceleration of the instrument package.

2.3 An instrument package weighing 300 lbs. is to be mounted on a flight vehicle. An elastic mounting is used to protect the package from vibration of the base. The base is vibrating with amplitude of 0.2 in. and frequency of 18 Hz. The spring constant of the mounting is set at k = 9,000 lb/ft., and the damping ratio of the mounting is $\varsigma = 0.03$. Determine the following:

(a) Maximum relative displacement of the package.
(b) Maximum force transmitted to the base.
(c) Maximum absolute acceleration.

2.4 Consider a gas turbine engine mounted on the rear fuselage of an aircraft. The engine weighs 4,450 N, and the engine mount deflects 2.5 mm downward under the weight. The turbine operates at 7,500 rpm. The engine is out of balance, and the maximum force transmitted to the airframe bulkhead is measured to be 110 N. Neglect the mass of the engine mount and assume $\varsigma = 0.1$. Determine the following:

(a) Effective spring constant k.
(b) Frequency of damped free vibration (rad/sec).
(c) em_0g (N-m) as a measure of mass unbalance.
(d) Magnitude of the centrifugal force.

2.5 An aircraft instrument weighing 130N needs to be isolated from vibration of a reciprocating engine with rpm ranging from 1300 to 1700. What is the spring constant (upper bound) of the mounting (or the cushion) for 95% isolation in acceleration? (That is, the maximum absolute acceleration allowed for the instrument is not to exceed 5% of the maximum acceleration of the base.)

2.6 A centrifugal pump weighs 550 N and operates at 1,200 rpm. The vertical spring constants of the mounting is 36,000 N/m. The amplitude of displacement due to mass unbalance is not to exceed 3 *mm*. Determine the following for a damping ratio of 0.01.

(a) Maximum mass unbalance allowed (in terms of $m_0 e$)
(b) Centrifugal force
(c) Force transmitted to the base

2.7 For the system shown in the sketch, mass m_A is connected to mass m_1 via a rigid lever resting on the two fulcrums. The distance between the left fulcrum and the right fulcrum is e and the distance between mass m_A and the left fulcrum is d. Rotation of the lever is assumed small.

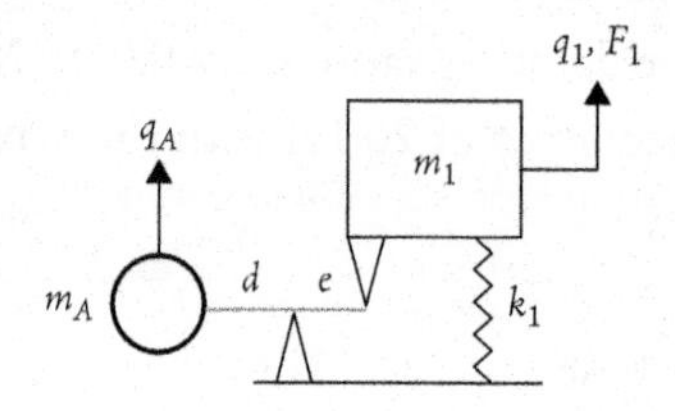

(a) Show that, from geometric consideration, displacements q_A and q_1 are related such that

$$q_A = \alpha q_1 \qquad \text{where } \alpha = -\frac{d}{e}$$

(b) Construct the equation of vertical motion for mass m_1 and another equation of angular motion for mass m_A rotating about the left fulcrum. Combine the two equations via the reaction force at the right fulcrum to show that

$$m_{eff}\ddot{q}_1 + k_1 q_1 = F_1$$

where

$$m_{eff} = m_1\left[1+\beta\alpha^2\right],\ \beta = \frac{m_A}{m_1}$$

and the natural frequency is $\omega_n = \sqrt{\dfrac{k_1}{m_{eff}}}$

(c) For $F_1 = F_0 \sin\Omega t$, find the expression for the force transmitted to the base. What is the force transmitted to the base if the following condition is satisfied?

$$k_1 + \Omega^2 m_A (1-\alpha)\alpha = 0$$

3 DYNAMIC RESPONSE OF MDOF SYSTEMS

In many practical situations, it is necessary to introduce multiple degrees of freedom (MDOF) to properly model dynamic behavior of a structure or system. In this chapter, we will consider dynamic systems that can be modeled using a collection of multiple masses, springs, and dampers. For more complicated structural systems, one can use the more powerful and versatile finite element method, which will be introduced in a later chapter. The primary topics to be covered in this chapter are as follows:

3.1 Equation of motion via Newton's second law
3.2 Free vibration of undamped MDOF systems
3.3 Forced vibration of undamped MDOF systems

In Section 3.1, we will apply Newton's second law of motion to construct the equation of motion for a MDOF system, which can be expressed in matrix form as follows:

$$\mathbf{M}\ddot{\mathbf{q}} + \mathbf{C}\dot{\mathbf{q}} + \mathbf{K}\mathbf{q} = \mathbf{F}$$

where $\mathbf{M}$: $N \times N$ mass matrix
$\mathbf{C}$: $N \times N$ damping matrix
$\mathbf{K}$: $N \times N$ stiffness matrix
$\mathbf{q}$: $N \times 1$ DOF vector
$\mathbf{F}$: $N \times 1$ load vector
N: the number of degrees of freedom

In Section 3.2, we will learn that when an undamped system undergoes free vibration, the system vibrates at certain frequencies called *natural frequencies* and with certain modes (or mode shapes) called *natural modes*. These natural frequencies and natural modes are dependent on system mass and stiffness properties. Mathematically, investigation of free vibration is an exercise in eigenvalue analysis.

In Section 3.3, we will learn that when damping is small and negligible, a MDOF system with N degrees of freedom can be transformed into a linear combination of N SDOF systems. These SDOF equations can be solved using the techniques that we have learned in Chapters 1 and 2.

In addition, we will consider such topics as steady-state response, first-order representation, or the state space vector form of equations of motion and numerical integration in time.

3.1 Equation of Motion via Newton's Second Law

Example 3.1.1 Consider a two-DOF system as shown in the sketch. It may be considered a crude model constructed to study longitudinal vibration of a rocket on a test stand.

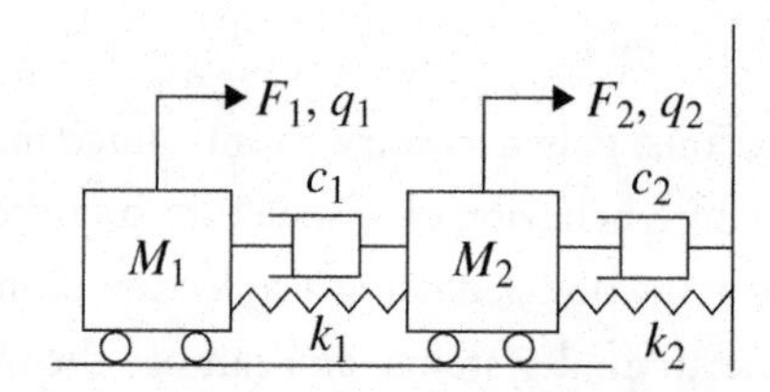

Figure 3.1 A two-DOF system.

The equation of motion is constructed as follows:

Mass 1:

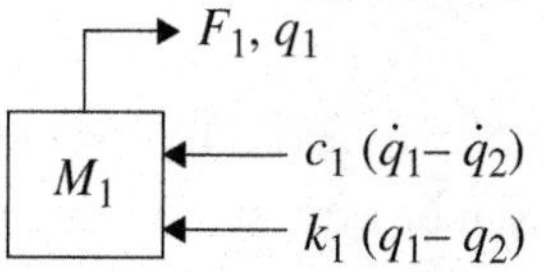

F_1, q_1

M_1

$c_1(\dot{q}_1 - \dot{q}_2)$

$k_1(q_1 - q_2)$

Figure 3.2 Free-body diagram for mass 1.

$$M_1\ddot{q}_1 = F_1 - k_1(q_1 - q_2) - c_1(\dot{q}_1 - \dot{q}_2)$$

$$M_1\ddot{q}_1 + c_1(\dot{q}_1 - \dot{q}_2) + k_1(q_1 - q_2) = F_1 \tag{3.1.1}$$

Mass 2:

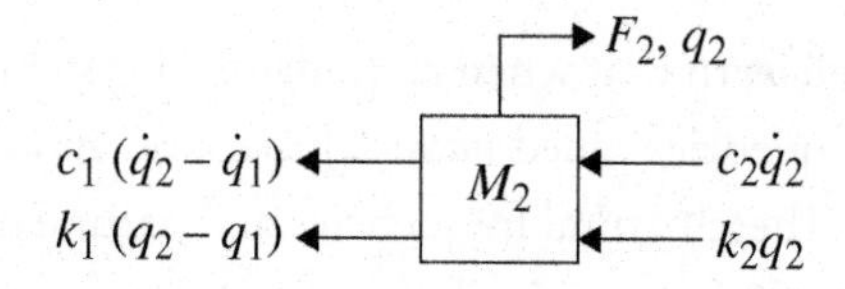

Figure 3.3 Free-body diagram for mass 2.

$$M_2\ddot{q}_2 = F_2 - k_1(q_2 - q_1) - k_2 q_2 - c_1(\dot{q}_2 - \dot{q}_1) - c_2\dot{q}_2$$

$$M_2\ddot{q}_2 - c_1\dot{q}_1 + (c_1 + c_2)\dot{q}_2 - k_1 q_1 + (k_1 + k_2)q_2 = F_2 \tag{3.1.2}$$

Equations (3.1.1) and (3.1.2) can be written in matrix form as follows:

$$\begin{bmatrix} M_1 & 0 \\ 0 & M_2 \end{bmatrix}\begin{Bmatrix} \ddot{q}_1 \\ \ddot{q}_2 \end{Bmatrix} + \begin{bmatrix} c_1 & -c_1 \\ -c_1 & c_1 + c_2 \end{bmatrix}\begin{Bmatrix} \dot{q}_1 \\ \dot{q}_2 \end{Bmatrix} + \begin{bmatrix} k_1 & -k_1 \\ -k_1 & k_1 + k_2 \end{bmatrix}\begin{Bmatrix} q_1 \\ q_2 \end{Bmatrix} = \begin{Bmatrix} F_1 \\ F_2 \end{Bmatrix} \tag{3.1.3}$$

or

$$\mathbf{M}\ddot{\mathbf{q}} + \mathbf{C}\dot{\mathbf{q}} + \mathbf{K}\mathbf{q} = \mathbf{F} \tag{3.1.4}$$

where $\mathbf{q} = \begin{Bmatrix} q_1 \\ q_2 \end{Bmatrix}$: DOF vector

$\mathbf{M} = \begin{bmatrix} M_1 & 0 \\ 0 & M_2 \end{bmatrix}$: mass matrix

$\mathbf{C} = \begin{bmatrix} c_1 & -c_1 \\ -c_1 & c_1 + c_2 \end{bmatrix}$: damping matrix

$\mathbf{K} = \begin{bmatrix} k_1 & -k_1 \\ -k_1 & k_1 + k_2 \end{bmatrix}$: stiffness matrix

$\mathbf{F} = \begin{Bmatrix} F_1 \\ F_2 \end{Bmatrix}$: load vector

Note:

A similar approach can be used to construct equations of motion for systems with more than two DOF.

3.2 Free Vibration of Undamped MDOF Systems

For free vibration ($\mathbf{F} = \mathbf{0}$) of an undamped system, the equation of motion is

$$\mathbf{M}\ddot{\mathbf{q}} + \mathbf{K}\mathbf{q} = \mathbf{0} \tag{3.2.1}$$

Equation (3.2.1) is a homogeneous equation of second order in time for **q**. The solution of equation (3.2.1) is harmonic in time and can be expressed as

$$\mathbf{q} = \boldsymbol{\varphi} e^{\pm i\omega t} \tag{3.2.2}$$

For a two-DOF system,

$$\begin{Bmatrix} q_1 \\ q_2 \end{Bmatrix} = \begin{Bmatrix} \phi_1 \\ \phi_2 \end{Bmatrix} e^{\pm i\omega t} \tag{3.2.3}$$

where

$e^{\pm i\omega t}$: oscillatory with frequency ω

$\boldsymbol{\varphi} = \begin{Bmatrix} \phi_1 \\ \phi_2 \end{Bmatrix}$: independent of time, called mode

Placing equation (3.2.2) into equation (3.2.1),

$$\mathbf{M}(\pm i\omega)^2 \boldsymbol{\varphi} e^{\pm i\omega t} + \mathbf{K}\boldsymbol{\varphi} e^{\pm i\omega t} = \mathbf{0} \rightarrow (\mathbf{K} - \omega^2\mathbf{M})\boldsymbol{\varphi} e^{\pm i\omega t} = \mathbf{0} \tag{3.2.4}$$

From equation (3.2.4),

$$(\mathbf{K} - \omega^2\mathbf{M})\boldsymbol{\varphi} = \mathbf{0} \tag{3.2.5}$$

Equation (3.2.5) is a homogeneous algebraic equation. For nontrivial $\boldsymbol{\varphi}$, the following equation must be satisfied:

$$\det\ (\mathbf{K} - \omega^2\mathbf{M}) = 0 \tag{3.2.6}$$

where *det* stands for the determinant.

For given **K** and **M**, equation (3.2.6) holds for specific values of ω^2. These specific values are called **eigenvalues.** For given ω, one can use equation (3.2.5) to determine $\boldsymbol{\varphi}$, called eigenvector. Note that equation (3.2.5) is a homogeneous equation. Accordingly, an eigenvector is determined with a constant multiple. In vibration, ω are called **undamped natural frequencies** and eigenvectors $\boldsymbol{\varphi}$ are called **natural modes.**

Example 3.2.1 Let's consider the system shown in the sketch.

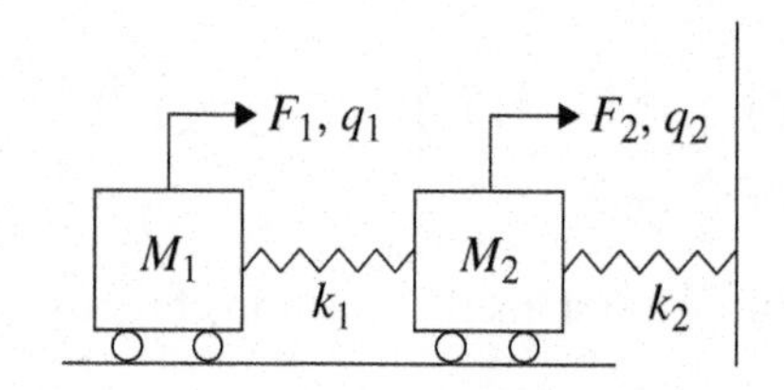

Figure 3.4 Two-DOF system with no damping.

The equation of motion is as follows:

$$\begin{bmatrix} M_1 & 0 \\ 0 & M_2 \end{bmatrix}\begin{Bmatrix} \ddot{q}_1 \\ \ddot{q}_2 \end{Bmatrix}+\begin{bmatrix} k_1 & -k_1 \\ -k_1 & k_1+k_2 \end{bmatrix}\begin{Bmatrix} q_1 \\ q_2 \end{Bmatrix}=\begin{Bmatrix} F_1 \\ F_2 \end{Bmatrix} \tag{3.2.7}$$

or

$$\mathbf{M}\ddot{\mathbf{q}}+\mathbf{K}\mathbf{q}=\mathbf{F} \tag{3.2.8}$$

For free vibration $(\mathbf{F}=\mathbf{0})$,

$$\mathbf{M}\ddot{\mathbf{q}}+\mathbf{K}\mathbf{q}=\mathbf{0} \tag{3.2.9}$$

Now, consider the following case:

$$M_1=m,\ M_2=2m,\ k_1=k_2=k, \tag{3.2.10}$$

Then,

$$\mathbf{M}=\begin{bmatrix} m & 0 \\ 0 & 2m \end{bmatrix}=m\begin{bmatrix} 1 & 0 \\ 0 & 2 \end{bmatrix} \tag{3.2.11}$$

$$\mathbf{K}=\begin{bmatrix} k & -k \\ -k & 2k \end{bmatrix}=k\begin{bmatrix} 1 & -1 \\ -1 & 2 \end{bmatrix} \tag{3.2.12}$$

(a) To determine the eigenvalues and thus natural frequencies, let's proceed as follows:

For free vibration,

$$(\mathbf{K}-\omega^2\mathbf{M})\boldsymbol{\varphi}=\mathbf{0} \tag{3.2.13}$$

With **K** and **M** as shown in equations (3.2.11) and (3.2.12), equation (3.2.13) is expressed as

$$\left(k\begin{bmatrix} 1 & -1 \\ -1 & 2 \end{bmatrix}-\omega^2 m\begin{bmatrix} 1 & 0 \\ 0 & 2 \end{bmatrix}\right)\begin{Bmatrix} \phi_1 \\ \phi_2 \end{Bmatrix}=\begin{Bmatrix} 0 \\ 0 \end{Bmatrix} \tag{3.2.14}$$

or

$$\left(\begin{bmatrix} 1 & -1 \\ -1 & 2 \end{bmatrix}-\bar{p}\begin{bmatrix} 1 & 0 \\ 0 & 2 \end{bmatrix}\right)\begin{Bmatrix} \phi_1 \\ \phi_2 \end{Bmatrix}=\begin{Bmatrix} 0 \\ 0 \end{Bmatrix} \tag{3.2.15}$$

where

$$\bar{p}=\frac{\omega^2 m}{k} \tag{3.2.16}$$

or

$$\begin{bmatrix} 1-\bar{p} & -1 \\ -1 & 2-2\bar{p} \end{bmatrix} \begin{Bmatrix} \phi_1 \\ \phi_2 \end{Bmatrix} = \begin{Bmatrix} 0 \\ 0 \end{Bmatrix} \tag{3.2.17}$$

For nontrivial $\begin{Bmatrix} \phi_1 \\ \phi_2 \end{Bmatrix}$,

$$\det \begin{bmatrix} 1-\bar{p} & -1 \\ -1 & 2-2\bar{p} \end{bmatrix} = 0 \tag{3.2.18}$$

or

$$\begin{aligned} &(1-\bar{p})(2-2\bar{p})-1=0 \\ &\rightarrow 2\bar{p}^2-4\bar{p}+1=0 \end{aligned} \tag{3.2.19}$$

From equation (3.2.19), we obtain

$$\bar{p} = 1 \pm \frac{1}{\sqrt{2}}$$

or

$$\bar{p}_1 = 1-\frac{1}{\sqrt{2}} \approx 0.293, \quad \bar{p}_2 = 1+\frac{1}{\sqrt{2}} \approx 1.707 \tag{3.2.20}$$

From equation (3.2.16),

$$\omega^2 = \bar{p}\frac{k}{m} \tag{3.2.21}$$

and

$$\omega_1^{\ 2} = \bar{p}_1 \frac{k}{m} = 0.293\frac{k}{m} \quad \rightarrow \quad \omega_1 = \sqrt{0.293\frac{k}{m}} \tag{3.2.22}$$

$$\omega_2^{\ 2} = \bar{p}_2 \frac{k}{m} = 1.707\frac{k}{m} \quad \rightarrow \quad \omega_2 = \sqrt{1.707\frac{k}{m}} \tag{3.2.23}$$

(b) To determine the eigenvectors and thus the natural modes of free vibration, let's proceed as follows:

Placing $\bar{p}_1$ in equation (3.2.20) into equation (3.2.17),

$$\begin{bmatrix} 1-\left(1-\frac{1}{\sqrt{2}}\right) & -1 \\ -1 & 2-2\left(1-\frac{1}{\sqrt{2}}\right) \end{bmatrix} \begin{Bmatrix} \phi_1 \\ \phi_2 \end{Bmatrix} = \begin{Bmatrix} 0 \\ 0 \end{Bmatrix} \tag{3.2.24}$$

$$\begin{bmatrix} \frac{1}{\sqrt{2}} & -1 \\ -1 & \sqrt{2} \end{bmatrix} \begin{Bmatrix} \phi_1 \\ \phi_2 \end{Bmatrix} = \begin{Bmatrix} 0 \\ 0 \end{Bmatrix} \tag{3.2.25}$$

Equation (3.2.25) can be expressed in two equations as follows:

$$\frac{1}{\sqrt{2}}\phi_1 - \phi_2 = 0 \rightarrow -\phi_1 + \sqrt{2}\phi_2 = 0 \qquad (3.2.26a)$$

$$-\phi_1 + \sqrt{2}\phi_2 = 0 \qquad (3.2.26b)$$

We see that equation (3.2.26a) is identical to equation (3.2.26b). So, the two equations are linearly dependent, and there is only one equation for two unknowns.

From equation (3.2.26),

$$\phi_2 = \frac{1}{\sqrt{2}}\phi_1 \qquad (3.2.27)$$

If we choose $\phi_1 = 1$, then $\phi_2 = \frac{1}{\sqrt{2}}$. In matrix form

$$\boldsymbol{\varphi}_1 = \begin{Bmatrix} \phi_1 \\ \phi_2 \end{Bmatrix}_1 = \begin{Bmatrix} 1 \\ 1/\sqrt{2} \end{Bmatrix} \qquad (3.2.28)$$

The above vector is called an eigenvector. Subscript "1" indicates that it corresponds to $\overline{p}_1$. Note that any constant multiple of the above eigenvector is also a solution to the equation.

Similarly, placing $\overline{p}_2$ in equation (3.2.20) into equation (3.2.17),

$$\begin{bmatrix} 1-\left(1+\frac{1}{\sqrt{2}}\right) & -1 \\ -1 & 2-2\left(1+\frac{1}{\sqrt{2}}\right) \end{bmatrix} \begin{Bmatrix} \phi_1 \\ \phi_2 \end{Bmatrix} = \begin{Bmatrix} 0 \\ 0 \end{Bmatrix} \qquad (3.2.29)$$

$$\begin{bmatrix} -\frac{1}{\sqrt{2}} & -1 \\ -1 & -\sqrt{2} \end{bmatrix} \begin{Bmatrix} \phi_1 \\ \phi_2 \end{Bmatrix} = \begin{Bmatrix} 0 \\ 0 \end{Bmatrix} \qquad (3.2.30)$$

Equation (3.2.30) can be expressed in two equations as follows:

$$-\frac{1}{\sqrt{2}}\phi_1 - \phi_2 = 0 \rightarrow -\phi_1 - \sqrt{2}\phi_2 = 0 \qquad (3.2.31a)$$

$$-\phi_1 - \sqrt{2}\phi_2 = 0 \qquad (3.2.31b)$$

We note that equation (3.2.31a) is identical to equation (3.2.31b). So, the two equations are linearly dependent, and there is only one equation for two unknowns.

From equation (3.2.31),

$$\phi_2 = -\frac{1}{\sqrt{2}}\phi_1$$

If we choose $\phi_1 = 1$, then $\phi_2 = -\frac{1}{\sqrt{2}}$. In matrix form

$$\boldsymbol{\varphi}_2 = \begin{Bmatrix} \phi_1 \\ \phi_2 \end{Bmatrix}_2 = \begin{Bmatrix} 1 \\ -1/\sqrt{2} \end{Bmatrix} \tag{3.2.32}$$

The above vector is called an eigenvector. Subscript "2" indicates that it corresponds to $\overline{p}_2$. Note that any constant multiple of the above eigenvector is also a solution to equation (3.2.30).

Summarizing:

The first mode:

$\omega_1 = \sqrt{0.293\frac{k}{m}}$: the first natural frequency, $\boldsymbol{\varphi}_1 = \begin{Bmatrix} \phi_1 \\ \phi_2 \end{Bmatrix}_1 = \begin{Bmatrix} 1 \\ 1/\sqrt{2} \end{Bmatrix}$: the first natural mode

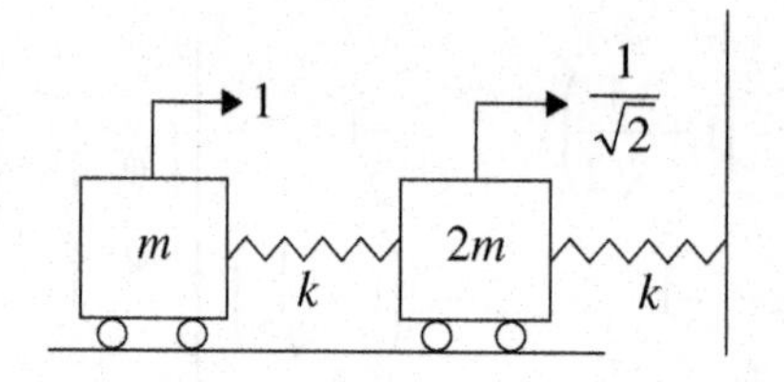

Figure 3.5a Mode 1.

The second mode:

$\omega_2 = \sqrt{1.707\frac{k}{m}}$: the second natural frequency, $\boldsymbol{\varphi}_2 = \begin{Bmatrix} \phi_1 \\ \phi_2 \end{Bmatrix}_2 = \begin{Bmatrix} 1 \\ -1/\sqrt{2} \end{Bmatrix}$: the second natural mode

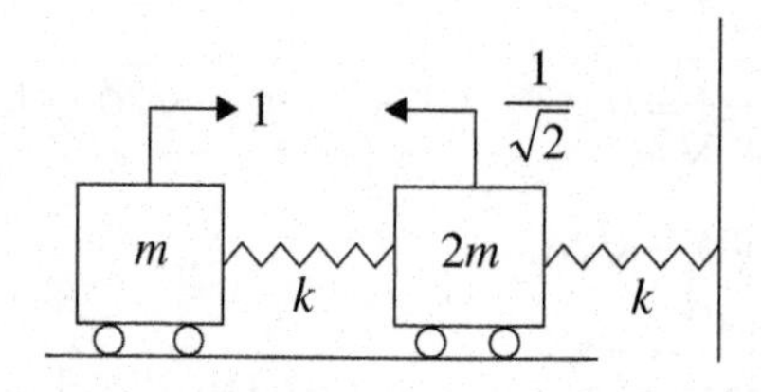

Figure 3.5b Mode 2.

Example 3.2.2 Consider a system of two masses connected by a spring.

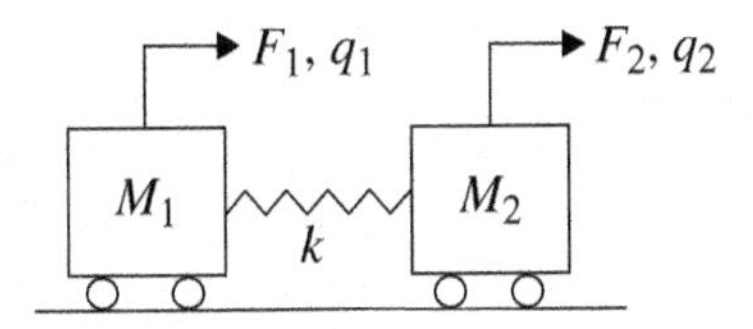

Figure 3.6 Two masses connected by a spring.

Note:

The system is allowed to undergo rigid body translation.

Equation of motion:

$$\begin{bmatrix} M_1 & 0 \\ 0 & M_2 \end{bmatrix} \begin{Bmatrix} \ddot{q}_1 \\ \ddot{q}_2 \end{Bmatrix} + \begin{bmatrix} k & -k \\ -k & k \end{bmatrix} \begin{Bmatrix} q_1 \\ q_2 \end{Bmatrix} = \begin{Bmatrix} F_1 \\ F_2 \end{Bmatrix} \tag{3.2.33}$$

or

$$\mathbf{M}\ddot{\mathbf{q}} + \mathbf{K}\mathbf{q} = \mathbf{F} \tag{3.2.34}$$

For free vibration,

$$\mathbf{M}\ddot{\mathbf{q}} + \mathbf{K}\mathbf{q} = \mathbf{0} \tag{3.2.35}$$

Let's consider the following cases: $M_2 = m$, $\dfrac{M_1}{M_2} = c$: mass ratio

(a) Determination of the eigenvalues and thus the natural frequencies

For free vibration,

$$(\mathbf{K} - \omega^2\mathbf{M})\boldsymbol{\varphi} = \mathbf{0} \tag{3.2.36}$$

Equation (3.2.36) can be expressed as

$$\left(k\begin{bmatrix} 1 & -1 \\ -1 & 1 \end{bmatrix} - \omega^2 m \begin{bmatrix} c & 0 \\ 0 & 1 \end{bmatrix} \right) \begin{Bmatrix} \phi_1 \\ \phi_2 \end{Bmatrix} = \begin{Bmatrix} 0 \\ 0 \end{Bmatrix} \tag{3.2.37}$$

or

$$\left(\begin{bmatrix} 1 & -1 \\ -1 & 1 \end{bmatrix} - \overline{p} \begin{bmatrix} c & 0 \\ 0 & 1 \end{bmatrix} \right) \begin{Bmatrix} \phi_1 \\ \phi_2 \end{Bmatrix} = \begin{Bmatrix} 0 \\ 0 \end{Bmatrix} \tag{3.2.38}$$

where
$$\bar{p} = \frac{\omega^2 m}{k} \tag{3.2.39}$$

or

$$\begin{bmatrix} 1-c\bar{p} & -1 \\ -1 & 1-\bar{p} \end{bmatrix} \begin{Bmatrix} \phi_1 \\ \phi_2 \end{Bmatrix} = \begin{Bmatrix} 0 \\ 0 \end{Bmatrix} \tag{3.2.40}$$

For nontrivial $\begin{Bmatrix} \phi_1 \\ \phi_2 \end{Bmatrix}$,

$$\det \begin{bmatrix} 1-c\bar{p} & -1 \\ -1 & 1-\bar{p} \end{bmatrix} = 0 \tag{3.2.41}$$

or

$$\begin{aligned} &(1-c\bar{p})(1-\bar{p})-1=0 \\ &\rightarrow 1-(1+c)\bar{p}+c\bar{p}^2-1=0 \\ &\rightarrow \bar{p}[c\bar{p}-(c+1)]=0 \end{aligned} \tag{3.2.42}$$

From equation (3.2.42), we obtain

$$\bar{p}=0,\ \frac{c+1}{c}$$

or

$$\bar{p}_1=0,\ \bar{p}_2=\frac{c+1}{c} \tag{3.2.43}$$

From equation (3.2.39),

$$\omega^2 = \bar{p}\frac{k}{m} \tag{3.2.44}$$

and

$$\omega_1^2 = \bar{p}_1\frac{k}{m}=0 \rightarrow \omega_1=0 \tag{3.2.45}$$

$$\omega_2^2 = \bar{p}_2\frac{k}{m}=\frac{c+1}{c}\frac{k}{m} \rightarrow \omega_2=\sqrt{\frac{c+1}{c}\frac{k}{m}} \tag{3.2.46}$$

(b) Determination of the eigenvectors and thus the natural modes of free vibration

Placing $\bar{p}_1$ in equation (3.2.43) into equation (3.2.40),

$$\begin{bmatrix} 1 & -1 \\ -1 & 1 \end{bmatrix} \begin{Bmatrix} \phi_1 \\ \phi_2 \end{Bmatrix} = \begin{Bmatrix} 0 \\ 0 \end{Bmatrix} \tag{3.2.47}$$

Equation (3.2.47) can be expressed in two equations as follows:

$$\phi_1 - \phi_2 = 0 \tag{3.2.48a}$$

$$-\phi_1 + \phi_2 = 0 \tag{3.2.48b}$$

We see that equation (3.2.48a) is identical to equation (3.2.48b). So, there is only one equation for two unknowns.

From equation (3.2.48), $$\phi_2 = \phi_1 \tag{3.2.49}$$

If we choose $\phi_1 = 1$, then $\phi_2 = 1$. In matrix form:

$$\boldsymbol{\varphi}_1 = \begin{Bmatrix} \phi_1 \\ \phi_2 \end{Bmatrix}_1 = \begin{Bmatrix} 1 \\ 1 \end{Bmatrix} \tag{3.2.50}$$

The above column vector is the eigenvector. We note that any constant multiple of the above eigenvector is also a solution to equation (3.2.47).

Similarly, placing $\overline{p}_2$ in equation (3.2.43) into equation (3.2.40),

$$\begin{bmatrix} 1-(c+1) & -1 \\ -1 & 1-\dfrac{c+1}{c} \end{bmatrix} \begin{Bmatrix} \phi_1 \\ \phi_2 \end{Bmatrix} = \begin{Bmatrix} 0 \\ 0 \end{Bmatrix} \tag{3.2.51}$$

$$\begin{bmatrix} -c & -1 \\ -1 & -1/c \end{bmatrix} \begin{Bmatrix} \phi_1 \\ \phi_2 \end{Bmatrix} = \begin{Bmatrix} 0 \\ 0 \end{Bmatrix} \tag{3.2.52}$$

Equation (3.2.52) can be expressed in two equations as follows:

$$-c\phi_1 - \phi_2 = 0 \tag{3.2.53a}$$

$$-\phi_1 - \frac{1}{c}\phi_2 = 0 \tag{3.2.53b}$$

We note that equation (3.2.53a) is identical to equation (3.2.53b). So, there is only one equation for two unknowns.

From equation (3.2.53), $$\phi_2 = -c\phi_1 \tag{3.2.54}$$

If we choose $\phi_1 = 1$, then $\phi_2 = -c$. In matrix form:

$$\boldsymbol{\varphi}_2 = \begin{Bmatrix} \phi_1 \\ \phi_2 \end{Bmatrix}_2 = \begin{Bmatrix} 1 \\ -c \end{Bmatrix} \tag{3.2.55}$$

The above column vector is the second eigenvector (corresponding to $\overline{p}_2$). We note that any constant multiple of the above eigenvector is also a solution to equation (3.2.52).

Summarizing:

The first mode:

$$\omega_1 = 0, \qquad \boldsymbol{\varphi}_1 = \begin{Bmatrix} \phi_1 \\ \phi_2 \end{Bmatrix}_1 = \begin{Bmatrix} 1 \\ 1 \end{Bmatrix} \tag{3.2.56}$$

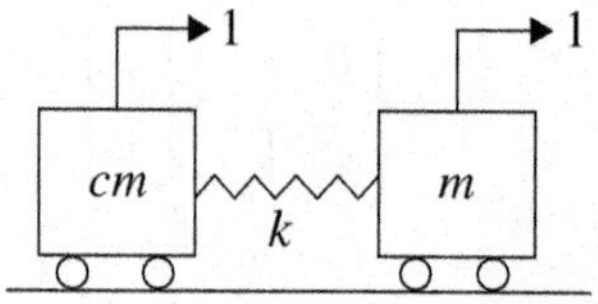

Figure 3.7a Mode 1 for rigid body translation.

Note:
Mode 1 is a rigid body mode and there is no strain energy stored in the spring.

The second mode:

$$\omega_2 = \sqrt{\frac{c+1}{c}\frac{k}{m}}, \qquad \boldsymbol{\varphi}_2 = \begin{Bmatrix} \phi_1 \\ \phi_2 \end{Bmatrix}_2 = \begin{Bmatrix} 1 \\ -c \end{Bmatrix} \tag{3.2.57}$$

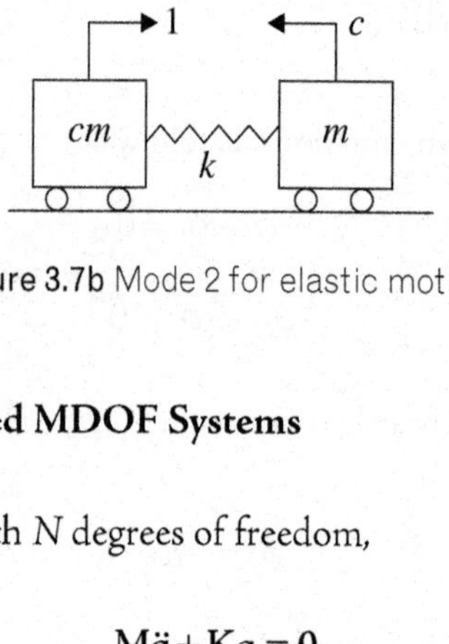

Figure 3.7b Mode 2 for elastic motion.

Summary: Free Vibration of Undamped MDOF Systems

For free vibration ($\mathbf{F} = \mathbf{0}$) of a system with N degrees of freedom,

$$\mathbf{M}\ddot{\mathbf{q}} + \mathbf{K}\mathbf{q} = \mathbf{0} \tag{3.2.58}$$

where $\mathbf{q}$ is an $N \times 1$ DOF vector. The above equation is homogeneous and admits a solution of the following form:

$$\mathbf{q} = \boldsymbol{\varphi} e^{pt} \tag{3.2.59}$$

For oscillatory response with no energy loss or gain, $p = \pm i\omega$ and

$$\mathbf{q} = \boldsymbol{\varphi} e^{\pm i\omega t} \tag{3.2.60}$$

Placing equation (3.2.60) into equation (3.2.58),

$$(\mathbf{K} - \omega^2 \mathbf{M})\boldsymbol{\varphi} e^{\pm i\omega t} = \mathbf{0} \tag{3.2.61}$$

From equation (3.2.61),

$$(\mathbf{K} - \omega^2 \mathbf{M})\boldsymbol{\varphi} = \mathbf{0} \tag{3.2.62}$$

Equation (3.2.62) is a homogeneous algebraic equation. For nontrivial $\boldsymbol{\varphi}$, the following equation must be satisfied:

$$\det\,(\mathbf{K} - \omega^2 \mathbf{M}) = 0 \tag{3.2.63}$$

Specific values of ω that satisfy equation (3.2.63) are called **eigenvalues.** For a system with N degrees of freedom, there are N eigenvalues counting multiple roots separately.

For each $\omega = \omega_i$, equation (3.2.62) is expressed as

$$(\mathbf{K} - \omega_i^2 \mathbf{M})\boldsymbol{\varphi}_i = \mathbf{0} \tag{3.2.64}$$

For given ω_i, one can use equation (3.2.64) to determine the corresponding eigenvector $\boldsymbol{\varphi}_i$. The mathematical exercise of determining eigenvalues and eigenvectors is called **eigenvalue analysis.**

From equation (3.2.64)

$$\mathbf{K}\boldsymbol{\varphi}_i = \omega_i^2 \mathbf{M}\boldsymbol{\varphi}_i \tag{3.2.65}$$

Note:

1) ω_i: natural frequency of mode number i.
   $\boldsymbol{\varphi}_i$: natural mode corresponding to ω_i
2) For a system with N DOFs, there are N natural frequencies and N natural modes.
3) **For convenience, ω_i are arranged in an increasing order of magnitude, starting from ω_1 such that** $\omega_1 \le \omega_2 \le \omega_3 \le \cdots\cdots \le \omega_N$.
4) Any constant multiple of an eigenvector is also an eigenvector. That is, an eigenvector (or a natural mode of free vibration) is determined within a constant multiple.
5) A natural mode provides the information on the relative magnitude among the degrees of freedom as the system undergoes free vibration at a natural frequency.

For eigenvalue analysis, we can write equation (3.2.62) into a standard form as follows:

$$\mathbf{K}\boldsymbol{\varphi} = \lambda \mathbf{M}\boldsymbol{\varphi} \tag{3.2.66}$$

where
$$\lambda = \omega^2 \tag{3.2.67}$$

Then, one can use MATLAB or any other software to compute eigenvalues and eigenvectors.

For the i-th mode,

$$\mathbf{K}\boldsymbol{\varphi}_i = \lambda_i \mathbf{M}\boldsymbol{\varphi}_i \tag{3.2.68}$$

Note:
Eigenvalue analysis can be carried out using MATLAB as follows.

Given equation $\mathbf{Ax} = \lambda \mathbf{Bx}$

use command [**x**, **D**] = eig (**A**, **B**)

to determine eigenvalues and eigenvectors. The output is as follows:
- **D**: diagonal matrix of eigenvalues.
- **x**: full matrix whose columns are the corresponding eigenvectors.

Orthogonality of Eigenvectors

For free vibration,

$$\mathbf{K}\boldsymbol{\varphi}_i = \lambda_i \mathbf{M}\boldsymbol{\varphi}_i \qquad (i = 1, 2, \cdots, N) \tag{3.2.69}$$

It can be shown that, for $r \neq s$,

$$\boldsymbol{\varphi}_r^T \mathbf{K}\boldsymbol{\varphi}_s = 0 \tag{3.2.70}$$

$$\boldsymbol{\varphi}_r^T \mathbf{M}\boldsymbol{\varphi}_s = 0 \tag{3.2.71}$$

This property is called **orthogonality of eigenvectors.**

Check:

1) Example 1

$$\boldsymbol{\varphi}_1^T \mathbf{K}\boldsymbol{\varphi}_2 = \begin{bmatrix} 1 & 1/\sqrt{2} \end{bmatrix} \begin{bmatrix} k & -k \\ -k & 2k \end{bmatrix} \begin{Bmatrix} 1 \\ -1/\sqrt{2} \end{Bmatrix} = 0$$

$$\boldsymbol{\varphi}_1^T \mathbf{M}\boldsymbol{\varphi}_2 = \begin{bmatrix} 1 & 1/\sqrt{2} \end{bmatrix} \begin{bmatrix} m & 0 \\ 0 & 2m \end{bmatrix} \begin{Bmatrix} 1 \\ -1/\sqrt{2} \end{Bmatrix} = 0$$

2) Example 2

$$\boldsymbol{\varphi}_1^T \mathbf{K} \boldsymbol{\varphi}_2 = \lfloor 1 \quad 1 \rfloor \begin{bmatrix} k & -k \\ -k & k \end{bmatrix} \begin{Bmatrix} 1 \\ -c \end{Bmatrix} = 0$$

$$\boldsymbol{\varphi}_1^T \mathbf{M} \boldsymbol{\varphi}_2 = \lfloor 1 \quad 1 \rfloor \begin{bmatrix} cm & 0 \\ 0 & m \end{bmatrix} \begin{Bmatrix} 1 \\ -c \end{Bmatrix} = 0$$

3.3 Forced Vibration of Undamped MDOF Systems

For an undamped N-DOF system under applied load,

equation of motion: $$\mathbf{M}\ddot{\mathbf{q}} + \mathbf{K}\mathbf{q} = \mathbf{F} \tag{3.3.1}$$

initial conditions: $$\mathbf{q}(0) = \mathbf{q}_0, \ \dot{\mathbf{q}}(0) = \dot{\mathbf{q}}_0 \tag{3.3.2}$$

Equation (3.3.1), subject to the initial conditions, may be solved by a numerical method. However, in an alternate approach called modal analysis, equation (3.3.1) is first transformed into N equations of SDOF systems. This can be done using the orthogonality of eigenvectors.

The unknown DOF vector $\mathbf{q}$ can be expressed as a linear combination of eigenvectors as follows:

$$\mathbf{q}(t) = \alpha_1 \boldsymbol{\varphi}_1 + \alpha_2 \boldsymbol{\varphi}_2 + \cdots\cdots + \alpha_N \boldsymbol{\varphi}_N \tag{3.3.3}$$

where $\alpha_1(t)$, $\alpha_2(t)$, ⋯⋯, $\alpha_N(t)$ are time-dependent coefficients, representing participation of individual modes to the system response at a given time.

Placing equation (3.3.3) into equation (3.3.1),

$$\mathbf{M}(\ddot{\alpha}_1 \boldsymbol{\varphi}_1 + \ddot{\alpha}_2 \boldsymbol{\varphi}_2 + \cdots\cdots + \ddot{\alpha}_N \boldsymbol{\varphi}_N) + \mathbf{K}(\alpha_1 \boldsymbol{\varphi}_1 + \alpha_2 \boldsymbol{\varphi}_2 + \cdots\cdots + \alpha_N \boldsymbol{\varphi}_N) = \mathbf{F} \tag{3.3.4}$$

Premultiplying equation (3.3.4) with $\boldsymbol{\varphi}_1^T$,

$$\begin{aligned} &\boldsymbol{\varphi}_1^T \mathbf{M}(\ddot{\alpha}_1 \boldsymbol{\varphi}_1 + \ddot{\alpha}_2 \boldsymbol{\varphi}_2 + \cdots\cdots + \ddot{\alpha}_N \boldsymbol{\varphi}_N) \\ &+ \boldsymbol{\varphi}_1^T \mathbf{K}(\alpha_1 \boldsymbol{\varphi}_1 + \alpha_2 \boldsymbol{\varphi}_2 + \cdots\cdots + \alpha_N \boldsymbol{\varphi}_N) = \boldsymbol{\varphi}_1^T \mathbf{F} \end{aligned} \tag{3.3.5}$$

Using the orthogonality of eigenvectors,

$$\boldsymbol{\varphi}_1^T \mathbf{M} \boldsymbol{\varphi}_1 \ddot{\alpha}_1 + \boldsymbol{\varphi}_1^T \mathbf{K} \boldsymbol{\varphi}_1 \alpha_1 = \boldsymbol{\varphi}_1^T \mathbf{F} \tag{3.3.6}$$

Recall that $$\mathbf{K}\boldsymbol{\varphi}_i = \omega_i^2\mathbf{M}\boldsymbol{\varphi}_i \qquad (i = 1, \cdots\cdots, N) \tag{3.3.7}$$

Placing equation (3.3.7) into equation (3.3.6),

$$\boldsymbol{\varphi}_1^T\mathbf{M}\boldsymbol{\varphi}_1\ddot{\alpha}_1 + \boldsymbol{\varphi}_1^T(\omega_1^2\mathbf{M}\boldsymbol{\varphi}_1)\alpha_1 = \boldsymbol{\varphi}_1^T\mathbf{F} \tag{3.3.8}$$

Introducing symbol m_1 defined as

$$m_1 = \boldsymbol{\varphi}_1^T\mathbf{M}\boldsymbol{\varphi}_1 \tag{3.3.9}$$

Then, equation (3.3.8) can be expressed as

$$m_1\ddot{\alpha}_1 + \omega_1^2 m_1\alpha_1 = \boldsymbol{\varphi}_1^T\mathbf{F} \tag{3.3.10}$$

In general, premultiplying equation (3.3.4) with $\boldsymbol{\varphi}_i^T$ and using the orthogonality of eigenvectors lead to

$$m_i\ddot{\alpha}_i + \omega_i^2 m_i\alpha_i = \boldsymbol{\varphi}_i^T\mathbf{F} \tag{3.3.11}$$

or $$\ddot{\alpha}_i + \omega_i^2\alpha_i = \frac{1}{m_i}\boldsymbol{\varphi}_i^T\mathbf{F} \tag{3.3.12}$$

where $$m_i = \boldsymbol{\varphi}_i^T\mathbf{M}\boldsymbol{\varphi}_i \tag{3.3.13}$$

$$(i = 1, 2, \ldots, N)$$

Equation (3.3.12) represents N decoupled SDOF system equations.

For $i = 1$,

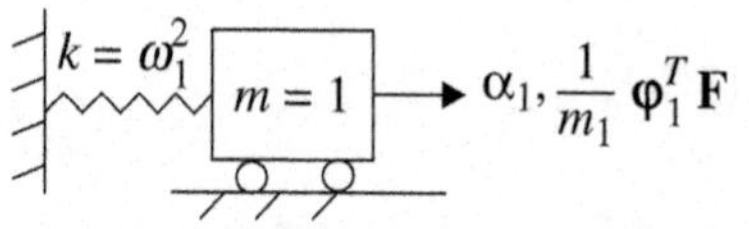

For $i = 2$,

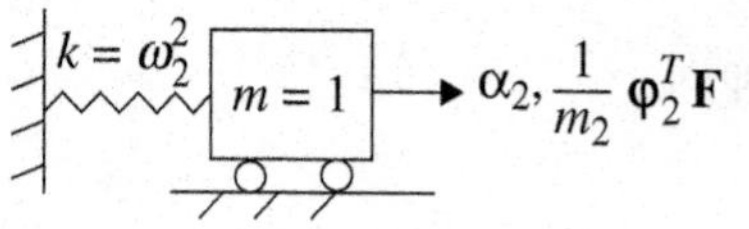

Similarly for $i = 3, \ldots, N$.

Figure 3.8 Decoupled SDOF systems.

So, instead of solving the original coupled equation (3.3.1) subject to initial conditions, we may solve the decoupled equation (3.3.12) for α_i subject to initial conditions. The appropriate initial conditions for α_i are determined as follows:

Recall $$\mathbf{q}(t) = \alpha_1\boldsymbol{\varphi}_1 + \alpha_2\boldsymbol{\varphi}_2 + \cdots\cdots + \alpha_N\boldsymbol{\varphi}_N$$

Then,

$$\boldsymbol{\varphi}_i^T \mathbf{M}\mathbf{q} = \boldsymbol{\varphi}_i^T \mathbf{M}(\alpha_1 \boldsymbol{\varphi}_1 + \alpha_2 \boldsymbol{\varphi}_2 + \cdots\cdots + \alpha_N \boldsymbol{\varphi}_N) = \alpha_i \boldsymbol{\varphi}_i^T \mathbf{M} \boldsymbol{\varphi}_i = \alpha_i m_i \tag{3.3.14}$$

From equation (3.3.14),

$$\alpha_i(t) = \frac{\boldsymbol{\varphi}_i^T \mathbf{M}\mathbf{q}(t)}{m_i} \tag{3.3.15}$$

and

$$\dot{\alpha}_i(t) = \frac{\boldsymbol{\varphi}_i^T \mathbf{M}\dot{\mathbf{q}}(t)}{m_i} \tag{3.3.16}$$

Accordingly, at $t = 0$,

$$\alpha_i(0) = \frac{\boldsymbol{\varphi}_i^T \mathbf{M}\mathbf{q}(0)}{m_i} \tag{3.3.17}$$

$$\dot{\alpha}_i(0) = \frac{\boldsymbol{\varphi}_i^T \mathbf{M}\dot{\mathbf{q}}(0)}{m_i} \tag{3.3.18}$$

Equations (3.3.17) and (3.3.18) provide the initial conditions to equation (3.3.12).

Example 3.3.1

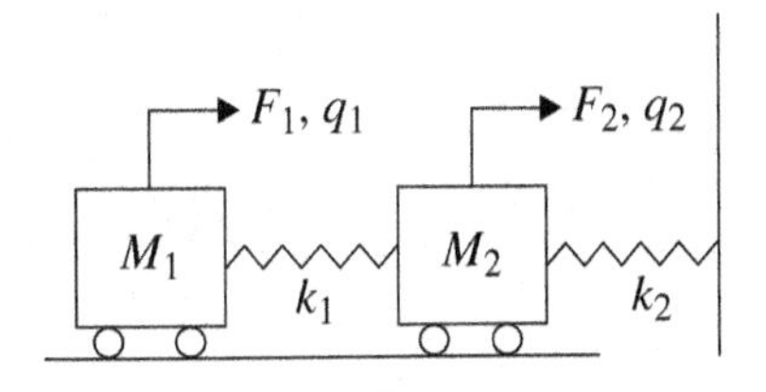

Figure 3.9 Two-DOF system under applied loads.

$$k_1 = k,\ k_2 = k,\ M_1 = m,\ M_2 = 2m$$

(A) The equation of motion:

$$\begin{bmatrix} m & 0 \\ 0 & 2m \end{bmatrix} \begin{Bmatrix} \ddot{q}_1 \\ \ddot{q}_2 \end{Bmatrix} + \begin{bmatrix} k & -k \\ -k & 2k \end{bmatrix} \begin{Bmatrix} q_1 \\ q_2 \end{Bmatrix} = \begin{Bmatrix} F_1 \\ F_2 \end{Bmatrix} \tag{3.3.19}$$

From the analysis of free vibration, we have obtained the following:

The first mode:

$$\omega_1 = \sqrt{0.293\frac{k}{m}}, \ \boldsymbol{\phi}_1 = \begin{Bmatrix} \phi_1 \\ \phi_2 \end{Bmatrix}_1 = \begin{Bmatrix} 1 \\ 1/\sqrt{2} \end{Bmatrix} \tag{3.3.20}$$

The second mode:

$$\omega_2 = \sqrt{1.707\frac{k}{m}}, \ \boldsymbol{\phi}_2 = \begin{Bmatrix} \phi_1 \\ \phi_2 \end{Bmatrix}_2 = \begin{Bmatrix} 1 \\ -1/\sqrt{2} \end{Bmatrix} \tag{3.3.21}$$

Then,

$$\mathbf{q}(t) = \alpha_1 \boldsymbol{\varphi}_1 + \alpha_2 \boldsymbol{\varphi}_2 \tag{3.3.22}$$

or

$$\begin{Bmatrix} q_1 \\ q_2 \end{Bmatrix} = \alpha_1 \begin{Bmatrix} 1 \\ 1/\sqrt{2} \end{Bmatrix} + \alpha_2 \begin{Bmatrix} 1 \\ -1/\sqrt{2} \end{Bmatrix} \tag{3.3.23}$$

$$\begin{aligned} q_1 &= \alpha_1 + \alpha_2 \\ q_2 &= \frac{1}{\sqrt{2}}(\alpha_1 - \alpha_2) \end{aligned} \tag{3.3.24}$$

(B) Equation of motion in terms of α_i:

$$\ddot{\alpha}_i + \omega_i^2 \alpha_i = \frac{1}{m_i} \boldsymbol{\varphi}_i^T \mathbf{F} \qquad (i = 1, 2) \tag{3.3.25}$$

$$m_1 = \boldsymbol{\varphi}_1^T \mathbf{M} \boldsymbol{\varphi}_1 = \begin{bmatrix} 1 & 1/\sqrt{2} \end{bmatrix} m \begin{bmatrix} 1 & 0 \\ 0 & 2 \end{bmatrix} \begin{Bmatrix} 1 \\ 1/\sqrt{2} \end{Bmatrix} = m \begin{bmatrix} 1 & \sqrt{2} \end{bmatrix} \begin{Bmatrix} 1 \\ 1/\sqrt{2} \end{Bmatrix} = 2m \tag{3.3.26}$$

$$m_2 = \boldsymbol{\varphi}_2^T \mathbf{M} \boldsymbol{\varphi}_2 = \begin{bmatrix} 1 & -1/\sqrt{2} \end{bmatrix} m \begin{bmatrix} 1 & 0 \\ 0 & 2 \end{bmatrix} \begin{Bmatrix} 1 \\ -1/\sqrt{2} \end{Bmatrix} = m \begin{bmatrix} 1 & -\sqrt{2} \end{bmatrix} \begin{Bmatrix} 1 \\ -1/\sqrt{2} \end{Bmatrix} = 2m \tag{3.3.27}$$

$$\boldsymbol{\varphi}_1^T \mathbf{F} = \begin{bmatrix} 1 & 1/\sqrt{2} \end{bmatrix} \begin{Bmatrix} F_1 \\ F_2 \end{Bmatrix} = F_1 + \frac{1}{\sqrt{2}} F_2 \tag{3.3.28}$$

$$\boldsymbol{\varphi}_2^T \mathbf{F} = \begin{bmatrix} 1 & -1/\sqrt{2} \end{bmatrix} \begin{Bmatrix} F_1 \\ F_2 \end{Bmatrix} = F_1 - \frac{1}{\sqrt{2}} F_2 \tag{3.3.29}$$

Accordingly, from equation (3.3.25),

$$\ddot{\alpha}_1 + \omega_1^2\alpha_1 = \frac{1}{2m}(F_1 + \frac{1}{\sqrt{2}}F_2) \tag{3.3.30}$$

$$\ddot{\alpha}_2 + \omega_2^2\alpha_2 = \frac{1}{2m}(F_1 - \frac{1}{\sqrt{2}}F_2) \tag{3.3.31}$$

For the initial conditions, recall that

$$\alpha_i(0) = \frac{\boldsymbol{\varphi}_i^T \mathbf{M}\mathbf{q}(0)}{m_i} \tag{3.3.32}$$

$$\dot{\alpha}_i(0) = \frac{\boldsymbol{\varphi}_i^T \mathbf{M}\dot{\mathbf{q}}(0)}{m_i} \tag{3.3.33}$$

(C) Consider now a load vector given as follows:

$$\mathbf{F} = \begin{Bmatrix} F_1 \\ F_2 \end{Bmatrix} = \begin{Bmatrix} P \\ 0 \end{Bmatrix} \tag{3.3.34}$$

where P is a given constant value. Then, from equations (3.3.30) and (3.3.31) in Section (B),

$$\ddot{\alpha}_1 + \omega_1^2\alpha_1 = \frac{P}{2m} \tag{3.3.35}$$

$$\ddot{\alpha}_2 + \omega_2^2\alpha_2 = \frac{P}{2m} \tag{3.3.36}$$

Equation (3.3.35) corresponds to a SDOF system subjected to a constant force. Also, equation (3.3.36) corresponds to a SDOF system subjected to a constant force.

For a system initially at rest,

$$\mathbf{q}(0) = 0,\ \dot{\mathbf{q}}(0) = 0 \tag{3.3.37}$$

Then, from equations (3.3.32) and (3.3.33) in Section (B),

$$\alpha_i(0) = 0,\ \dot{\alpha}_i(0) = 0 \tag{3.3.38}$$

The solution to equation (3.3.35), subject to the initial conditions in equation (3.3.38), is as follows:

$$\alpha_1 = C_1 \cos\omega_1 t + D_1 \sin\omega_1 t + \frac{P}{2m\omega_1^2} \tag{3.3.39}$$

and

$$\dot{\alpha}_1 = \omega_1(-C_1 \sin\omega_1 t + D_1 \cos\omega_1 t) \tag{3.3.40}$$

For the system initially at rest,

$$\alpha_1(0) = 0,\ \dot{\alpha}_1(0) = 0 \tag{3.3.41}$$

Applying the initial conditions to equations (3.3.39) and (3.3.40),

$$C_1 + \frac{P}{2m\omega_1^2} = 0 \ \rightarrow\ C_1 = -\frac{P}{2m\omega_1^2} \tag{3.3.42}$$

$$\omega_1 D_1 = 0 \ \rightarrow\ D_1 = 0 \tag{3.3.43}$$

Placing equations (3.3.42) and (3.3.43) into equation (3.3.39),

$$\alpha_1 = \frac{P}{2m\omega_1^2}(1 - \cos\omega_1 t) \tag{3.3.44}$$

Using equation (3.3.20) in Section (A),

$$\alpha_1 = \frac{P}{0.586k}(1 - \cos\omega_1 t) \tag{3.3.45}$$

Following a similar procedure, we can show that

$$\alpha_2 = \frac{P}{2m\omega_2^2}(1 - \cos\omega_2 t) \tag{3.3.46}$$

Using equation (3.3.21) in Section (A),

$$\alpha_2 = \frac{P}{3.414k}(1 - \cos\omega_2 t) \tag{3.3.47}$$

(D) Consider a load vector given as follows:

$$\mathbf{F} = \begin{Bmatrix} F_1 \\ F_2 \end{Bmatrix} = \begin{Bmatrix} A \\ 0 \end{Bmatrix} \sin\Omega t \tag{3.3.48}$$

From equations (3.3.30) and (3.3.31) in Section (B),

$$\ddot{\alpha}_1 + \omega_1^2 \alpha_1 = \frac{A}{2m} \sin\Omega t \tag{3.3.49}$$

$$\ddot{\alpha}_2 + \omega_2^2 \alpha_2 = \frac{A}{2m} \sin\Omega t \tag{3.3.50}$$

Note:

If $\Omega = \omega_1$, α_1 is in resonance and $\mathbf{q}(t) = \alpha_1 \boldsymbol{\varphi}_1 + \alpha_2 \boldsymbol{\varphi}_2 \approx \alpha_1 \boldsymbol{\varphi}_1$.

If $\Omega = \omega_2$, α_2 is in resonance and $\mathbf{q}(t) = \alpha_1 \boldsymbol{\varphi}_1 + \alpha_2 \boldsymbol{\varphi}_2 \approx \alpha_2 \boldsymbol{\varphi}_2$.

Accordingly, resonance can be used to excite a particular mode.

(E) Consider now free vibration as a special case:

For free vibration, $F_1 = 0,\ F_2 = 0$

Then, from equations (3.3.30) and (3.3.31) in Section (B),

$$\ddot{\alpha}_1 + \omega_1^2 \alpha_1 = 0 \tag{3.3.51}$$

$$\ddot{\alpha}_2 + \omega_2^2 \alpha_2 = 0 \tag{3.3.52}$$

For α_1, the general solution is expressed as

$$\alpha_1 = C_1 \cos \omega_1 t + D_1 \sin \omega_1 t \tag{3.3.53}$$

where coefficients C_1 and D_1 are determined via applying the initial conditions.

For α_2, the general solution is expressed as

$$\alpha_2 = C_2 \cos \omega_2 t + D_2 \sin \omega_2 t \tag{3.3.54}$$

where coefficients C_2 and D_2 are determined via applying the initial conditions.

If the initial conditions are given as

$$\begin{aligned} &q_1(0) = 0,\ q_2(0) = 0, \\ &\dot{q}_1(0) = a,\ \dot{q}_2(0) = 0 \end{aligned} \tag{3.3.55}$$

where a is a given constant value. Then,

$$\alpha_1(0) = \frac{\boldsymbol{\varphi}_1^T \mathbf{M} \mathbf{q}(0)}{m_1} = \frac{1}{2m} \begin{bmatrix} 1 & 1/\sqrt{2} \end{bmatrix} m \begin{bmatrix} 1 & 0 \\ 0 & 2 \end{bmatrix} \begin{Bmatrix} 0 \\ 0 \end{Bmatrix} = 0 \tag{3.3.56a}$$

$$\alpha_2(0) = \frac{\boldsymbol{\varphi}_2^T \mathbf{M} \mathbf{q}(0)}{m_2} = \frac{1}{2m} \begin{bmatrix} 1 & -1/\sqrt{2} \end{bmatrix} m \begin{bmatrix} 1 & 0 \\ 0 & 2 \end{bmatrix} \begin{Bmatrix} 0 \\ 0 \end{Bmatrix} = 0 \tag{3.3.56b}$$

$$\dot{\alpha}_1(0) = \frac{\boldsymbol{\varphi}_1^T \mathbf{M} \dot{\mathbf{q}}(0)}{m_1} = \frac{1}{2m} \begin{bmatrix} 1 & 1/\sqrt{2} \end{bmatrix} m \begin{bmatrix} 1 & 0 \\ 0 & 2 \end{bmatrix} \begin{Bmatrix} a \\ 0 \end{Bmatrix} = \frac{a}{2} \tag{3.3.56c}$$

$$\dot{\alpha}_2(0) = \frac{\boldsymbol{\varphi}_2^T \mathbf{M} \dot{\mathbf{q}}(0)}{m_2} = \frac{1}{2m} \begin{bmatrix} 1 & -1/\sqrt{2} \end{bmatrix} m \begin{bmatrix} 1 & 0 \\ 0 & 2 \end{bmatrix} \begin{Bmatrix} a \\ 0 \end{Bmatrix} = \frac{a}{2} \tag{3.3.56d}$$

Example 3.3.2 Consider a system of two masses connected by a spring:

$$M_2 = m, \quad \frac{M_1}{M_2} = c$$

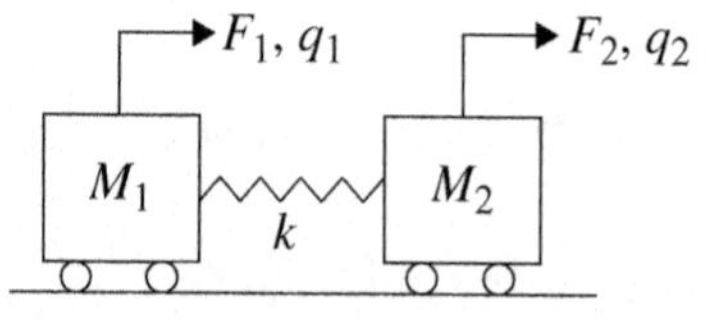

Figure 3.10 A system of two masses connected by a spring under applied loads.

(A) The equation of motion:

$$\begin{bmatrix} cm & 0 \\ 0 & m \end{bmatrix} \begin{Bmatrix} \ddot{q}_1 \\ \ddot{q}_2 \end{Bmatrix} + \begin{bmatrix} k & -k \\ -k & k \end{bmatrix} \begin{Bmatrix} q_1 \\ q_2 \end{Bmatrix} = \begin{Bmatrix} F_1 \\ F_2 \end{Bmatrix} \tag{3.3.57}$$

From the eigenvalue analysis of free vibration, we have obtained the following:

The first mode:

$$\omega_1 = 0, \qquad \boldsymbol{\varphi}_1 = \begin{Bmatrix} \phi_1 \\ \phi_2 \end{Bmatrix}_1 = \begin{Bmatrix} 1 \\ 1 \end{Bmatrix} \tag{3.3.58}$$

The second mode:

$$\omega_2 = \sqrt{\frac{c+1}{c}\frac{k}{m}}, \qquad \boldsymbol{\varphi}_2 = \begin{Bmatrix} \phi_1 \\ \phi_2 \end{Bmatrix}_2 = \begin{Bmatrix} 1 \\ -c \end{Bmatrix} \tag{3.3.59}$$

Now, for $c = 2$,

$$\omega_2 = \sqrt{\frac{3}{2}\frac{k}{m}}, \qquad \boldsymbol{\varphi}_2 = \begin{Bmatrix} \phi_1 \\ \phi_2 \end{Bmatrix}_2 = \begin{Bmatrix} 1 \\ -2 \end{Bmatrix} \text{ or } \begin{Bmatrix} -1/2 \\ 1 \end{Bmatrix} \tag{3.3.60}$$

Then, $\mathbf{q}$ can be expressed as

$$\mathbf{q} = \alpha_1 \boldsymbol{\varphi}_1 + \alpha_2 \boldsymbol{\varphi}_2 \tag{3.3.61}$$

or

$$\begin{Bmatrix} q_1 \\ q_2 \end{Bmatrix} = \alpha_1 \begin{Bmatrix} 1 \\ 1 \end{Bmatrix} + \alpha_2 \begin{Bmatrix} -1/2 \\ 1 \end{Bmatrix} \tag{3.3.62}$$

$$q_1 = \alpha_1 - \frac{1}{2}\alpha_2 \qquad (3.3.63)$$
$$q_2 = \alpha_1 + \alpha_2$$

(B) Equation of motion in terms of α_i :

$$\ddot{\alpha}_i + \omega_i^2 \alpha_i = \frac{1}{m_i} \boldsymbol{\varphi}_i^T \mathbf{F} \qquad (i = 1, 2) \qquad (3.3.64)$$

For $i = 1$,

$$\omega_1 = 0$$

$$\ddot{\alpha}_1 = \frac{1}{m_1} \boldsymbol{\varphi}_1^T \mathbf{F} \qquad (3.3.65)$$

$$m_1 = \boldsymbol{\varphi}_1^T \mathbf{M} \boldsymbol{\varphi}_1 = \lfloor 1 \quad 1 \rfloor m \begin{bmatrix} 2 & 0 \\ 0 & 1 \end{bmatrix} \begin{Bmatrix} 1 \\ 1 \end{Bmatrix} = 3m : \text{total mass} \qquad (3.3.66a)$$

$$\boldsymbol{\varphi}_1^T \mathbf{F} = \lfloor 1 \quad 1 \rfloor \begin{Bmatrix} F_1 \\ F_2 \end{Bmatrix} = F_1 + F_2 : \text{total force} \qquad (3.3.66b)$$

Then, from equation (3.3.65),

$$\ddot{\alpha}_1 = \frac{1}{3m}(F_1 + F_2) \qquad (3.3.67)$$

Note:
Equation (3.3.67) represents the motion of a rigid body with mass $3m$ subjected to a total force of $F_1 + F_2$.

For $i = 2$,

$$\ddot{\alpha}_2 + \omega_2^2 \alpha_2 = \frac{1}{m_2} \boldsymbol{\varphi}_2^T \mathbf{F} \qquad (3.3.68)$$

$$m_2 = \boldsymbol{\varphi}_2^T \mathbf{M} \boldsymbol{\varphi}_2 = \lfloor -1/2 \quad 1 \rfloor m \begin{bmatrix} 2 & 0 \\ 0 & 1 \end{bmatrix} \begin{Bmatrix} -1/2 \\ 1 \end{Bmatrix} = \frac{3}{2} m \qquad (3.3.69a)$$

$$\boldsymbol{\varphi}_2^T \mathbf{F} = \lfloor -1/2 \quad 1 \rfloor \begin{Bmatrix} F_1 \\ F_2 \end{Bmatrix} = F_2 - \frac{1}{2} F_1 \qquad (3.3.69b)$$

Then, from equation (3.3.68),

$$\ddot{\alpha}_2 + \omega_2^2 \alpha_2 = \frac{2}{3m}(F_2 - \frac{1}{2} F_1) \qquad (3.3.70)$$

(C) Consider the load vector given as follows:

$$\mathbf{F} = \begin{Bmatrix} F_1 \\ F_2 \end{Bmatrix} = \begin{Bmatrix} 0 \\ P \end{Bmatrix} \tag{3.3.71}$$

Then, from equations (3.3.67) and (3.3.70) in Section (B),

$$\ddot{\alpha}_1 = \frac{P}{3m} \tag{3.3.72}$$

$$\ddot{\alpha}_2 + \omega_2^2 \alpha_2 = \frac{2}{3m} P \tag{3.3.73}$$

If P is constant,

$$\dot{\alpha}_1 = \frac{P}{3m} t + C_1, \ \alpha_1 = \frac{P}{6m} t^2 + C_1 t + D_1 \tag{3.3.74}$$

For a system initially at rest,

$$C_1 = 0, \ D_1 = 0 \tag{3.3.75}$$

and

$$\dot{\alpha}_1 = \frac{P}{3m} t, \ \alpha_1 = \frac{P}{6m} t^2 \tag{3.3.76}$$

Also, we can show that

$$\alpha_2 = \frac{2P}{3m\omega_2^2}(1 - \cos\omega_2 t) \tag{3.3.77}$$

Summary:

For a system with N degrees of freedom,

$$\ddot{\alpha}_i + \omega_i^2 \alpha_i = \frac{1}{m_i} \boldsymbol{\varphi}_i^T \mathbf{F} \tag{3.3.78}$$

1) If $\mathbf{F} \sim \sin\Omega t$ and $\Omega \sim \omega_i$, then α_i is in resonance and

$$\mathbf{q}(t) = \alpha_1 \boldsymbol{\varphi}_1 + \alpha_2 \boldsymbol{\varphi}_2 + \cdots\cdots + \alpha_N \boldsymbol{\varphi}_N \approx \alpha_i \boldsymbol{\varphi}_i \tag{3.3.79}$$

So, we can use resonance to excite a particular natural mode.

2) If $\boldsymbol{\varphi}_i^T \mathbf{F} = 0$, then from equation (3.3.78),

$$\ddot{\alpha}_i + \omega_i^2 \alpha_i = 0 \tag{3.3.80}$$

Equation (3.3.80) represents free vibration for α_i.

3) $\mathbf{q}(t) = \alpha_1 \boldsymbol{\varphi}_1 + \alpha_2 \boldsymbol{\varphi}_2 + \cdots\cdots + \alpha_N \boldsymbol{\varphi}_N$
Note that α_i with higher frequencies are stiffer and harder to excite.

Accordingly, in practical problems involving aerospace structures and other structures, only a few lowest modes are excited, even for a system modeled with a large number of DOF. Then, $\mathbf{q}$ can be approximated as

$$\mathbf{q}(t) = \alpha_1\boldsymbol{\varphi}_1 + \alpha_2\boldsymbol{\varphi}_2 + \cdots\cdots + \alpha_P\boldsymbol{\varphi}_P$$

where $P << N$.

3.4 Additional Topics

3.4.1 Steady-State Response of MDOF Systems

Consider a MDOF System with damping subject to harmonic loading $\mathbf{F} = \mathbf{F}_0 \sin\Omega t$. The equation of motion is then

$$\mathbf{M}\ddot{\mathbf{q}} + \mathbf{C}\dot{\mathbf{q}} + \mathbf{K}\mathbf{q} = \mathbf{F}_0 \sin\Omega t \tag{3.4.1}$$

The particular solution to the above equation can be expressed as

$$\mathbf{q} = \mathbf{A}\sin\Omega t + \mathbf{B}\cos\Omega t \tag{3.4.2}$$

The column vectors **A** and **B** can be determined via introducing equation (3.4.2) into equation (3.4.1). We will revisit this topic in a later chapter within the context of vibration absorbers.

3.4.2 First-Order Representation: State Space Vector Form

Given the equation of motion,

$$\mathbf{M}\ddot{\mathbf{q}} + \mathbf{C}\dot{\mathbf{q}} + \mathbf{K}\mathbf{q} = \mathbf{F} \tag{3.4.3}$$

Introduce a new variable v such that

$$\dot{\mathbf{q}} = \mathbf{v} \tag{3.4.4}$$

Placing equation (3.4.4) into equation (3.4.3),

$$\mathbf{M}\dot{\mathbf{v}} + \mathbf{C}\mathbf{v} + \mathbf{K}\mathbf{q} = \mathbf{F} \tag{3.4.5}$$

For free vibration analysis ($\mathbf{F} = 0$), we can combine equations (3.4.4) and (3.4.5) as follows:

$$\begin{bmatrix} \mathbf{I} & 0 \\ 0 & \mathbf{M} \end{bmatrix} \begin{Bmatrix} \dot{\mathbf{q}} \\ \dot{\mathbf{v}} \end{Bmatrix} - \begin{bmatrix} 0 & \mathbf{I} \\ -\mathbf{K} & -\mathbf{C} \end{bmatrix} \begin{Bmatrix} \mathbf{q} \\ \mathbf{v} \end{Bmatrix} = \begin{Bmatrix} 0 \\ 0 \end{Bmatrix} \tag{3.4.6}$$

where I is an identity matrix.

Equation (3.4.6) can be expressed as

$$\mathbf{B}\dot{\mathbf{x}} - \mathbf{A}\mathbf{x} = \mathbf{0} \tag{3.4.7}$$

where

$$\mathbf{x} = \begin{Bmatrix} \mathbf{q} \\ \mathbf{v} \end{Bmatrix} \tag{3.4.8}$$

$$\mathrm{B} = \begin{bmatrix} \mathrm{I} & 0 \\ 0 & \mathrm{M} \end{bmatrix} \tag{3.4.9}$$

$$\mathrm{A} = \begin{bmatrix} 0 & \mathrm{I} \\ -\mathrm{K} & -\mathrm{C} \end{bmatrix} \tag{3.4.10}$$

Equation (3.4.7) is a first-order homogeneous equation. A solution to equation (3.4.7) is of the following form:

$$\mathbf{x} = \boldsymbol{\varphi} e^{\lambda t} \tag{3.4.11}$$

Placing equation (3.4.11) into equation (3.4.7),

$$\begin{aligned} &\mathbf{B}\boldsymbol{\varphi}\lambda e^{\lambda t} - \mathbf{A}\boldsymbol{\varphi} e^{\lambda t} = \mathbf{0} \rightarrow (\mathbf{A} - \lambda\mathbf{B})\boldsymbol{\varphi} e^{\lambda t} = \mathbf{0} \\ &\rightarrow (\mathbf{A} - \lambda\mathbf{B})\boldsymbol{\varphi} = \mathbf{0} \end{aligned} \tag{3.4.12}$$

or

$$\mathbf{A}\boldsymbol{\varphi} = \lambda\mathbf{B}\boldsymbol{\varphi} \tag{3.4.13}$$

For given A and B, equation (3.4.13) is a standard equation for an eigenvalue analysis.

The eigenvalues λ_k $(k = 1, 2, \cdots\cdots)$ can be expressed as

$$\lambda_k = \mathrm{Re}(\lambda_k) + i\,\mathrm{Im}(\lambda_k) = \sigma_k \pm i\omega_k \qquad (\omega_k \geq 0) \tag{3.4.14}$$

where

$$\sigma_k = \mathrm{Re}(\lambda_k)$$

Then,

$$e^{\lambda_k t} = e^{(\sigma_k \pm i\omega_k)t} = e^{\sigma_k t} e^{\pm i\omega_k t} = e^{\sigma_k t}(\cos\omega_k t \pm i \sin\omega_k t) \tag{3.4.15}$$

where $e^{\sigma_k t}$ ~ change of amplitude with time ($\sigma_k < 0$ with damping)

$(\cos\omega_k t \pm i \sin\omega_k t)$ ~ oscillation with frequency ω_k

3.4.3 Numerical Integration in Time

Consider a MDOF model with the equation of motion,

$$\mathbf{M\ddot{q}} + \mathbf{C\dot{q}} + \mathbf{Kq} = \mathbf{F} \tag{3.4.16}$$

For numerical integration in time, we can work directly with the above equation. Alternatively, we can convert the above second-order equation to a first-order equation as in the previous section by introducing a new variable **v** such that

$$\mathbf{\dot{q}} = \mathbf{v} \tag{3.4.17}$$

Placing equation (3.4.17) into equation (3.4.16),

$$\mathbf{M\dot{v}} + \mathbf{Cv} + \mathbf{Kq} = \mathbf{F} \tag{3.4.18}$$

or

$$\mathbf{\dot{v}} = \mathbf{M}^{-1}(\mathbf{F} - \mathbf{Cv} - \mathbf{Kq}) \tag{3.4.19}$$

Equations (3.4.17) and (3.4.19) can be combined into a single matrix equation as follows:

$$\begin{Bmatrix} \mathbf{\dot{q}} \\ \mathbf{\dot{v}} \end{Bmatrix} = \begin{Bmatrix} \mathbf{v} \\ \mathbf{M}^{-1}(\mathbf{F} - \mathbf{Cv} - \mathbf{Kq}) \end{Bmatrix} \tag{3.4.20}$$

Equation (3.4.20) can be expressed as

$$\mathbf{\dot{x}} = \mathbf{f}(\mathbf{x}, t) \tag{3.4.21}$$

where

$$\mathbf{x} = \begin{Bmatrix} \mathbf{q} \\ \mathbf{v} \end{Bmatrix} \tag{3.4.22}$$

$$\mathbf{f}(\mathbf{x}, t) = \begin{Bmatrix} \mathbf{v} \\ \mathbf{M}^{-1}(\mathbf{F} - \mathbf{Cv} - \mathbf{Kq}) \end{Bmatrix} \tag{3.4.23}$$

For numerical integration of the first order (in time) equations, we can use the Euler method described in Chapter 1 or a more accurate method such as the fourth-order Runge-Kutta (RK4) method.

Chapter 3 Problem Sets

3.1 For a two-DOF system, the mass matrix, stiffness matrix, and the natural modes are given as follows:

$$\mathbf{M} = m\begin{bmatrix} 4 & 0 \\ 0 & 2 \end{bmatrix}, \quad \mathbf{K} = k\begin{bmatrix} 3 & -1 \\ -1 & A \end{bmatrix}, \quad \boldsymbol{\varphi}_1 = \begin{Bmatrix} 1 \\ 1 \end{Bmatrix}, \quad \boldsymbol{\varphi}_2 = \begin{Bmatrix} 1 \\ B \end{Bmatrix}$$

(a) Find the numerical values of A and B.

(b) Find the natural frequencies of the system.
(c) Is the system allowed to undergo rigid body motion?

3.2 Consider a three-DOF system shown below.

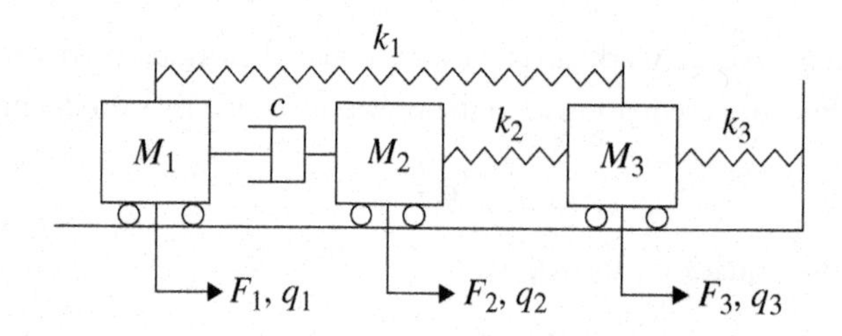

(a) Draw a free-body diagram for each mass to derive the equation of motion.
(b) Express the equation of motion in matrix form. Identify the mass matrix, the damping matrix, the stiffness matrix, and the load vector.

3.3 For the system shown in Problem 2,

$$M_1 = M_2 = M_3 = m$$
$$k_1 = k_2 = k_3 = k$$

(a) Assume no damping ($c = 0$). Carry out an eigenvalue analysis to determine the natural frequencies and the natural modes. Scale such that the largest (in magnitude) entry in each eigenvector is equal to 1.
(b) Sketch the modes.
(c) Check the orthogonality between mode 1 and mode 2.

3.4 The two-DOF system shown in the sketch may represent a crude model of a rocket on a test stand.

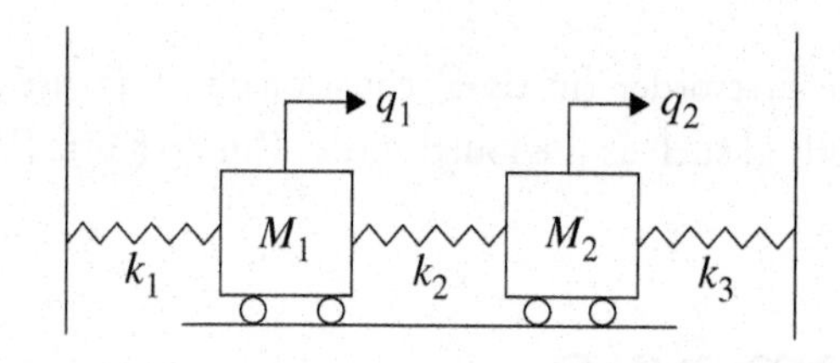

$M_1 = \frac{1}{2}M,\ M_2 = \frac{1}{2}M$, M: total mass $\qquad k_1 = k_2 = k_3 = k$

(a) Draw a free-body diagram for each mass and apply Newton's second law to construct the equation of motion. Express the equation motion in matrix form.
(b) Determine the natural frequencies ω_1 and ω_2 of the model.

(c) Determine the natural modes $\boldsymbol{\varphi}_1$ and $\boldsymbol{\varphi}_2$ of the model. Scale the modes such that the largest (in magnitude) entry in each mode is equal to 1.
(d) Confirm the orthogonality of natural modes.

3.5 Shown below is a crude model of a rocket on a launch pad.

$M_1 = M_3 = 0.25M, \quad M_2 = 0.5M, \quad M\text{: total mass,}$
$k_1 = k_2 = k,\ k_3 = 0.5k$

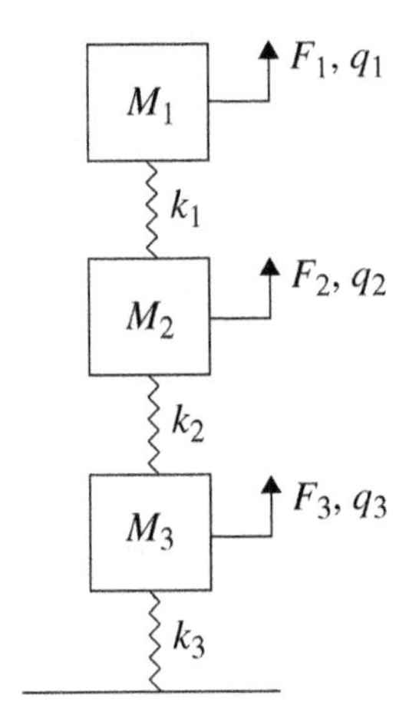

(a) Construct the mass matrix.
(b) Construct the stiffness matrix.
(c) Determine the natural frequencies and the natural modes. For the natural modes, scale such that the largest (in magnitude) entry in each eigenvector is equal to 1. Sketch the modes.

Note:
Introduce $\bar{p} = \omega^2 \dfrac{M}{k}$.

3.6 The 3-DOF system shown in the sketch represents a crude model for a jet sled on a frictionless track undergoing longitudinal vibration.

(a) Construct the mass matrix.
(b) Construct the stiffness matrix.
(c) Determine the natural frequencies and the natural modes. Sketch the modes.
(d) Confirm orthogonality of the modes.

Note:
Introduce $\bar{p} = \omega^2 \dfrac{M}{k}$. For the natural modes, scale such that the largest entry (in magnitude) in each eigenvector is equal to 1.

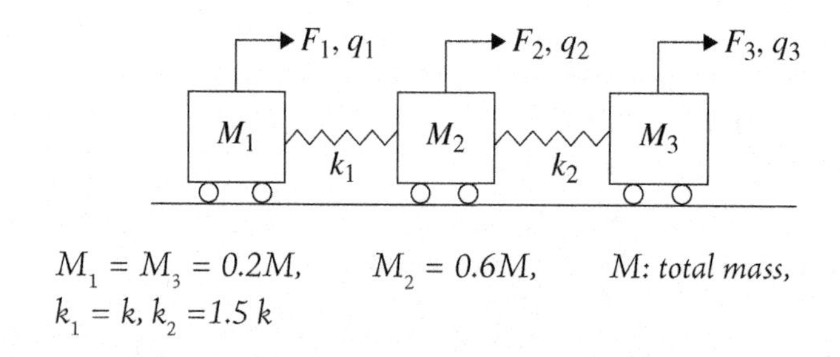

$M_1 = M_3 = 0.2M,$ $M_2 = 0.6M,$ M: *total mass,*
$k_1 = k, k_2 = 1.5\,k$

3.7 Consider the model of a jet sled on a horizontal track shown in the previous problem. The jet sled, initially at rest, is subjected to a blast loading delivered at the tail by an explosive charge, followed by a constant thrust of P applied immediately after the blast loading.

Note:

For simplicity, the effect of the blast is represented in the form of impulse Io on M_1.
The track is assumed frictionless, and the mass loss due to fuel burn is neglected.

(a) Determine the initial conditions corresponding to the impulse.
(b) Derive the equation for α_1 corresponding to the rigid body mode. Also, determine the initial conditions. Determine $\alpha_1(t)$.
(c) Derive the equation for α_2 corresponding to an elastic mode. Also, determine the initial conditions. Determine $\alpha_2(t)$.
(d) Derive the equation for α_3 corresponding to an elastic mode. Also, determine the initial conditions. Determine $\alpha_3(t)$.
(e) Determine the nodal displacement vector $\boldsymbol{q}$.
(f) Determine the force in each spring corresponding to the displacement in (e).

3.8 Consider a two-DOF system with the mass matrix and the stiffness matrix given as follows:

$$\mathbf{M} = m\begin{bmatrix} 1 & 0 \\ 0 & 2 \end{bmatrix}, \qquad \mathbf{K} = k\begin{bmatrix} 1 & -1 \\ -1 & 2 \end{bmatrix},$$

A force was applied to the system which was initially at rest. It turns out that the recorded acceleration of the ensuing motion can be expressed as

$$\ddot{q}_1 = A\left(\cos\omega_1 t + \cos\omega_2 t\right)$$
$$\ddot{q}_2 = 0.707A\left(\cos\omega_1 t - \cos\omega_2 t\right)$$

where A is a given constant. Determine the following:

(a) velocity and displacement of each mass.
(b) force acting on each mass in terms of A.

4 ENERGY APPROACH

In the previous chapters, we have applied Newton's second law to construct the equation of motion of a system. In this chapter, we will introduce an alternate approach that is energy based. This method, called the *Lagrange equation* approach, is more convenient when dealing with a system with a large number of degrees of freedom, especially when it involves angular displacements. We will not attempt to introduce a formal proof of the Lagrange equation approach in this chapter. Instead, we will apply it to a few example problems to demonstrate that its application indeed results in equations of motion that can be obtained by the application of Newton's second law. Specific topics covered are as follows:

4.1 Kinetic energy and potential energy of dynamic systems
4.2 Equation of motion via the Lagrange equation
4.3 Damping effect

In Section 4.1, we will construct the kinetic energy and potential energy of simple systems, neglecting the effect of damping. Here, we will observe that for a system with rotational or angular degree of freedom, the kinetic energy can be a function of angular displacement as well as angular velocity. Subsequently, in Section 4.2, we will introduce the Lagrange equation without proof and then apply it to several example problems to appreciate its validity and usefulness. In Section 4.3, we will discuss how the effect of damping can be incorporated either as an externally applied force or introducing a dissipation function. The Lagrange equation approach will be used in later chapters to examine the stability of dynamic systems and the construction of equation of motion via the finite element method.

4.1 Kinetic Energy and Potential Energy of Dynamic Systems

Example 4.1.1 A SDOF system.

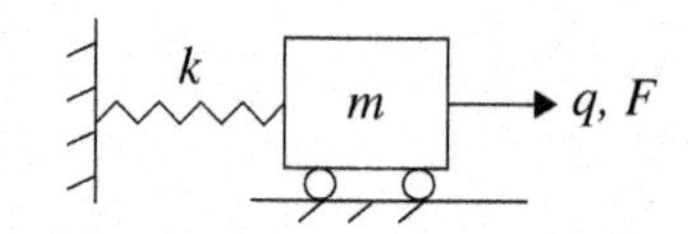

Figure 4.1 Undamped SDOF system.

$$\text{The kinetic energy: } T = \frac{1}{2}m\dot{q}^2 \tag{4.1.1}$$

$$\text{The potential energy: } V = U = \frac{1}{2}kq^2 \tag{4.1.2}$$

where U is the strain energy

Example 4.1.2 A simple pendulum (or a hovering helicopter with a sling load).

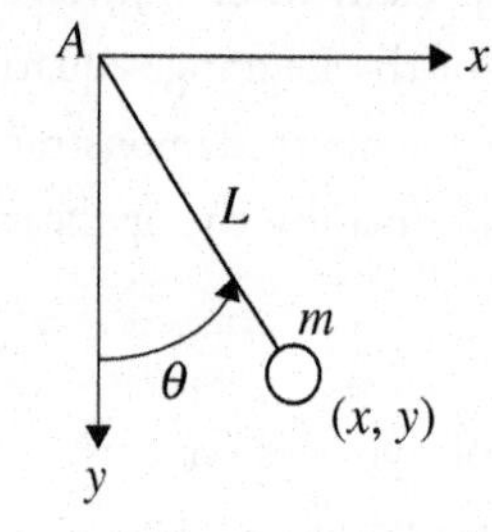

A: fixed pivot point
L: length of the string

Figure 4.2 Simple pendulum.

Assumptions:
1) The string is light and assumed massless.
2) The mass at the end of the string is assumed a concentrated mass.

$$\text{The kinetic energy: } \quad T = \frac{1}{2}m(\dot{x}^2 + \dot{y}^2) \tag{4.1.3}$$

The x and y coordinates of the mass can be expressed in terms of angle θ as

$$x = L\sin\theta, \quad y = L\cos\theta \tag{4.1.4}$$

Taking time derivatives of equation (4.1.4),

$$\begin{aligned} \dot{x} &= \frac{dx}{dt} = \frac{dx}{d\theta}\frac{d\theta}{dt} = (L\cos\theta)\dot{\theta} \\ \dot{y} &= \frac{dy}{dt} = \frac{dy}{d\theta}\frac{d\theta}{dt} = (-L\sin\theta)\dot{\theta} \end{aligned} \tag{4.1.5}$$

Placing equation (4.1.5) into equation (4.1.3),

$$T = \frac{1}{2} m (L\dot{\theta})^2 \quad (4.1.6)$$

or

$$T = \frac{1}{2} mL^2 \dot{\theta}^2 = \frac{1}{2} I \dot{\theta}^2$$

where $I = mL^2$: mass moment of inertia (4.1.7)

The potential energy: If the pivot point height is used as a reference,

$$V = -mgL\cos\theta \quad (4.1.8)$$

Example 4.1.3 The kinetic energy of a rigid body rotating about an axis.

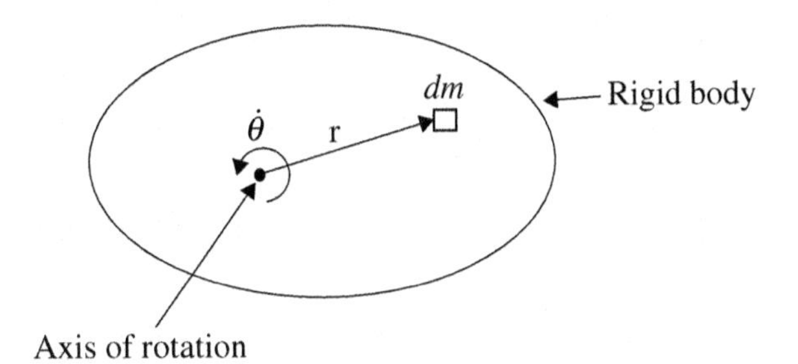

Figure 4.3 Rigid body rotating about an axis.

$\dot{\theta}$: angular velocity (rad/sec) or rotational speed
$dm = \rho dV$ where ρ: mass/volume and V: volume

dT : kinetic energy of mass dm

$$dT = \frac{1}{2}(dm)(r\dot{\theta})^2 \quad (4.1.9)$$

For the entire rigid body,

$$T = \int dT = \int \frac{1}{2} r^2 \dot{\theta}^2 \, dm = \frac{1}{2} \dot{\theta}^2 \int r^2 dm$$

or

$$T = \frac{1}{2} I \dot{\theta}^2 \quad (4.1.10)$$

where

$$I = \int r^2 dm = \int r^2 \rho dV \quad (4.1.11)$$

is the mass moment of inertia with respect to the axis of rotation.

Example 4.1.4 The two-mass system, connected by a string as shown below, may represent a helicopter carrying a space capsule picked up from the water. The helicopter is in level fight.

The kinetic energy:

$$T = \frac{1}{2}M_1\dot{x}_1^2 + \frac{1}{2}M_2(\dot{x}_2^2 + \dot{y}_2^2)$$

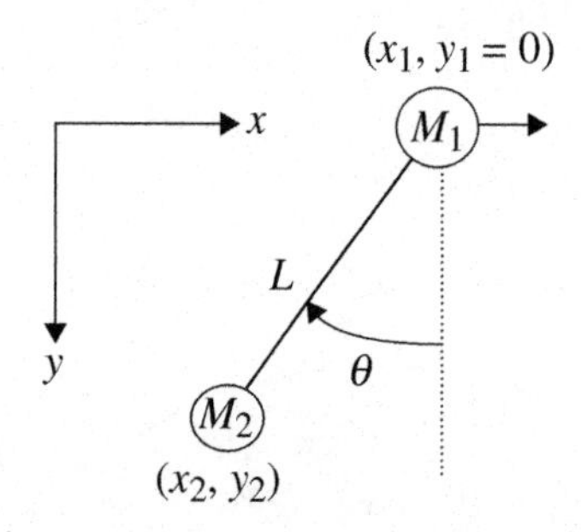

Figure 4.4 System of two masses connected by a string.

$$x_2 = x_1 - L\sin\theta,\ y_2 = L\cos\theta$$

$$\dot{x}_2 = \dot{x}_1 - L\dot{\theta}\cos\theta,\ \dot{y}_2 = -L\dot{\theta}\sin\theta$$

$$\dot{x}_2^2 + \dot{y}_2^2 = (\dot{x}_1 - L\dot{\theta}\cos\theta)^2 + (-L\dot{\theta}\sin\theta)^2 = \dot{x}_1^2 - 2L\dot{x}_1\dot{\theta}\cos\theta + L^2\dot{\theta}^2$$

$$T = \frac{1}{2}M_1\dot{x}_1^2 + \frac{1}{2}M_2(\dot{x}_1^2 - 2L\dot{x}_1\dot{\theta}\cos\theta + L^2\dot{\theta}^2) \qquad (4.1.12)$$

Note:

(1) The $-M_2L\dot{x}_1\dot{\theta}\cos\theta$ term in the kinetic energy represents the coupling between the linear motion in the horizontal direction and the angular motion.

(2) Also, note that the kinetic energy is a function of θ as well as $\dot{\theta}$ and $\dot{x}_1$.

The potential energy:

$$V = -M_2gL\cos\theta \qquad (4.1.13)$$

4.2 Equation of Motion via the Lagrange Equation

Consider a system with N degrees of freedom $(q_1, q_2 \, \dots\dots \, q_N)$ subjected to applied forces, or moments $F_1, F_2, \dots\dots, F_N$ corresponding to $q_1, q_2 \, \dots\dots \, q_N$. The kinetic energy T and the potential energy V of the system can be expressed as

$$\begin{aligned} T &= T(\dot{q}_1, \dot{q}_2, \dots\dots, \dot{q}_N, q_1, q_2, \dots\dots, q_N) \\ V &= V(q_1, q_2, \dots\dots, q_N) \end{aligned} \quad (4.2.1)$$

Note:

1) The kinetic energy can be a function of q_i as well as $\dot{q}_i$ when a system has angular displacements as degrees of freedom.
2) Strain energy U is an example of potential energy.

It can then be shown that the dynamic equation of motion for the system can be obtained from the following equation:

$$\frac{d}{dt}\left(\frac{\partial T}{\partial \dot{q}_i}\right) - \frac{\partial T}{\partial q_i} + \frac{\partial V}{\partial q_i} = F_i \quad (i = 1 \sim N) \quad (4.2.2)$$

where F_i are the applied forces/moments corresponding to qi

Note:

One can prove the statement involving equation (4.2.2) using the concept of virtual displacement. However, at this point, we will not attempt to prove the above statement. Instead, we will apply the above equation to simple example cases to appreciate the veracity of the statement. We will then apply it to other systems.

Equation (4.2.2) can be expressed in terms of a scalar quantity L, called the **Lagrangian**, defined as follows:

$$L = T - V \quad (4.2.3)$$

Then, equation (4.2.2) can be expressed as follows:

$$\frac{d}{dt}\left(\frac{\partial L}{\partial \dot{q}_i}\right) - \frac{\partial L}{\partial q_i} = F_i \quad (i = 1 \sim N) \quad (4.2.4)$$

Equation (4.2.2) or equation (4.2.4) is called the **Lagrange equation.** In this chapter and in subsequent chapters, we will work with equation (4.2.2).

Example 4.2.1 Consider the SDOF system shown in Figure 4.1.

$$q_1 = q, \; F_1 = F$$

$$T = \frac{1}{2}m\dot{q}^2, \quad V = U = \frac{1}{2}kq^2 \tag{4.2.5}$$

$$\frac{d}{dt}\left(\frac{\partial T}{\partial \dot{q}}\right) = \frac{d}{dt}(m\dot{q}) = m\ddot{q}, \qquad \frac{\partial T}{\partial q} = 0, \qquad \frac{\partial U}{\partial q} = kq \tag{4.2.6}$$

So, from the Lagrange equation,

$$m\ddot{q} + kq = F \tag{4.2.7}$$

Example 4.2.2 A disk and torsional spring system.

k_θ : torsional spring constant representing torsional stiffness of a shaft

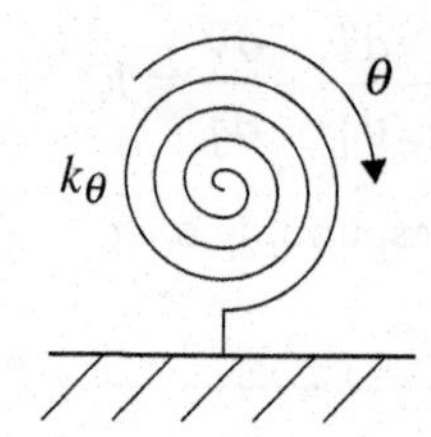

Figure 4.5 Torsional spring.

$$T_{STATIC} = k_\theta \theta_{STATIC}$$

$$k_\theta = \frac{T_{STATIC}}{\theta_{STATIC}}$$

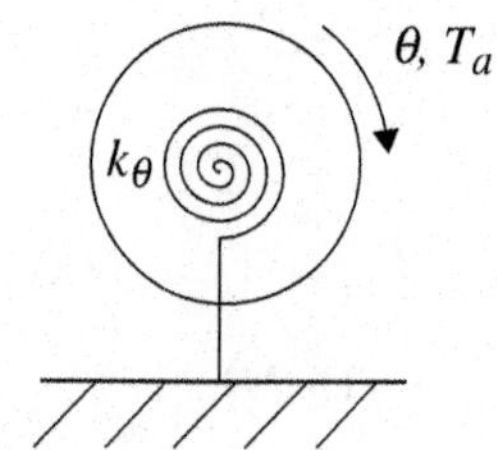

I : mass moment of inertia of the disk
T_a : applied torque

Figure 4.6 Rotating body with torsional spring.

$$T = \frac{1}{2}I\dot{\theta}^2, \qquad U = \frac{1}{2}k_\theta \theta^2,$$

$$q_1 = \theta, \qquad F_1 = T_a$$

Applying the Lagrange equation,

$$I\ddot{\theta} + k_\theta \theta = T_a$$

Example 4.2.3 A two-DOF system.

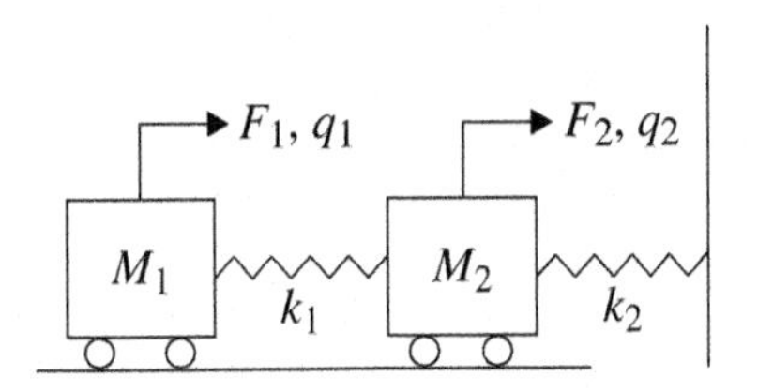

Figure 4.7 Two-DOF system with no damping.

Kinetic energy:

$$\text{For mass 1, kinetic energy } T_1 = \frac{1}{2} M_1 \dot{q}_1^2 \tag{4.2.8}$$

$$\text{For mass 2, kinetic energy } T_2 = \frac{1}{2} M_2 \dot{q}_2^2 \tag{4.2.9}$$

$$\text{Total kinetic energy } T = T_1 + T_2$$

$$T = \frac{1}{2} M_1 \dot{q}_1^2 + \frac{1}{2} M_2 \dot{q}_2^2 \tag{4.2.10}$$

Potential energy:

$$\text{For the spring with } k_1, \text{ strain energy } U_1 = \frac{1}{2} k_1 (q_1 - q_2)^2 \tag{4.2.11}$$

$$\text{For the spring with } k_2, \text{ strain energy } U_2 = \frac{1}{2} k_2 q_2^2 \tag{4.2.12}$$

$$\text{Total strain energy } U = U_1 + U_2$$

$$U = \frac{1}{2} k_1 (q_1 - q_2)^2 + \frac{1}{2} k_2 q_2^2 \tag{4.2.13}$$

Lagrange equation:

With $V = U$, the two Lagrange equations are as follows:

$$\text{For } i = 1, \quad \frac{d}{dt}\left(\frac{\partial T}{\partial \dot{q}_1}\right) - \frac{\partial T}{\partial q_1} + \frac{\partial U}{\partial q_1} = F_1 \tag{4.2.14}$$

$$\text{For } i = 2, \quad \frac{d}{dt}\left(\frac{\partial T}{\partial \dot{q}_2}\right) - \frac{\partial T}{\partial q_2} + \frac{\partial U}{\partial q_2} = F_2 \tag{4.2.15}$$

For $i = 1$,

$$\frac{d}{dt}\left(\frac{\partial T}{\partial \dot{q}_1}\right) = \frac{d}{dt}(M_1\dot{q}_1) = M_1\ddot{q}_1, \quad \frac{\partial T}{\partial q_1} = 0$$
$$\frac{\partial U}{\partial q_1} = k_1(q_1 - q_2) \tag{4.2.16}$$

Placing equation (4.2.16) into equation (4.2.14),

$$M_1\ddot{q}_1 + k_1(q_1 - q_2) = F_1 \tag{4.2.17}$$

For $i = 2$,

$$\frac{d}{dt}\left(\frac{\partial T}{\partial \dot{q}_2}\right) = \frac{d}{dt}(M_2\dot{q}_2) = M_2\ddot{q}_2, \quad \frac{\partial T}{\partial q_2} = 0$$
$$\frac{\partial U}{\partial q_2} = k_1(q_1 - q_2)(-1) + k_2 q_2 \tag{4.2.18}$$

Placing equation (4.2.18) into equation (4.2.15),

$$M_2\ddot{q}_2 - k_1 q_1 + (k_1 + k_2) q_2 = F_2 \tag{4.2.19}$$

Equations (4.2.17) and (4.2.19) can be written in matrix form as follows:

$$\begin{bmatrix} M_1 & 0 \\ 0 & M_2 \end{bmatrix}\begin{Bmatrix} \ddot{q}_1 \\ \ddot{q}_2 \end{Bmatrix} + \begin{bmatrix} k_1 & -k_1 \\ -k_1 & k_1 + k_2 \end{bmatrix}\begin{Bmatrix} q_1 \\ q_2 \end{Bmatrix} = \begin{Bmatrix} F_1 \\ F_2 \end{Bmatrix} \tag{4.2.20}$$

or

$$\mathbf{M}\ddot{\mathbf{q}} + \mathbf{K}\mathbf{q} = \mathbf{F} \tag{4.2.21}$$

where

$$\mathbf{M} = \begin{bmatrix} M_1 & 0 \\ 0 & M_2 \end{bmatrix} : \text{mass matrix} \tag{4.2.22}$$

$$\mathbf{K} = \begin{bmatrix} k_1 & -k_1 \\ -k_1 & k_1 + k_2 \end{bmatrix} : \text{stiffness matrix} \tag{4.2.23}$$

$$\mathbf{F} = \begin{Bmatrix} F_1 \\ F_2 \end{Bmatrix} : \text{load vector} \tag{4.2.24}$$

Example 4.2.4 A single pendulum.

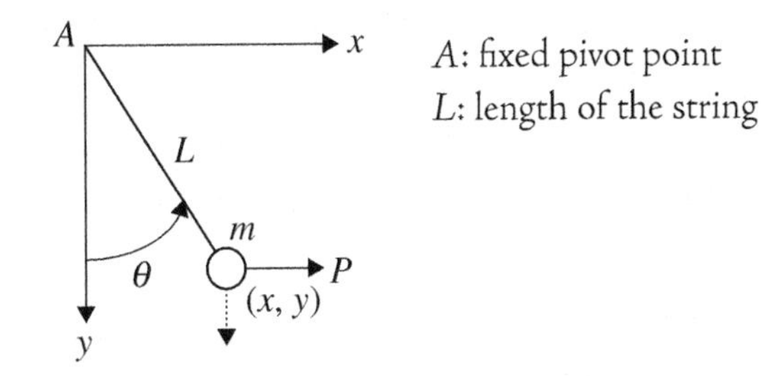

Figure 4.8 Simple pendulum subjected to a horizontal force.

The x and y coordinates of the mass can be expressed in terms of angle θ as

$$x = L\sin\theta, \quad y = L\cos\theta \tag{4.2.25}$$

Kinetic energy

The kinetic energy can be expressed as

$$T = \frac{1}{2}m(L\dot{\theta})^2 \tag{4.2.26}$$

Potential energy

If the position of the mass at $\theta = 0$ is used as a reference point, the potential energy due to gravity can be expressed as

$$V = mg(L - L\cos\theta) = mgL(1 - \cos\theta) \tag{4.2.27}$$

Alternately, if the pivot point is used as a reference,

$$V = -mgL\cos\theta \tag{4.2.28}$$

External load

Applied load P, acting horizontally in the x direction, is not directly related to θ. To find the load corresponding to θ, let's consider incremental work done by the applied load P, expressed as follows:

$$dW = Pdx = Pd(L\sin\theta) = PL\cos\theta d\theta = F_1 d\theta \tag{4.2.29}$$

From the above equation, we can identify F_1 as

$$F_1 = PL\cos\theta \tag{4.2.30}$$

The Lagrange equation is

$$\frac{d}{dt}\left(\frac{\partial T}{\partial \dot{q}_1}\right) - \frac{\partial T}{\partial q_1} + \frac{\partial V}{\partial q_1} = F_1 \tag{4.2.31}$$

or, with $q_1 = \theta$,

$$\frac{d}{dt}\left(\frac{\partial T}{\partial \dot{\theta}}\right) - \frac{\partial T}{\partial \theta} + \frac{\partial V}{\partial \theta} = F_1 \tag{4.2.32}$$

Then, the equation of motion is

$$mL^2\ddot{\theta} + mgL\sin\theta = PL\cos\theta \tag{4.2.33}$$

Equation (4.2.33) describes a nonlinear angular motion under applied load P. For small θ,

$$\sin\theta \approx \theta\,,\ \cos\theta \approx 1 \tag{4.2.34}$$

Then, from equation (4.2.33),

$$mL^2\ddot{\theta} + mgL\theta = PL \tag{4.2.35}$$

For free vibration ($P = 0$),

$$\ddot{\theta} + \frac{g}{L}\theta = 0 \tag{4.2.36}$$

and the natural frequency of free vibration is as follows:

$$\omega_n = \sqrt{\frac{g}{L}} \tag{4.2.37}$$

4.3 Damping Effect

Consider a SDOF system with a damper:

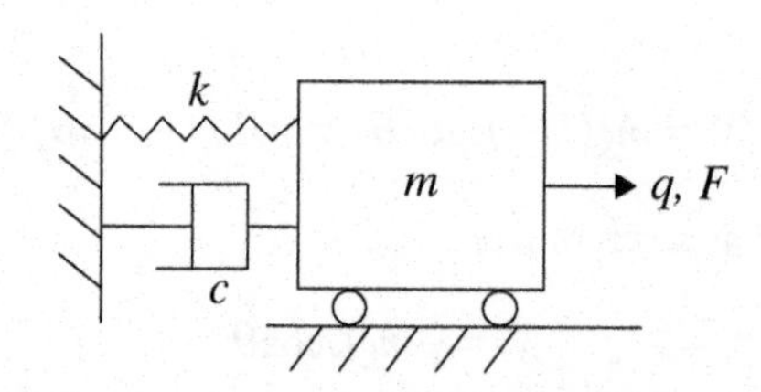

Figure 4.9 SDOF system with damping.

$$T = \frac{1}{2}m\dot{q}^2 \qquad V = U = \frac{1}{2}kq^2 \tag{4.3.1}$$

We can treat the damping force as an external force as follows:

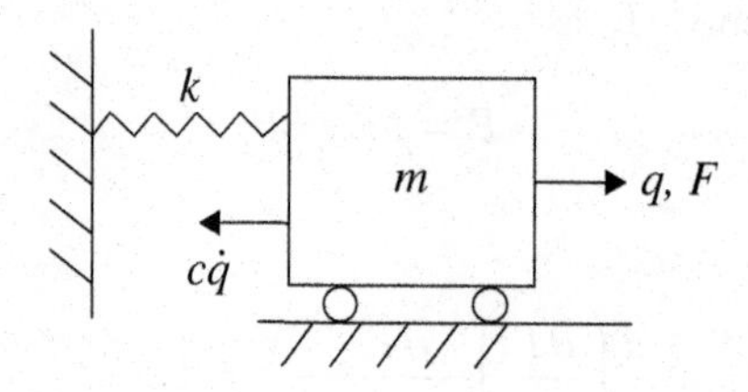

Figure 4.10 SDOF system with damping treated as an external force.

$$F_1 = F - c\dot{q} \tag{4.3.2}$$

Applying the Lagrange equation,

$$\frac{d}{dt}\left(\frac{\partial T}{\partial \dot{q}}\right) - \frac{\partial T}{\partial q} + \frac{\partial V}{\partial q} = F_1 \tag{4.3.3}$$

$$m\ddot{q} + kq = F_1 = F - c\dot{q} \tag{4.3.4}$$

and

$$m\ddot{q} + c\dot{q} + kq = F \tag{4.3.5}$$

Dissipation Function:

Alternatively, we can take into account the damping effect as follows:

Spring force $= kq$

Damping force $= c\dot{q}$

Strain energy: $U = \frac{1}{2}kq^2$ (4.3.6)

and

$$\frac{\partial U}{\partial q} = kq \tag{4.3.7}$$

Noting the similarity between the damping force expression and the spring force expression, we can introduce, for convenience, a dissipation function D defined as follows:

$$D = \frac{1}{2}c\dot{q}^2 \tag{4.3.8}$$

Then,

$$\frac{\partial D}{\partial \dot{q}} = c\dot{q} \tag{4.3.9}$$

and

$$F_1 = F - c\dot{q} = F - \frac{\partial D}{\partial \dot{q}} \tag{4.3.10}$$

Accordingly, the Lagrange equation can then be expressed as follows:

$$\frac{d}{dt}\left(\frac{\partial T}{\partial \dot{q}}\right) - \frac{\partial T}{\partial q} + \frac{\partial V}{\partial q} + \frac{\partial D}{\partial \dot{q}} = F \tag{4.3.11}$$

In general,

$$\frac{d}{dt}\left(\frac{\partial T}{\partial \dot{q}_i}\right) - \frac{\partial T}{\partial q_i} + \frac{\partial V}{\partial q_i} + \frac{\partial D}{\partial \dot{q}_i} = F_i \quad (i = 1 \sim N) \tag{4.3.12}$$

Example:

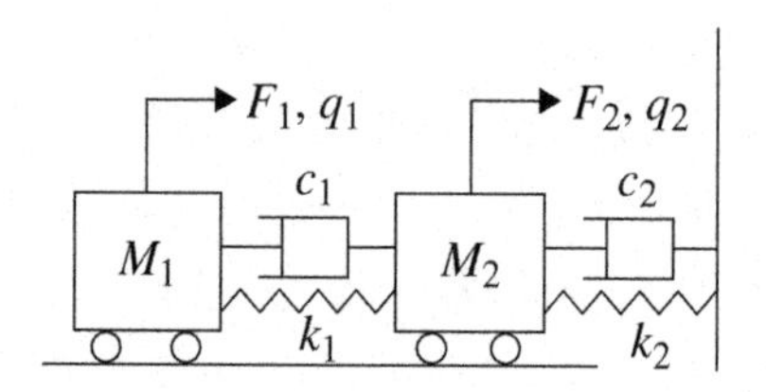

Figure 4.11 SDOF system with two dampers.

$$U = \frac{1}{2}k_1(q_1 - q_2)^2 + \frac{1}{2}k_2q_2^2 \tag{4.3.13}$$

$$D = \frac{1}{2}c_1(\dot{q}_1 - \dot{q}_2)^2 + \frac{1}{2}c_2\dot{q}_2^2 \tag{4.3.14}$$

Note that the dissipation function is not a potential function. It was introduced for mathematical convenience.

Chapter 4 Problem Sets

4.1 Consider a two-DOF system shown in the sketch

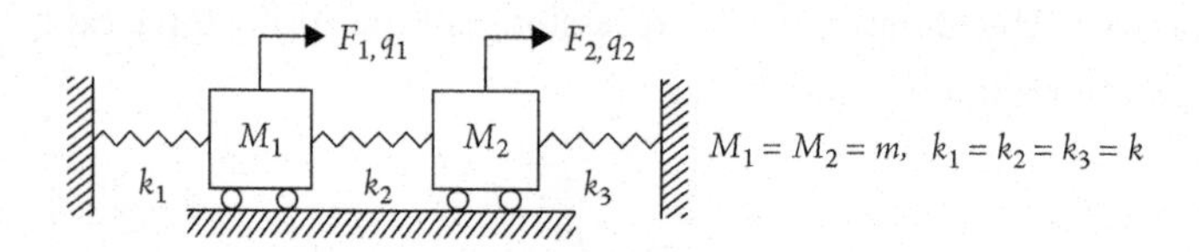

(a) Apply the energy approach to construct the equation of motion. Conform that the equation of motion is identical to the one from the Newton's second law.

(b) Express the equation of motion in matrix form.

4.2 Consider a three-DOF system shown below.

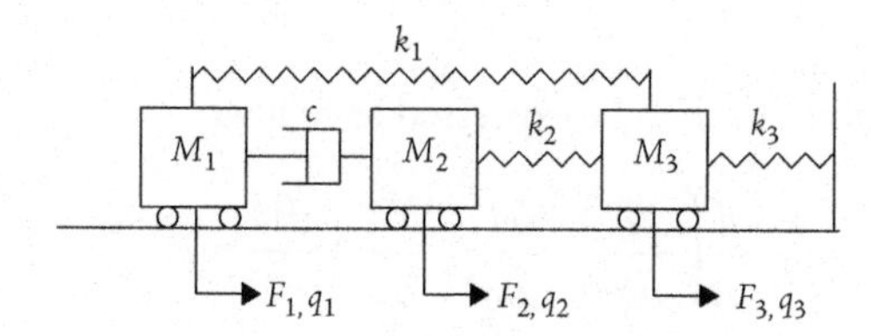

(a) Construct the expression for the kinetic energy, strain energy and dissipation (or damping) function of the system.

(b) Apply the energy approach to derive the equation of motion.
(c) Express the equation of motion in matrix form. Check whether the equation of motion is identical to the one based on the Newton's second law.

4.3 Consider a SDOF system undergoing vertical motion with an mass unbalance represented by a single mass m_o with offset distance e from the axis of rotation as shown in the sketch. The rotational speed is Ω rad/sec and the total mass of the system including the unbalanced mass is M. Construct the equation of motion using the Lagrange equation approach.

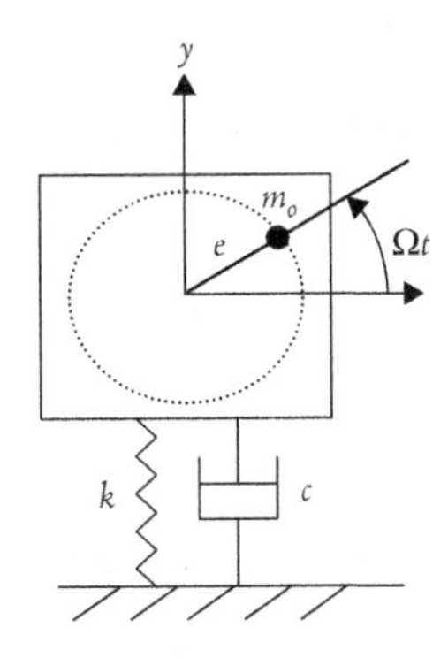

4.4 Consider a system of a concentrated mass M, a vertical spring with constant K and two rigid bars as shown in the sketch. The sketch shows an initially straight body of length $2L$ in the displaced position with angle θ. Applied force P remains always horizontal. The rigid bars are assumed massless. Ignore the gravity effect for simplicity. Hinge C is fixed. Hinge A and B are fixed in the vertical direction, but free to translate horizontally. The linear spring remains always vertical. Note that this may represent an SDOF model of an slender body under compressive force P with the spring representing bending stiffness of the body.

(a) Express position (x, y) of mass M in terms of length L and angle θ.
(b) Construct the potential energy expression in terms of angle θ.
(c) Construct the kinetic energy expression.
(d) Find F_1 corresponding to θ. Note that $dW = P(dx)_A = F_1 d\theta$
(e) Derive the equation of motion for θ via the Lagrange equation approach.
(f) Assume small θ and simplify the equation of motion.

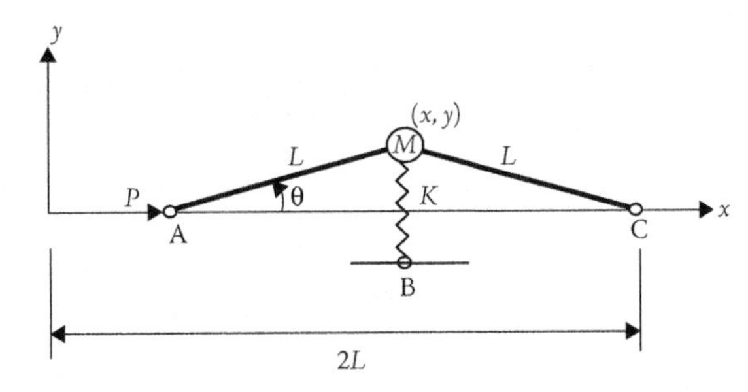

4.5 For the system shown in the sketch, mass m_A is connected to mass m_1 via a rigid lever resting on the two fulcrums. The distance between the left fulcrum and the right fulcrum is e and the distance between mass

m_A and the left fulcrum is d. Rotation of the lever is assumed small. From geometric consideration, one can show that displacements q_A and q_1 are related such that

$$q_A = \alpha q_1 \qquad \text{where } \alpha = -\frac{d}{e}$$

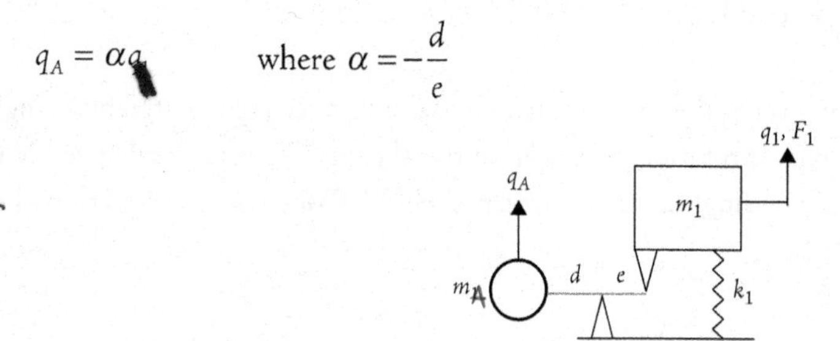

(a) Construct the kinetic energy expression.
(b) Use the Lagrange equation approach to show that the equation of motion can be expressed as

$$m_{eff}\ddot{q}_1 + k_1 q_1 = F_1$$

where

$$m_{eff} = m_1\left[1+\beta\alpha^2\right],\ \beta = \frac{m_A}{m_1}$$

4.6 A payload appended to a flight vehicle is modeled as a concentrated mass M, placed at the end of a rod of length L, undergoing rotational motion about pivot point A as shown in the sketch. The rod is assumed rigid and massless. The torsional spring represents bending stiffness of the pylon. Point A is moving with a prescribed vertical displacement of $q(t)$ where $q(t)$ is measured from the $y = 0$ position.

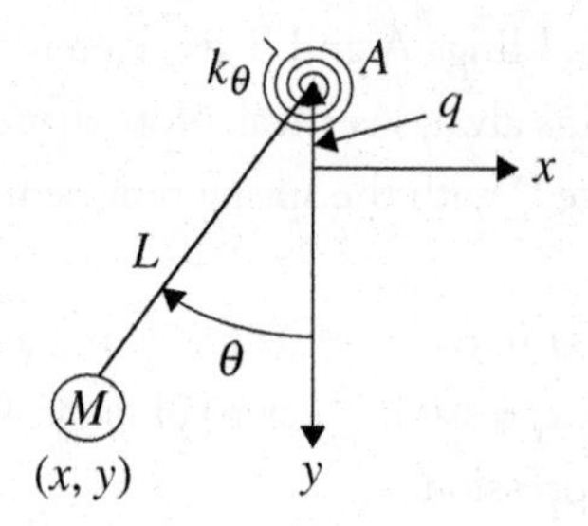

(a) Construct the potential energy expression.
(b) Construct the kinetic energy expression.
(c) Derive the equation of motion for θ via the Lagrange equation approach.
(d) Assume small θ and simplify the equation of motion to $I\ddot{\theta} + k_{eff}\theta = 0$.
(Note that k_{eff}, the effective spring constant, includes a time-varying component.)
(e) Find the expression for k_{eff} for $q = B\cos\Omega t$.

4.7 Do the following for the two-DOF system with a single pendulum attached to a moving block as shown below.

(a) Construct the kinetic energy expression.
(b) Construct the potential energy expression. Identify the reference point from which the gravity potential is measured.

(c) Find F_1 and F_2 corresponding to q and θ.
(d) Derive the equation of motion using the Lagrange equation approach.

M_1: mass of the block
M_2: mass attached at the end of the string
P : horizontal force applied to mass M_2
q : horizontal displacement of mass M_1
L : length of the string
x_2, y_2 : Cartesian coordinates of M_2

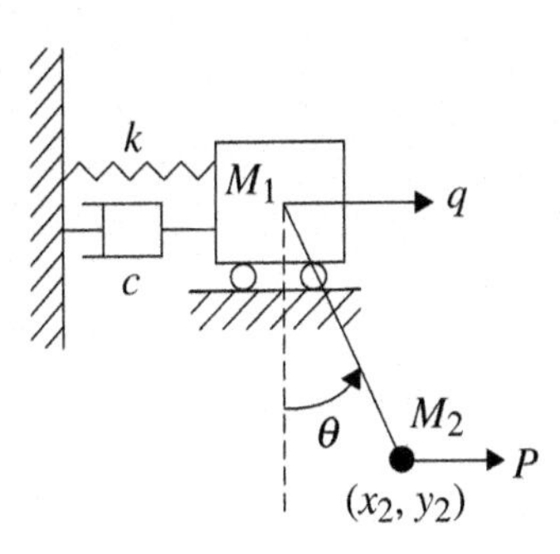

5 DYNAMIC STABILITY

A system undergoing dynamic motion can experience instability, where the system exhibits excessive vibration that does not decay with time, resulting in fatigue damage and failure of the system. As an example, one may consider a slender flexible body such as a rocket in flight undergoing bending motion while subjected to a thrust force with no vector control. Accordingly, the thrust axis is always in parallel with the body axis as it undergoes bending deflection. This type of applied force is called a **follower force**. More mundane examples are a garden hose or a fire hose spewing water. In these cases, the coupling between the thrust and the deformation of the slender body could lead to dynamic instability if the thrust level is high enough.

Another example of dynamic instability is the aircraft wing flutter. An aircraft wing in flight vibrates when it is subjected to disturbances caused by gust or sudden maneuver. At low speeds, the vibration dies out because of structural and aerodynamic damping. However, if the speed is high enough, the wing vibration does not damp out. This phenomenon is called **wing flutter**. The flutter can cause wing fatigue damage and catastrophic failure. At the flutter speed, the wing draws energy from airflow to sustain vibration caused by initial disturbances. Other aerodynamic surfaces such as elevator, rudder, and aileron may experience flutter. Examples of wing or tail flutter include many race planes in the 1920s and 1930s and the North American FJ-4 Fury in the early 1950s.

Flutter is a dynamic instability phenomenon caused by the interaction among structural, aerodynamic, and inertia forces. Aerospace vehicles must be free of flutter within their flight envelope.

In this chapter, we will consider dynamic stability of the two examples mentioned above. For this, we will introduce simple models with two degrees of freedom and then apply the Lagrange equation approach to construct the equation of motion. We will note that, under the assumption of small displacement, the analysis of dynamic stability turns out to be an exercise in eigenvalue analysis.

5.1 Follower Force Problem

To capture the essence of dynamic response of the slender flexible body undergoing bending vibration subject to a follower force, one may construct a model with two concentrated masses (M_1, M_2) and two torsional springs (K_1, K_2) as shown below. This sketch shows a double-pendulum with two torsional springs subjected to a follower force at the bottom. The torsional springs are added to represent bending stiffness of the slender body. One may consider this a crude model of a rocket vertically placed on a test stand. To simplify the discussion, we will assume no mass loss and no gravity condition.

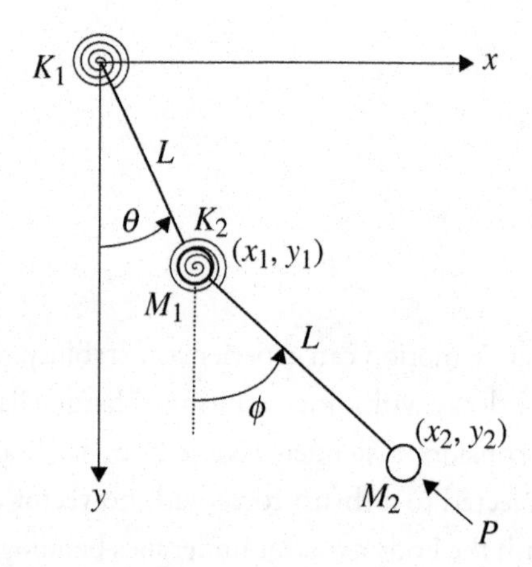

Figure 5.1 Two-DOF model with a follower force.

5.1.1 Equation of Motion

The kinetic energy of the system:

$$T = \frac{1}{2}M_1(\dot{x}_1^{\,2} + \dot{y}_1^{\,2}) + \frac{1}{2}M_2(\dot{x}_2^{\,2} + \dot{y}_2^{\,2}) \tag{5.1.1}$$

From the sketch,

$$x_1 = L\sin\theta, \quad y_1 = L\cos\theta \tag{5.1.2}$$

$$\dot{x}_1 = (L\cos\theta)\dot{\theta}, \quad \dot{y}_1 = -(L\sin\theta)\dot{\theta} \tag{5.1.3}$$

$$x_2 = x_1 + L\sin\phi, \quad y_2 = y_1 + L\cos\phi \tag{5.1.4}$$

$$\begin{aligned} \dot{x}_2 &= \dot{x}_1 + (L\cos\phi)\dot{\phi} = L\dot{\theta}\cos\theta + L\dot{\phi}\cos\phi \\ \dot{y}_2 &= \dot{y}_1 + (-L\sin\phi)\dot{\phi} = -L\dot{\theta}\sin\theta - L\dot{\phi}\sin\phi \end{aligned} \tag{5.1.5}$$

Placing equations (5.1.3) and (5.1.5) into equation (5.1.1),

$$T = \frac{1}{2}(M_1 + M_2)L^2\dot{\theta}^2 + \frac{1}{2}M_2L^2\dot{\phi}^2 + M_2L^2\dot{\theta}\dot{\phi}\cos(\phi - \theta) \tag{5.1.6}$$

Note:

$$T = T(\dot{\theta},\ \dot{\phi},\ \theta,\ \phi) \tag{5.1.7}$$

For small angles, $\cos(\phi - \theta) \approx 1$ and

$$T = \frac{1}{2}(M_1 + M_2)L^2\dot{\theta}^2 + \frac{1}{2}M_2L^2\dot{\phi}^2 + M_2L^2\dot{\theta}\dot{\phi} \tag{5.1.8}$$

Note:

$$T = T(\dot{\theta},\ \dot{\phi}) \sim \text{independent of } \phi \text{ and } \theta$$

The strain energy of the system:

$$V = U = \frac{1}{2}K_1\theta^2 + \frac{1}{2}K_2(\phi - \theta)^2 \tag{5.1.9}$$

The Lagrange equations are

$$\begin{aligned} \frac{d}{dt}\left(\frac{\partial T}{\partial \dot{\theta}}\right) - \frac{\partial T}{\partial \theta} + \frac{\partial V}{\partial \theta} &= F_1 \\ \frac{d}{dt}\left(\frac{\partial T}{\partial \dot{\phi}}\right) - \frac{\partial T}{\partial \phi} + \frac{\partial V}{\partial \phi} &= F_2 \end{aligned} \tag{5.1.10}$$

For $M_1 = 2M_0$, $M_2 = M_0$

$$T = \frac{1}{2}(3M_0L^2)\dot{\theta}^2 + \frac{1}{2}M_0L^2\dot{\phi}^2 + M_0L^2\dot{\theta}\dot{\phi} \tag{5.1.11}$$

For $K_1 = K_2 = K$

$$V = U = \frac{1}{2}K\theta^2 + \frac{1}{2}K(\phi - \theta)^2 \tag{5.1.12}$$

Placing equations (5.1.11) and (5.1.12) into equation (5.1.10),

$$\begin{aligned} 3M_0L^2\ddot{\theta} + M_0L^2\ddot{\phi} + 2K\theta - K\phi &= F_1 \\ M_0L^2\ddot{\theta} + M_0L^2\ddot{\phi} + K(\phi - \theta) &= F_2 \end{aligned} \tag{5.1.13}$$

In matrix form:

$$M_0L^2\begin{bmatrix} 3 & 1 \\ 1 & 1 \end{bmatrix}\begin{Bmatrix} \ddot{\theta} \\ \ddot{\phi} \end{Bmatrix} + K\begin{bmatrix} 2 & -1 \\ -1 & 1 \end{bmatrix}\begin{Bmatrix} \theta \\ \phi \end{Bmatrix} = \begin{Bmatrix} F_1 \\ F_2 \end{Bmatrix} \tag{5.1.14}$$

To find the expressions for F_1 and F_2, let's consider the incremental work done by the thrust P as follows:

$$\begin{aligned} dW &= -(P\sin\phi)dx_2 - (P\cos\phi)dy_2 \\ &= -(P\sin\phi)(L\cos\theta d\theta + L\cos\phi d\phi) - (P\cos\phi)(-L\sin\theta d\theta - L\sin\phi d\phi) \end{aligned} \tag{5.1.15}$$

or

$$dW = -PL(\sin\phi\cos\theta - \cos\phi\sin\theta)d\theta = F_1 d\theta + F_2 d\phi \tag{5.1.16}$$

where

$$\begin{aligned} F_1 &= -PL(\sin\phi\cos\theta - \cos\phi\sin\theta) = -PL\sin(\phi - \theta) \\ F_2 &= 0 \end{aligned} \tag{5.1.17}$$

Note:

F_1 is dependent on angular displacement.

For small angles,

$$F_1 = -PL(\phi - \theta) \tag{5.1.18}$$

In matrix form:

$$\begin{Bmatrix} F_1 \\ F_2 \end{Bmatrix} = PL \begin{Bmatrix} \theta - \phi \\ 0 \end{Bmatrix} = PL \begin{bmatrix} 1 & -1 \\ 0 & 0 \end{bmatrix} \begin{Bmatrix} \theta \\ \phi \end{Bmatrix} \tag{5.1.19}$$

Placing equation (5.1.19) into equation (5.1.14),

$$M_0 L^2 \begin{bmatrix} 3 & 1 \\ 1 & 1 \end{bmatrix} \begin{Bmatrix} \ddot{\theta} \\ \ddot{\phi} \end{Bmatrix} + K \begin{bmatrix} 2 & -1 \\ -1 & 1 \end{bmatrix} \begin{Bmatrix} \theta \\ \phi \end{Bmatrix} = PL \begin{bmatrix} 1 & -1 \\ 0 & 0 \end{bmatrix} \begin{Bmatrix} \theta \\ \phi \end{Bmatrix} \tag{5.1.20}$$

or

$$M_0 L^2 \begin{bmatrix} 3 & 1 \\ 1 & 1 \end{bmatrix} \begin{Bmatrix} \ddot{\theta} \\ \ddot{\phi} \end{Bmatrix} + K \left(\begin{bmatrix} 2 & -1 \\ -1 & 1 \end{bmatrix} - \frac{PL}{K} \begin{bmatrix} 1 & -1 \\ 0 & 0 \end{bmatrix} \right) \begin{Bmatrix} \theta \\ \phi \end{Bmatrix} = \begin{Bmatrix} 0 \\ 0 \end{Bmatrix} \tag{5.1.21}$$

or

$$M_0 L^2 \begin{bmatrix} 3 & 1 \\ 1 & 1 \end{bmatrix} \begin{Bmatrix} \ddot{\theta} \\ \ddot{\phi} \end{Bmatrix} + K \begin{bmatrix} 2 - \overline{P} & -1 + \overline{P} \\ -1 & 1 \end{bmatrix} \begin{Bmatrix} \theta \\ \phi \end{Bmatrix} = \begin{Bmatrix} 0 \\ 0 \end{Bmatrix} \tag{5.1.22}$$

with

$$\overline{P} = \frac{PL}{K} : \text{nondimensional thrust parameter} \tag{5.1.23}$$

Equation (5.1.22) can be expressed symbolically as

$$\mathbf{M}\ddot{\mathbf{q}} + \mathbf{K}_{eff}\mathbf{q} = \mathbf{0} \tag{5.1.24}$$

where

$$\mathbf{M} = M_0 L^2 \begin{bmatrix} 3 & 1 \\ 1 & 1 \end{bmatrix} : \text{mass matrix}$$

$$\mathbf{K}_{eff} = K\begin{bmatrix} 2-\overline{P} & -1+\overline{P} \\ -1 & 1 \end{bmatrix} \text{: effective stiffness matrix}$$

Note that $\mathbf{K}_{eff}$ is dependent on $\overline{P}$ and NONSYMMETRIC.

We can further simplify the above equation by introducing a nondimesional time as follows:

Divide equation (5.1.22) by K such that:

$$\frac{M_0 L^2}{K}\begin{bmatrix} 3 & 1 \\ 1 & 1 \end{bmatrix}\begin{Bmatrix} \ddot{\theta} \\ \ddot{\phi} \end{Bmatrix} + \begin{bmatrix} 2-\overline{P} & -1+\overline{P} \\ -1 & 1 \end{bmatrix}\begin{Bmatrix} \theta \\ \phi \end{Bmatrix} = \begin{Bmatrix} 0 \\ 0 \end{Bmatrix} \tag{5.1.25}$$

Introduce a scaled time "τ" defined as follows:

$$\tau = at \tag{5.1.26}$$

Then,

$$\dot{\theta} = \frac{d\theta}{dt} = \frac{d\theta}{d\tau}\frac{d\tau}{dt} = a\frac{d\theta}{d\tau} \tag{5.1.27}$$

$$\ddot{\theta} = \frac{d^2\theta}{dt^2} = a^2\frac{d^2\theta}{d\tau^2} \tag{5.1.28}$$

Also,

$$\ddot{\phi} = \frac{d^2\phi}{dt^2} = a^2\frac{d^2\phi}{d\tau^2} \tag{5.1.29}$$

Placing equations (5.1.28) and (5.1.29) into equation (5.1.25),

$$a^2\frac{M_0 L^2}{K}\begin{bmatrix} 3 & 1 \\ 1 & 1 \end{bmatrix}\begin{Bmatrix} \dfrac{d^2\theta}{d\tau^2} \\ \dfrac{d^2\phi}{d\tau^2} \end{Bmatrix} + \begin{bmatrix} 2-\overline{P} & -1+\overline{P} \\ -1 & 1 \end{bmatrix}\begin{Bmatrix} \theta \\ \phi \end{Bmatrix} = \begin{Bmatrix} 0 \\ 0 \end{Bmatrix} \tag{5.1.30}$$

We can choose a such that

$$a^2\frac{M_0 L^2}{K} = 1$$

or

$$a = \sqrt{\frac{K}{M_0 L^2}} \tag{5.1.31}$$

Then,

$$\begin{bmatrix} 3 & 1 \\ 1 & 1 \end{bmatrix}\begin{Bmatrix} \dfrac{d^2\theta}{d\tau^2} \\ \dfrac{d^2\phi}{d\tau^2} \end{Bmatrix} + \begin{bmatrix} 2-\overline{P} & -1+\overline{P} \\ -1 & 1 \end{bmatrix}\begin{Bmatrix} \theta \\ \phi \end{Bmatrix} = \begin{Bmatrix} 0 \\ 0 \end{Bmatrix} \tag{5.1.32}$$

with
$$\tau = t\sqrt{\frac{K}{M_0 L^2}} \tag{5.1.33}$$

Equation (5.1.32) can be expressed symbolically as

$$\mathbf{M}\ddot{\mathbf{q}} + \mathbf{K}_{eff}\mathbf{q} = \mathbf{0} \tag{5.1.34}$$

where
$$\mathbf{M} = \begin{bmatrix} 3 & 1 \\ 1 & 1 \end{bmatrix} \tag{5.1.35}$$

$$\ddot{\mathbf{q}} = \begin{Bmatrix} \dfrac{d^2\theta}{d\tau^2} \\ \dfrac{d^2\phi}{d\tau^2} \end{Bmatrix} \tag{5.1.36}$$

$$\mathbf{K}_{eff} = \begin{bmatrix} 2-\overline{P} & -1+\overline{P} \\ -1 & 1 \end{bmatrix} \tag{5.1.37}$$

$$\mathbf{q} = \begin{Bmatrix} \theta \\ \phi \end{Bmatrix} \tag{5.1.38}$$

We can use equation (5.1.32) to examine the stability for given $\overline{P}$.

5.1.2 Static Behavior

For static condition, the equation of motion is reduced to

$$\left(\begin{bmatrix} 2-\overline{P} & -1+\overline{P} \\ -1 & 1 \end{bmatrix}\right)\begin{Bmatrix} \theta \\ \phi \end{Bmatrix} = \begin{Bmatrix} 0 \\ 0 \end{Bmatrix} \tag{5.1.39}$$

For nontrivial solution (i.e., non-straight configuration),

$$\det\begin{bmatrix} 2-\overline{P} & -1+\overline{P} \\ -1 & 1 \end{bmatrix} = 0 \tag{5.1.40}$$

However, the determinant of the above matrix is

$$2-\overline{P}+\overline{P}-1 = 1 \neq 0 \tag{5.1.41}$$

and the solution to equation (5.1.39) is

$$\begin{Bmatrix} \theta \\ \phi \end{Bmatrix} = \begin{Bmatrix} 0 \\ 0 \end{Bmatrix} \tag{5.1.42}$$

So, the system does not buckle statically and remains straight. However, it can be dynamically unstable if the thrust level is high enough.

5.1.3 Dynamic Behavior

Equation of motion:

$$\mathbf{M}\ddot{\mathbf{q}}+\mathbf{K}_{eff}\mathbf{q}=\mathbf{0} \tag{5.1.43}$$

The solution to equation (5.1.43) is of the form

$$\mathbf{q}=\varphi e^{\lambda\tau} \tag{5.1.44}$$

Placing equation (5.1.44) into equation (5.1.43),

$$\left(\mathbf{K}_{eff}+\lambda^2\mathbf{M}\right)\varphi=\mathbf{0} \tag{5.1.45}$$

For nontrivial φ,

$$\det\left(\mathbf{K}_{eff}+\lambda^2\mathbf{M}\right)=0 \tag{5.1.46}$$

The eigenvalues λ_k ($k=1,2$), which are the solutions of equation (5.1.46), can be expressed as

$$\lambda_k=\mathrm{Re}(\lambda_k)+i\,\mathrm{Im}(\lambda_k)=\sigma_k\pm i\omega_k \qquad (\omega_k>0) \tag{5.1.47}$$

where

$$\sigma_k=\mathrm{Re}(\lambda_k) \tag{5.1.48}$$

Then,

$$e^{\lambda_k\tau}=e^{(\sigma_k\pm i\omega_k)\tau}=e^{\sigma_k\tau}e^{\pm i\omega_k\tau}=e^{\sigma_k\tau}(\cos\omega_k\tau\pm i\sin\omega_k\tau) \tag{5.1.49}$$

where $e^{\sigma_k\tau}$ ~ change of amplitude with time

$(\cos\omega_k\tau\pm i\sin\omega_k\tau)$ ~ oscillation with "frequency" ω_k

Stability criteria: If $\sigma_k=\mathrm{Re}(\lambda_k)>0$ for any k, the amplitude of vibration excited by initial disturbance will grow in time. The system is then said to be dynamically unstable.

Expressing K and M as

$$\mathbf{K}_{eff}=\begin{bmatrix}k_{11} & k_{12}\\ k_{21} & k_{22}\end{bmatrix},\quad \mathbf{M}=\begin{bmatrix}m_{11} & m_{12}\\ m_{21} & m_{22}\end{bmatrix} \tag{5.1.50}$$

Equation (5.1.46) can be written as

$$A\lambda^4+B\lambda^2+C=0 \tag{5.1.51}$$

where

$$\begin{aligned}A&=m_{11}m_{22}-m_{12}m_{21}\\ B&=k_{11}m_{22}+k_{22}m_{11}-k_{12}m_{21}-k_{21}m_{12}\\ C&=k_{11}k_{22}-k_{12}k_{21}\end{aligned} \tag{5.1.52}$$

From equation (5.1.51),

$$\lambda^2=\frac{-B\pm\sqrt{B^2-4AC}}{2A}$$

We can observe as follows:

(1) For small $\overline{P}$, $B^2-4AC>0$ and $\lambda^2<0$, and $\sigma_k=\mathrm{Re}(\lambda_k)=0$ for all k, $\lambda=\pm i\omega_1$, $\pm i\omega_2$ and thus the system is dynamically stable.

(2) As $\overline{P}$ increases, $B^2-4AC=0$ and we observe double roots for λ with $\omega_1=\omega_2$.

(3) As $\overline{P}$ further increases, $B^2-4AC<0$, and the real part of one of the eigenvalues becomes positive and the system becomes dynamically unstable.

So, the transition to dynamic instability occurs at $B^2-4AC=0$. Frequencies ω_1 and ω_2 approach each other as $\overline{P}\to\overline{P}_F$. This phenomenon is called frequency coalescence. For $\mathbf{M}$ and $\mathbf{K}_{eff}$ given in equations (5.1.35) and (5.1.37), $A=2$, $B=7-2\overline{P}$ and $C=1$. Then from $B^2-4AC=0$, one can determine that $\overline{P}_F=2.086$.

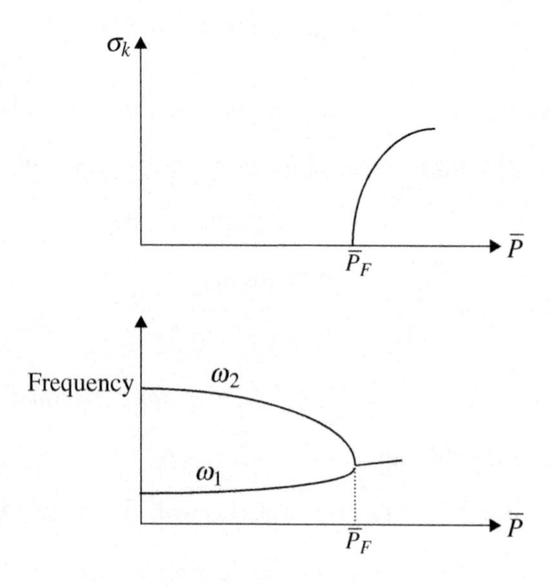

Figure 5.2 Real part and frequency plots of two-DOF model under a follower force.

Note:

We can check how the body behaves if the thrust line remains always vertical via thrust vector control.

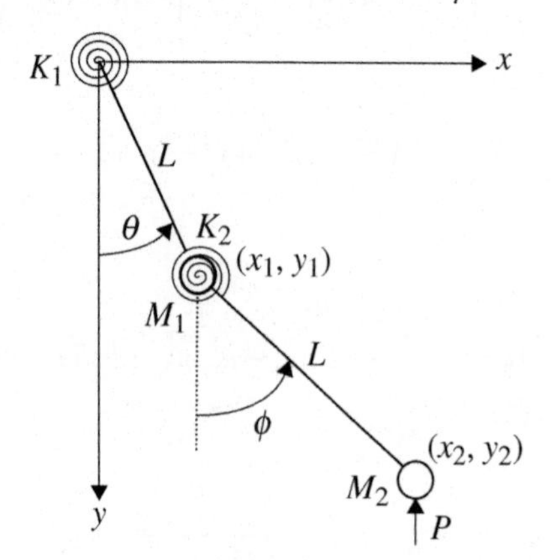

Figure 5.3 Two-DOF model under applied force with no directional change.

We can consider the incremental work done by the thrust

$$dW = -Pdy_2 = -PL(-\sin\theta d\theta - \sin\phi d\phi) = F_1 d\theta + F_2 d\phi$$

to show that $F_1 = PL\sin\theta,\ F_2 = PL\sin\phi$

Assuming small angles, the equation of motion can then be expressed as

$$\begin{bmatrix} 3 & 1 \\ 1 & 1 \end{bmatrix} \begin{Bmatrix} \dfrac{d^2\theta}{d\tau^2} \\ \dfrac{d^2\phi}{d\tau^2} \end{Bmatrix} + \begin{bmatrix} 2-\overline{P} & -1 \\ -1 & 1-\overline{P} \end{bmatrix} \begin{Bmatrix} \theta \\ \phi \end{Bmatrix} = \begin{Bmatrix} 0 \\ 0 \end{Bmatrix}$$

Does it buckle under static condition? For static case, the equation reduces to

$$\begin{bmatrix} 2-\overline{P} & -1 \\ -1 & 1-\overline{P} \end{bmatrix} \begin{Bmatrix} \theta \\ \phi \end{Bmatrix} = \begin{Bmatrix} 0 \\ 0 \end{Bmatrix} \quad (5.1.53)$$

For nontrivial solution (i.e., non-straight configuration),

$$\det \begin{bmatrix} 2-\overline{P} & -1 \\ -1 & 1-\overline{P} \end{bmatrix} = 0 \quad (5.1.54)$$

$$\overline{P}^2 - 3\overline{P} + 1 = 0 \quad (5.1.55)$$

Solving the above equation,

$$\overline{P} = \frac{3 \pm \sqrt{5}}{2} \quad (5.1.56)$$

The smaller of the two values corresponds to the critical load (i.e., the buckling load).

$$\overline{P}_{cr} = \frac{3-\sqrt{5}}{2} \approx 0.3820 \quad (5.1.57)$$

Placing the above value of $\overline{P}_{cr}$ into equation (5.1.53), we can determine the eigenvector (i.e., the buckling mode) as follows:

$$\begin{Bmatrix} \theta \\ \phi \end{Bmatrix} = \begin{Bmatrix} 0.6180 \\ 1 \end{Bmatrix} \quad (5.1.58)$$

Note that for given $\overline{P}$ ($< \overline{P}_{cr}$), one can carry out free vibration analysis to determine the natural frequencies and the natural modes. The system is stable as long as it does not buckle statically.

5.2 Dynamic Aeroelasticity

We will first consider aircraft wing flutter using a simple two-DOF model to appreciate the importance of inertia coupling between bending motion and torsional motion of the wing. We will then briefly introduce other aeroelastic phenomena such as panel flutter and stall flutter.

5.2.1 A Model Wing

A model wing with two degrees of freedom as shown in the sketch can represent the essential characteristics of the behaviorv of a real wing.

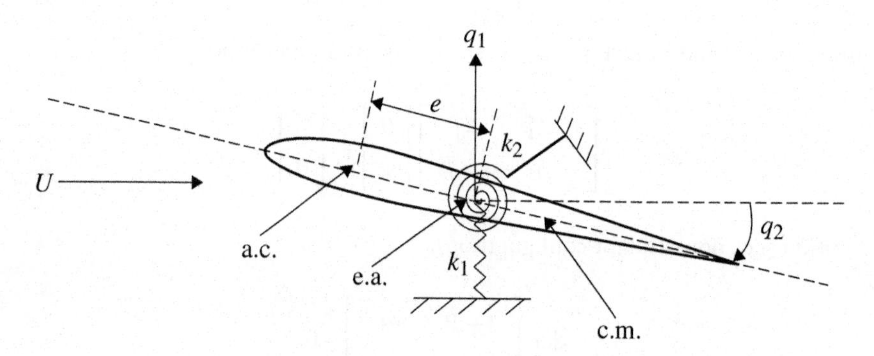

Figure 5.4 Two-DOF model wing.

U: flight speed or upstream velocity
q_1 : vertical displacement
q_2 : rotation angle
k_1 : linear spring constant representing bending stiffness of the wing
k_2 : torsional spring constant representing torsional stiffness of the wing
e: distance between the aerodynamic center (a.c.) and the elastic axis (e.a.)

Note:

(1) The elastic axis is the locus of shear center.
(2) We use the elastic axis as the reference to structurally decouple bending from torsion.
(3) q_1 and q_2 are measured from the static equilibrium.

The equation of motion:

For the two-DOF model, the equation of motion can be derived via applying the Lagrange equation as follows:

Strain energy:

$$V = \frac{1}{2}k_1 q_1^2 + \frac{1}{2}k_2 q_2^2 \tag{5.2.1}$$

Kinetic energy:

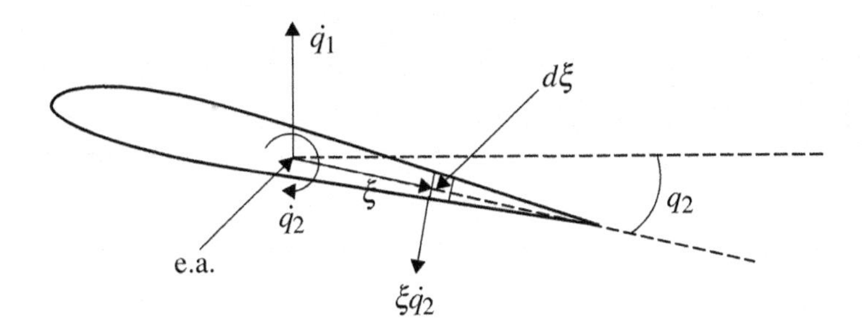

Figure 5.5 Two-DOF model wing undergoing vertical and rotational motion.

ξ : coordinate along the chord starting from the elastic axis
$\hat{m}$: mass per chord length
dT : kinetic energy of small mass of length $d\xi$

$$\begin{aligned} dT &= \frac{1}{2}(\hat{m}d\xi)[(\dot{q}_1 - \xi\dot{q}_2\cos q_2)^2 + (\xi\dot{q}_2\sin q_2)^2] \\ &= \frac{1}{2}(\hat{m}d\xi)[\dot{q}_1^2 - 2\xi\dot{q}_1\dot{q}_2\cos q_2 + \xi^2\dot{q}_2^2\ (\cos^2 q_2 + \sin^2 q_2)] \\ &= \frac{1}{2}(\hat{m}d\xi)[\dot{q}_1^2 - 2\xi\dot{q}_1\dot{q}_2\cos q_2 + \xi^2\dot{q}_2^2] \end{aligned} \tag{5.2.2}$$

$$\begin{aligned} T &= \int dT = \frac{1}{2}\int(\dot{q}_1^2 - 2\xi\dot{q}_1\dot{q}_2\cos q_2 + \xi^2\dot{q}_2^2)\hat{m}d\xi \\ &= \frac{1}{2}\dot{q}_1^2\int\hat{m}\,d\xi - \dot{q}_1\dot{q}_2\cos q_2\int\xi\hat{m}d\xi + \frac{1}{2}\dot{q}_2^2\int\xi^2\hat{m}\,d\xi \end{aligned} \tag{5.2.3}$$

Carrying out the integrations from the leading edge to the trailing edge,

$$T = \frac{1}{2}M\dot{q}_1^2 - S_\alpha\dot{q}_1\dot{q}_2\cos q_2 + \frac{1}{2}I_\alpha\dot{q}_2^2 \tag{5.2.4}$$

where

$M = \int\hat{m}\,d\xi$: total mass of the wing

$S_\alpha = \int\xi\hat{m}d\xi$: static moment of mass about the elastic axis

$I_\alpha = \int\xi^2\hat{m}\,d\xi$: mass moment of inertia about the elastic axis

Note:

The second term in equation (5.2.4) represents **inertia coupling** between the vertical (bending) motion and the rotational (torsional) motion. S_α is a measure of the c.m. offset from the e.a. and also a measure of inertia coupling. If the c.m. coincides with the e.a., $S_\alpha = 0$ and there is no inertia coupling.

For small rotation, $\cos q_2 \approx 1$ and

$$T = \frac{1}{2}M\dot{q}_1^2 - S_\alpha \dot{q}_1 \dot{q}_2 + \frac{1}{2}I_\alpha \dot{q}_2^2 \tag{5.2.5}$$

Incremental work done:

$$dW = F_1 dq_1 + F_2 dq_2$$

Aerodynamic force and moment:

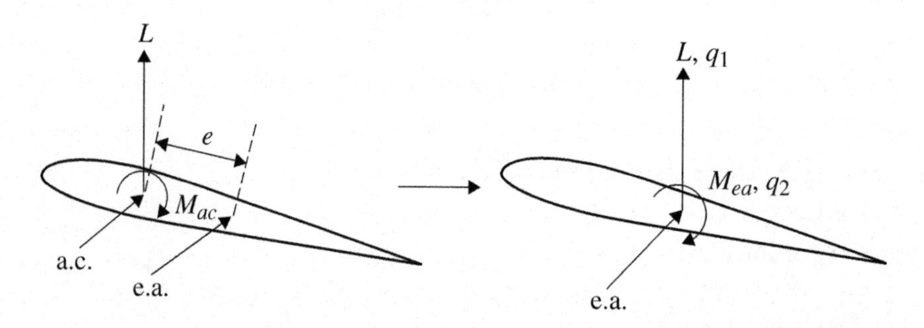

Figure 5.6 Aerodynamic lift and moment acting on the model wing.

M_{ea} : aerodynamic moment with respect to the elastic axis

$$M_{ea} = M_{ac} + Le\cos q_2 \approx M_{ac} + Le \tag{5.2.6}$$

Note:
For small rotation, the moment due to drag can be neglected.

Applying the Lagrange equation,

$$\frac{d}{dt}\left(\frac{\partial T}{\partial \dot{q}_1}\right) - \frac{\partial T}{\partial q_1} + \frac{\partial V}{\partial q_1} = F_1 \;\rightarrow\; M\ddot{q}_1 - S_\alpha \ddot{q}_2 + k_1 q_1 = L \tag{5.2.7a}$$

$$\frac{d}{dt}\left(\frac{\partial T}{\partial \dot{q}_2}\right) - \frac{\partial T}{\partial q_2} + \frac{\partial V}{\partial q_2} = F_2 \;\rightarrow\; -S_\alpha \ddot{q}_1 + I_\alpha \ddot{q}_2 + k_2 q_2 = M_{ea} \tag{5.2.7b}$$

where $F_1 = L,\ F_2 = M_{ea}$

More on aerodynamic loads:

Adopting quasi-steady aerodynamic theory,

$$L = qS\frac{\partial C_L}{\partial \alpha}\alpha_{eff} \tag{5.2.8}$$

where α_{eff}, the effective angle of attack, is expressed as follows:

$$\alpha_{eff} = q_2 - \frac{\dot{q}_1}{U} \tag{5.2.9}$$

So,
$$L = qS\frac{\partial C_L}{\partial \alpha}\left(q_2 - \frac{\dot{q}_1}{U}\right) \tag{5.2.10}$$

q: dynamic pressure
S: planform area of the model wing
U: flight speed
$\frac{\partial C_L}{\partial \alpha}$: lift slope of the model wing

Note:
To appreciate the second term in equation (5.2.9), let's consider an airfoil section moving upward with velocity $\dot{q}_1$ as shown below:

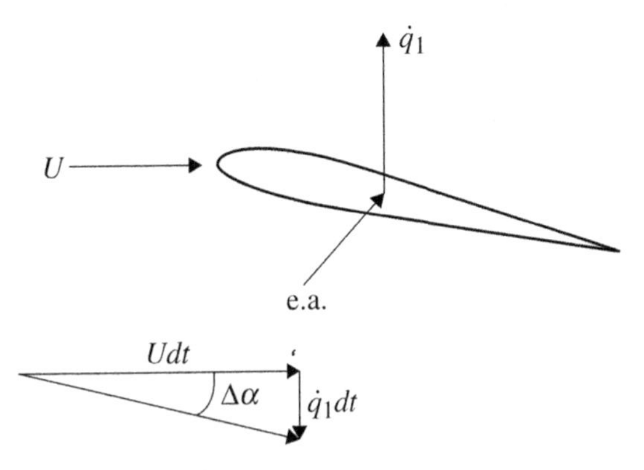

Figure 5.7 Change in effective AOA due to vertical motion of the wing.

The displacement of an air particle over time dt, as seen by an observer moving with the airfoil, is shown in the sketch:

Decrease in angle of attack:
$$\Delta\alpha = \frac{\dot{q}_1 dt}{Udt} = \frac{\dot{q}_1}{U} \tag{5.2.11}$$

Also, from aerodynamics,
$$M_{ac} = qSc\frac{\partial C_M}{\partial \dot{\alpha}}\dot{q}_2 \tag{5.2.12}$$

where c: the chord length.

Note:
Equation (5.2.12) shows that M_{ac} is dependent on angular velocity, while M_{ac} is constant with respect to angle of attack.

Then,
$$M_{ea} = eL + M_{ac} = eqS\frac{\partial C_L}{\partial \alpha}\left(q_2 - \frac{\dot{q}_1}{U}\right) + qSc\frac{\partial C_M}{\partial \dot{\alpha}}\dot{q}_2 \tag{5.2.13}$$

In equations (5.2.10) and (5.2.13), the velocity-dependent ($\dot{q}_1$ and $\dot{q}_2$) terms represent "aerodynamic damping."

In summary, the equations of motion of the 2-DOF model wing are

$$M\ddot{q}_1 - S_\alpha \ddot{q}_2 + k_1 q_1 = L \tag{5.2.14}$$

$$I_\alpha \ddot{q}_2 - S_\alpha \ddot{q}_1 + k_2 q_2 = M_{ea} \tag{5.2.15}$$

where

$$L = qS\frac{\partial C_L}{\partial \alpha}\left(q_2 - \frac{\dot{q}_1}{U}\right) \tag{5.2.16}$$

$$M_{ea} = eL + M_{ac} = eqS\frac{\partial C_L}{\partial \alpha}\left(q_2 - \frac{\dot{q}_1}{U}\right) + qSc\frac{\partial C_M}{\partial \dot{\alpha}}\dot{q}_2 \tag{5.2.17}$$

Placing equations (5.2.16) and (5.2.17) into equations (5.2.14) and (5.2.15) and rearranging,

$$M\ddot{q}_1 + qS\frac{\partial C_L}{\partial \alpha}\frac{1}{U}\dot{q}_1 + k_1 q_1 = S_\alpha \ddot{q}_2 + qS\frac{\partial C_L}{\partial \alpha}q_2 \tag{5.2.18}$$

$$I_\alpha \ddot{q}_2 + qSc\left(-\frac{\partial C_M}{\partial \dot{\alpha}}\right)\dot{q}_2 + (k_{eff})_{torsion} q_2 = S_\alpha \ddot{q}_1 - eqS\frac{\partial C_L}{\partial \alpha}\frac{1}{U}\dot{q}_1 \tag{5.2.19}$$

where

$$(k_{eff})_{torsion} = k_2 - eqS\frac{\partial C_L}{\partial \alpha} \tag{5.2.20}$$

Equation (5.2.18) represents a vertical vibration (bending) driven by rotational (torsional) displacement and acceleration, while equation (5.2.19) represents a rotational vibration driven by vertical acceleration and velocity.

Static Case: Wing Divergence

For static case, equations (5.2.18) and (5.2.19) reduce to

$$k_1 q_1 = qS\frac{\partial C_L}{\partial \alpha}q_2 \tag{5.2.21}$$

$$(k_{eff})_{torsion}\, q_2 = 0 \tag{5.2.22}$$

where

$$(k_{eff})_{torsion} = k_2 - eqS\frac{\partial C_L}{\partial \alpha} : \text{effective torsional spring constant} \tag{5.2.23}$$

k_2 : torsional spring constant representing torsional stiffness of the wing

$-eqS\frac{\partial C_L}{\partial \alpha}$: aerodynamic torsional spring constant

Note that $(k_{eff})_{torsion}$ decreases as the air speed (thus dynamic pressure q) increases. If the speed is high enough, $(k_{eff})_{torsion} = 0$ and the wing loses the torsional stiffness, the wing will fail statically in torsion. This phenomenon is called *wing divergence*. The dynamic pressure q_D at wing divergence is determined from the $k_{eff} = 0$ condition, i.e.,

$$k_2 - eq_D S\frac{\partial C_L}{\partial \alpha} = 0 \tag{5.2.24}$$

Then,

$$q_D = \frac{k_2}{eS\dfrac{\partial C_L}{\partial \alpha}} \tag{5.2.25}$$

and the wing divergence speed U_D is

$$U_D = \sqrt{\frac{2q_D}{\rho}} \tag{5.2.26}$$

where ρ : air density

Note:

1) Wing divergence is a **static** phenomenon.
2) To increase q_D, we can try to decrease the offset distance e between the $a.c.$ and the $e.a.$ **The most important single parameter for wing divergence is the offset distance e.**
3) To increase q_D, we can also try to increase the torsional stiffness. However, this may lead to increase in weight.

Dynamic Case: Inertia Coupling and Flutter

(A) What if c.m. coincides with e.a. ($S_\alpha = 0$)?

Setting $S_\alpha = 0$ and ignoring the aerodynamic damping, the equation of motion reads as follows:

$$M\ddot{q}_1 + k_1 q_1 = qS\frac{\partial C_L}{\partial \alpha}q_2 \tag{5.2.27}$$

$$I_\alpha \ddot{q}_2 + (k_{eff})_{torsion} q_2 = 0 \tag{5.2.28}$$

For $(k_{eff})_{torsion} > 0$, equation (5.2.28) represents free vibration in torsion with the natural frequency of

$$\omega_{torsion} = \sqrt{\frac{(k_{eff})_{torsion}}{I_\alpha}}.$$

Equation (5.2.27) represents a SDOF system of q_1 subjected to a force proportional to q_2.

$$\omega_{bending} = \sqrt{\frac{k_1}{M}} \neq \omega_{torsion}$$

The amplitudes of q_1 and q_2 do not grow with time and there is no flutter. In equations (5.2.27) and (5.2.28), structural damping and aerodynamic damping are not present. However, in the presence of damping, torsional free vibration (with DOF q_2) dies out, and thus the vertical motion (with DOF q_1) also dies out.

(B) Consider now a wing section moving with upward acceleration. For a wing with c.m. behind e.a. ($S_\alpha > 0$), the inertia force acting through c.m. induces a moment that rotates the section clockwise around the elastic axis. This increases AOA and the lift, which promotes the upward motion—destabilizing.

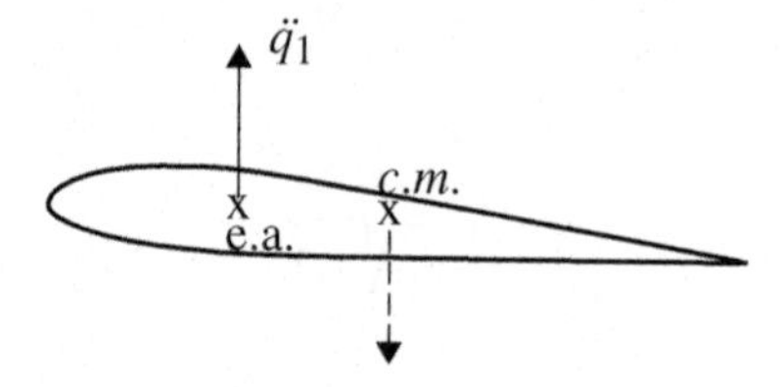

Figure 5.8a Wing center of mass behind elastic axis.

For a wing with c.m. ahead of e.a. ($S_\alpha < 0$), upward acceleration rotates the section counterclockwise. This decreases AOA and the lift, which hinders the upward motion—stabilizing.

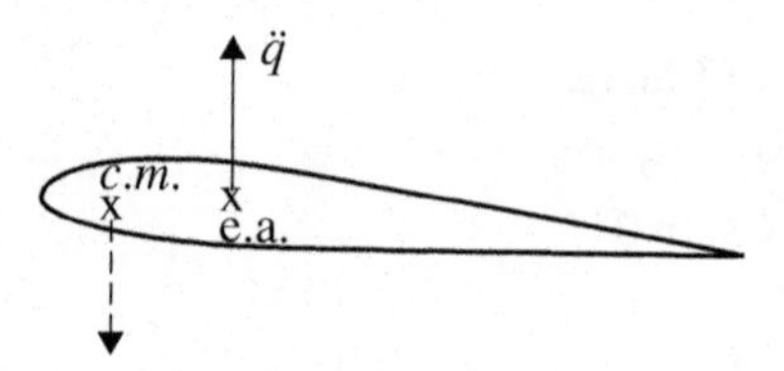

Figure 5.8b Wing center of mass ahead of elastic axis.

If c.m. coincides with e.a., vertical acceleration does not induce rotation. There is no inertia coupling between bending and torsion.

Note:

1) The c.m. of a wing section is usually behind the e.a.
2) **Inertia coupling** (with $S_\alpha > 0$) **is the source of dynamic instability called wing flutter.**

Flutter prevention via mass balancing:

Mass balancing (moving the wing c.m. forward closer to the elastic axis) is used to prevent or delay occurrence of flutter via eliminating or reducing the inertia coupling. Examples of mass balancing are as follows:

1) Helicopter rotor blades: lead weights can be placed close to the leading edge.
2) Control surfaces (aileron, rudder, or elevator) or tabs: a rod or a horn can be used to place a mass ahead of the hinge axis.

5.2.2 Flutter analysis

Equation of motion in matrix form:

The equations of motion of the 2-DOF model wing are:

$$M\ddot{q}_1 - S_\alpha \ddot{q}_2 + k_1 q_1 = L \tag{5.2.29}$$

$$I_\alpha \ddot{q}_2 - S_\alpha \ddot{q}_1 + k_2 q_2 = M_{ea} \tag{5.2.30}$$

where

$$L = qS\frac{\partial C_L}{\partial \alpha}\left(q_2 - \frac{\dot{q}_1}{U}\right) \tag{5.2.31}$$

$$M_{ea} = eL + M_{ac} = eqS\frac{\partial C_L}{\partial \alpha}\left(q_2 - \frac{\dot{q}_1}{U}\right) + qSc\frac{\partial C_M}{\partial \dot{\alpha}}\dot{q}_2 \tag{5.2.32}$$

Equations (5.2.29) and (5.2.30) can be expressed in matrix form as

$$\begin{bmatrix} M & -S_\alpha \\ -S_\alpha & I_\alpha \end{bmatrix}\begin{Bmatrix} \ddot{q}_1 \\ \ddot{q}_2 \end{Bmatrix} + \begin{bmatrix} k_1 & 0 \\ 0 & k_2 \end{bmatrix}\begin{Bmatrix} q_1 \\ q_2 \end{Bmatrix} = \begin{Bmatrix} L \\ M_{ea} \end{Bmatrix} \tag{5.2.33}$$

or

$$\mathbf{M}\ddot{\mathbf{q}} + \mathbf{K}\mathbf{q} = \mathbf{F} \tag{5.2.34}$$

where

$$\mathbf{q} = \begin{Bmatrix} q_1 \\ q_2 \end{Bmatrix} \tag{5.2.35}$$

$$\mathbf{M} = \begin{bmatrix} M & -S_\alpha \\ -S_\alpha & I_\alpha \end{bmatrix} \tag{5.2.36}$$

$$\mathbf{K} = \begin{bmatrix} k_1 & 0 \\ 0 & k_2 \end{bmatrix} \tag{5.2.37}$$

$$\mathbf{F} = \begin{Bmatrix} L \\ M_{ea} \end{Bmatrix} \tag{5.2.38}$$

In matrix form, the load vector F can be expressed as

$$\mathbf{F} = \begin{Bmatrix} L \\ M_{ea} \end{Bmatrix} = qS\begin{bmatrix} 0 & \frac{\partial C_L}{\partial \alpha} \\ 0 & e\frac{\partial C_L}{\partial \alpha} \end{bmatrix}\begin{Bmatrix} q_1 \\ q_2 \end{Bmatrix} - qS\begin{bmatrix} \frac{\partial C_L}{\partial \alpha}\frac{1}{U} & 0 \\ e\frac{\partial C_L}{\partial \alpha}\frac{1}{U} & -c\frac{\partial C_M}{\partial \dot{\alpha}} \end{bmatrix}\begin{Bmatrix} \dot{q}_1 \\ \dot{q}_2 \end{Bmatrix} \tag{5.2.39}$$

or

$$\mathbf{F} = q\mathbf{K}_a\mathbf{q} - q\mathbf{C}_a\dot{\mathbf{q}} \tag{5.2.40}$$

where

$$\mathbf{K}_a = S\begin{bmatrix} 0 & \dfrac{\partial C_L}{\partial \alpha} \\ 0 & e\dfrac{\partial C_L}{\partial \alpha} \end{bmatrix} \tag{5.2.41}$$

$$\mathbf{C}_a = S\begin{bmatrix} \dfrac{\partial C_L}{\partial \alpha}\dfrac{1}{U} & 0 \\ e\dfrac{\partial C_L}{\partial \alpha}\dfrac{1}{U} & -c\dfrac{\partial C_M}{\partial \dot{\alpha}} \end{bmatrix} \tag{5.2.42}$$

Note:

The load vector F is dependent on q, $\mathbf{q}$ and $\dot{\mathbf{q}}$.

Then, the equation of motion is

$$\mathbf{M}\ddot{\mathbf{q}} + \mathbf{K}\mathbf{q} = \mathbf{F} = q\mathbf{K}_a\mathbf{q} - q\mathbf{C}_a\dot{\mathbf{q}}$$

$$\mathbf{M}\ddot{\mathbf{q}} + q\mathbf{C}_a\dot{\mathbf{q}} + (\mathbf{K} - q\mathbf{K}_a)\mathbf{q} = \mathbf{0}$$

or

$$\mathbf{M}\ddot{\mathbf{q}} + \mathbf{C}\dot{\mathbf{q}} + \mathbf{K}_{eff}\mathbf{q} = \mathbf{0} \tag{5.2.43}$$

where

$\mathbf{C} = q\mathbf{C}_a$: aerodynamic damping matrix

$\mathbf{K}_{eff} = \mathbf{K} - q\mathbf{K}_a$: effective stiffness matrix

$\mathbf{K}$: structural stiffness matrix

$-q\mathbf{K}_a$: (nonsymmetric) aerodynamic stiffness matrix

Note that
$$\mathbf{K}_{eff} = \begin{bmatrix} k_1 & -qS\dfrac{\partial C_L}{\partial \alpha} \\ 0 & k_2 - qSe\dfrac{\partial C_L}{\partial \alpha} \end{bmatrix} \tag{5.2.44}$$

The above homogeneous equation describes a free vibration following initial disturbances due to gust or sudden control input. If, at a certain flight condition, the amplitude of free vibration does not die out with time, the wing is said to be in flutter.

The dynamic pressure at which flutter occurs can be determined as follows:

Neglecting damping the equation of motion simplifies to

$$\mathbf{M}\ddot{\mathbf{q}} + \mathbf{K}_{eff}\mathbf{q} = \mathbf{0} \tag{5.2.45}$$

A solution to equation (5.2.45) is of the form

$$\mathbf{q} = \boldsymbol{\varphi} e^{\lambda t} \tag{5.2.46}$$

Placing equation (5.2.46) into equation (5.2.45),

$$\left(\mathbf{K}_{eff} + \lambda^2 \mathbf{M}\right)\boldsymbol{\varphi} = \mathbf{0} \tag{5.2.47}$$

For nontrivial φ,

$$\det\left(\mathbf{K}_{eff} + \lambda^2 \mathbf{M}\right) = 0 \tag{5.2.48}$$

from which one can find eigenvalues $\lambda = \lambda_1, \lambda_2$.

Following the procedure used for the follower force problem discussed previously, equation (5.2.48) can be expressed as

$$A\lambda^4 + B\lambda^2 + C = 0 \tag{5.2.49}$$

where

$$\begin{aligned} A &= MI_\alpha - S_\alpha^2 \\ B &= I_\alpha k_1 + M\left(k_2 - qSe\frac{\partial C_L}{\partial \alpha}\right) - qS\frac{\partial C_L}{\partial \alpha} S_\alpha \\ C &= k_1\left(k_2 - qSe\frac{\partial C_L}{\partial \alpha}\right) \end{aligned} \tag{5.2.50}$$

From equation (5.2.49),

$$\lambda^2 = \frac{-B \pm \sqrt{B^2 - 4AC}}{2A}$$

We can then observe as follows:

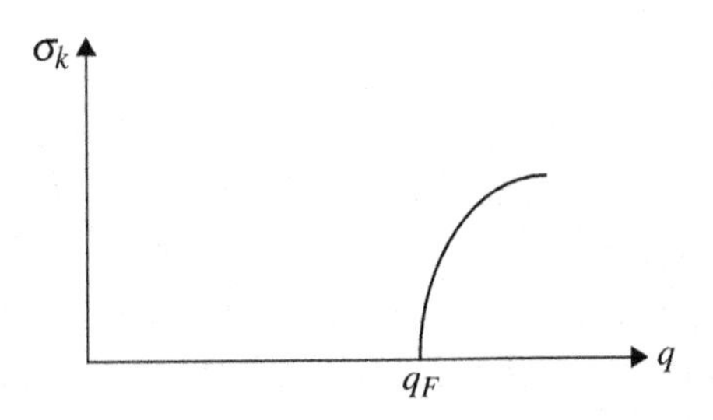

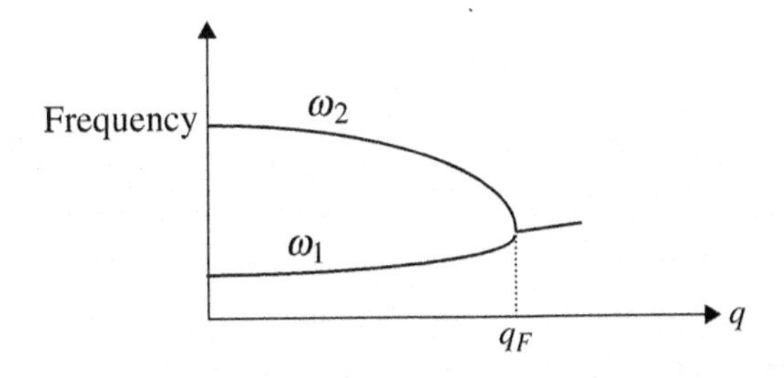

Figure 5.9 Real part and frequency plots.

(1) For small dynamic pressure q, $B^2 - 4AC > 0$ and $\lambda^2 < 0$, and $\sigma_k = \text{Re}(\lambda_k) = 0$ for all k, $\lambda = \pm i\omega_1, \ \pm i\omega_2$ and thus the system is dynamically stable and free of flutter.
(2) As q increases, $B^2 - 4AC = 0$ and we observe double roots for λ with $\omega_1 = \omega_2$.
(3) As q further increases, $B^2 - 4AC < 0$, and the real part of one of the eigenvalues becomes positive, and the wing exhibits flutter.

So, the transition to flutter occurs at $B^2 - 4AC = 0$. Frequencies ω_1 and ω_2 approach each other as $q \to q_F$. This is called frequency coalescence.

Limit Cycle Oscillation

In the present wing model, bending stiffness and torsional stiffness of the wing are represented by a vertical spring of constant k_1 and a rotational spring of constant k_2. However, the structural response of the wing can be nonlinear, exhibiting stiffening behavior. In this case, the wing will oscillate with finite amplitude, which itself undergoes undulation. This phenomenon is called a **limit cycle oscillation** (LCO). To appreciate the LCO, the reader is encouraged to do an exercise problem given at the end of this chapter.

5.2.3 Other Dynamic Phenomena

Panel Flutter:

For thin panels exposed to supersonic flow on one side, vibration of the panels induces changes in the local angle of attack, which in turn interacts with the airflow. From the aerodynamic theory, for a thin panel exposed to supersonic flow on one side, the aerodynamic pressure change p_a due to the panel deflection can be expressed as

$$p_a = -\frac{\rho U^2}{\sqrt{M^2 - 1}} \left(\frac{\partial w}{\partial x} + \frac{M^2 - 2}{M^2 - 1} \frac{1}{U} \frac{\partial w}{\partial t} \right)$$

where ρ : air density
U : upstream air speed
M : Mach number
w : vertical displacement of the panel
x : coordinate parallel with U

When the speed is high enough, the panel will experience flutter. Historical examples of panel flutter include German V-2 rockets in World War II, North American X-15 hypersonic rocket-powered aircraft, and the *Saturn V* moon rocket.

Stall Flutter:

Stall flutter is a predominantly torsional vibration that does not damp out. Stall flutter may occur in rotating components such as propellers, turbine blades, and compressor blades. If the rotational speed of a propeller is high, the blade twist will become large enough to cause a blade stall. The blade may then experience a stall flutter. The stall flutter speed can be raised via increasing the torsional stiffness.

Stall flutter can also occur in non-aeronautical structures. Examples are suspension bridges, tall buildings, and transmission wires. The suspension bridge across the Tacoma Narrows in the state of Washington was destroyed due to stall flutter on November 7, 1940, only several months after its opening. For transmission wires, the formation of ice could trigger a stall flutter called *galloping*.

Free Play of Control Surfaces:
Free play occurs due to loose joints in attachment of control surface to a wing. There is some free play in all aircraft. Oscillations due to free play may cause wear and fatigue. Free play tends to increase over time as the aircraft is in service.

5.2.4 Real Wings and Other Aerodynamic Surfaces

For realistic wings or other aerodynamic surfaces, one may introduce finite element modeling. Then, it can be shown that the equation of motion is symbolically identical to that for the model wing with 2-DOF.

Applying the finite element modeling, the equation of motion can be expressed symbolically as

$$\mathbf{M}\ddot{\mathbf{q}} + \mathbf{K}\mathbf{q} = \mathbf{F} \tag{5.2.51}$$

where $\mathbf{F}$ can be expressed symbolically as follows:

$$\mathbf{F} = q\mathbf{K}_a\mathbf{q} - q\mathbf{C}_a\dot{\mathbf{q}} \tag{5.2.52}$$

Note that $\mathbf{F}$ is linearly dependent on q, $\mathbf{q}$ and $\dot{\mathbf{q}}$. Also, equation (5.2.52) is symbolically identical to that for the model wing. Placing equation (5.2.52) into equation (5.2.51),

$$\mathbf{M}\ddot{\mathbf{q}} + \mathbf{K}\mathbf{q} = q\mathbf{K}_a\mathbf{q} - q\mathbf{C}_a\dot{\mathbf{q}} \tag{5.2.53}$$

or

$$\mathbf{M}\ddot{\mathbf{q}} + \mathbf{C}\dot{\mathbf{q}} + \mathbf{K}_{eff}\mathbf{q} = \mathbf{0} \tag{5.2.54}$$

where $\mathbf{C} = q\mathbf{C}_a$: aerodynamic damping matrix

$\mathbf{K}_{eff} = \mathbf{K} - q\mathbf{K}_a$: effective stiffness matrix

$\mathbf{K}$: structural stiffness matrix

$-q\mathbf{K}_a$: (nonsymmetric) aerodynamic stiffness matrix

Equation (5.2.54) is a second-order homogeneous equation that describes a free vibration following initial disturbances due to gust or sudden control input. We can carry out eigenvalue analysis to investigate dynamic stability.

(1) Flutter analysis when damping is neglected:
With no damping, the equation of motion reduces to

$$\mathbf{M}\ddot{\mathbf{q}} + \mathbf{K}_{eff}\mathbf{q} = \mathbf{0} \tag{5.2.55}$$

A solution to equation (5.2.55) is of the form

$$\mathbf{q} = \boldsymbol{\varphi}e^{\lambda t} \tag{5.2.56}$$

Placing equation (5.2.56) into equation (5.2.55),

$$\left(\mathbf{K}_{eff}+\lambda^2\mathbf{M}\right)\boldsymbol{\varphi}=0 \tag{5.2.57}$$

For nontrivial $\boldsymbol{\varphi}$,

$$\det\left(\mathbf{K}_{eff}+\lambda^2\mathbf{M}\right)=0 \tag{5.2.58}$$

Solve for $\lambda=\lambda_1,\lambda_2,\cdots,\lambda_n$. Alternatively, equation (5.2.57) can be expressed as

$$\mathbf{K}_{eff}\boldsymbol{\varphi}=\Lambda\mathbf{M}\boldsymbol{\varphi} \tag{5.2.59}$$

where $\Lambda=-\lambda^2$ (5.2.60)

is a complex number. Equation (5.2.59) is a standard equation for eigenvalue analysis. For a given flight condition (i.e., given dynamic pressure), we can find eigenvalues Λ_k from equation (5.2.59) and then determine λ_k from equation (5.2.60).

The eigenvalues λ_k $(k=1,2,\cdots\cdots)$ can be expressed as

$$\lambda_k=\mathrm{Re}(\lambda_k)+i\,\mathrm{Im}(\lambda_k)=\sigma_k\pm i\omega_k\quad(\omega_k>0) \tag{5.2.61}$$

where

$$\sigma_k=\mathrm{Re}(\lambda_k)$$

Then,

$$e^{\lambda_k t}=e^{(\sigma_k\pm i\omega_k)t}=e^{\sigma_k t}e^{\pm i\omega_k t}=e^{\sigma_k t}(\cos\omega_k t\pm i\sin\omega_k t) \tag{5.2.62}$$

where $e^{\sigma_k t}$ ~ change of amplitude with time

$(\cos\omega_k t\pm i\sin\omega_k t)$ ~ oscillation with frequency ω_k

Flutter criteria:

1) If $\sigma_k=\mathrm{Re}(\lambda_k)<0$ for all k, the vibration excited by initial disturbance will die out. The system is stable and free of flutter.
2) If $\sigma_k=\mathrm{Re}(\lambda_k)>0$ for any k, the vibration excited by initial disturbance will grow in time. The system experiences flutter.

At small q, $\sigma_k=\mathrm{Re}(\lambda_k)<0$ for all k, and there is no flutter. When aerodynamic damping is ignored, $\sigma_k=0$ before the flutter occurs.

At $q=q_F$, σ_k becomes positive.

q_F: dynamic pressure at flutter

The two lowest frequencies ω_1 and ω_2 approach each other as $q\to q_F$.

Under the assumption of no damping, $\omega_1=\omega_2$ at q_F. This is frequency coalescence.

(2) Flutter analysis with damping included:

In this case, we can convert equation (5.2.54) into a first-order (in time) equation as follows: Introduce a new variable **v** such that

$$\dot{\mathbf{q}} = \mathbf{v} \tag{5.2.63}$$

Placing equation (5.2.63) into equation (5.2.54),

$$\mathbf{M}\dot{\mathbf{v}} + \mathbf{C}\mathbf{v} + \mathbf{K}_{eff}\mathbf{q} = \mathbf{0} \tag{5.2.64}$$

Equations (5.2.63) and (5.2.64) can be combined as follows:

$$\begin{bmatrix} \mathbf{I} & \mathbf{0} \\ \mathbf{0} & \mathbf{M} \end{bmatrix} \begin{Bmatrix} \dot{\mathbf{q}} \\ \dot{\mathbf{v}} \end{Bmatrix} - \begin{bmatrix} \mathbf{0} & \mathbf{I} \\ -\mathbf{K}_{eff} & -\mathbf{C} \end{bmatrix} \begin{Bmatrix} \mathbf{q} \\ \mathbf{v} \end{Bmatrix} = \begin{Bmatrix} \mathbf{0} \\ \mathbf{0} \end{Bmatrix} \tag{5.2.65}$$

where **I** is an identity matrix. Equation (5.2.65) can be expressed as

$$\mathbf{B}\dot{\mathbf{z}} - \mathbf{A}\mathbf{z} = \mathbf{0} \tag{5.2.66}$$

where

$$\mathbf{z} = \begin{Bmatrix} \mathbf{q} \\ \mathbf{v} \end{Bmatrix} \tag{5.2.67}$$

$$\mathrm{B} = \begin{bmatrix} \mathbf{I} & \mathbf{0} \\ \mathbf{0} & \mathbf{M} \end{bmatrix} \tag{5.2.68}$$

$$\mathrm{A} = \begin{bmatrix} \mathbf{0} & \mathbf{I} \\ -\mathbf{k}_{eff} & -\mathbf{C} \end{bmatrix} \tag{5.2.69}$$

Equation (5.2.66) is a first-order homogeneous equation. A solution to equation (5.2.66) is of the following form:

$$\mathbf{z} = \varphi e^{\lambda t} \tag{5.2.70}$$

Placing equation (5.2.70) into equation (5.2.66),

$$\begin{aligned} &\mathbf{B}\varphi\lambda e^{\lambda t} - \mathbf{A}\varphi e^{\lambda t} = \mathbf{0}, \ \rightarrow (\mathbf{A} - \lambda\mathbf{B})\varphi e^{\lambda t} = \mathbf{0} \\ &\rightarrow (\mathbf{A} - \lambda\mathbf{B})\varphi = \mathbf{0} \end{aligned} \tag{5.2.71}$$

or

$$\mathbf{A}\varphi = \lambda\mathbf{B}\varphi \tag{5.2.72}$$

Note:
(1) For given **A** and **B**, equation (5.2.72) is a standard equation for an eigenvalue analysis.
(2) With damping, $\omega_1 \neq \omega_2$ at q_F, but they are close to each other.

Chapter 5 Problem Sets

5.1 Consider the two-DOF model introduced in class as a crude model of a slender and flexible LV (with no TVC) on a vertical test stand. Using a scaled time "τ" defined as

$$\tau = t\sqrt{\frac{K}{M_0 L^2}}$$

the equation of motion for the two-DOF model can be written as

$$\mathbf{M}\ddot{\mathbf{q}} + \mathbf{K}_{eff}\mathbf{q} = \mathbf{0}$$

where

$$\mathrm{M} = \begin{bmatrix} 3 & 1 \\ 1 & 1 \end{bmatrix}, \quad \ddot{\mathrm{q}} = \begin{Bmatrix} \dfrac{d^2\theta}{d\tau^2} \\ \dfrac{d^2\phi}{d\tau^2} \end{Bmatrix}, \quad \mathrm{q} = \begin{Bmatrix} \theta \\ \phi \end{Bmatrix}$$

$$\mathrm{K}_{eff} = \begin{bmatrix} 2-\overline{P} & -1+\overline{P} \\ -1 & 1 \end{bmatrix}$$

The initial disturbances are expressed as the initial conditions given as follows:

$$\theta(0) = 0,\ \phi(0) = 0,\ \dot{\theta}(0) = 0,\ \dot{\phi}(0) = 0.1$$

Use the Euler method to plot θ and φ over 100 units in scaled time for the following $\overline{P}$.

(a) $\overline{P} = 1.8$. Does the amplitude grow with time?
(b) $\overline{P} = 2.3$. Does the amplitude grow with time?

5.2 Do the following to investigate dynamic stability of the system described in problem 5.1.

(a) Plot the real part of the eigenvalues versus $\overline{P}$.
(b) Plot two frequencies versus $\overline{P}$.
(c) Determine $\overline{P}_F$ at which the LV structure becomes dynamically unstable.

5.3 Conduct a literature search on "pogo instability" of launch vehicles and submit a three-page typed report that includes the following:

(a) What is pogo instability? Why does it occur?
(b) Historical examples
(c) How to prevent pogo instability
(d) List of references.

5.4 Consider a subsonic model wing with properties given as follows:

$$M = 8.7 \text{ slug}, S_\alpha = 5.4 \text{ slug-ft}, I_\alpha = 84 \text{ slug-ft}^2$$

$$k_1 = 6.3 \times 10^4 \text{ lb/ft}, k_2 = 1.3 \times 10^6 \text{ lb-ft/rad}$$

$$c = 5.0 \text{ ft}, e = 0.19\text{ft}, S = 150 \text{ ft}^2, \frac{\partial C_L}{\partial \alpha} = 1.87\pi$$

Neglect aerodynamic damping and do the following:

Case 1:
(a) Determine q_D and U_D at wing divergence. Assume sea level conditions.
(b) Plot dynamic pressure q versus $\text{Re}(\lambda_k)$. Determine the dynamic pressure q_F at the onset of flutter. Determine the flutter speed U_F at sea level.
(c) Plot q versus ω_1 and ω_2. Do the frequencies coalesce?

Case 2: Repeat Case 1 with $e = 0.38$ft. Comment on the effect of e on wing divergence and flutter. Does it significantly affect the flutter speed as well as the wing divergence speed?

Case 3: Repeat Case 1 with $S_\alpha = 0.05 \times 30$ slug-ft. Comment on the effect of S_α on wing divergence and flutter.

Case 4: Repeat Case 1 with $S_\alpha = -0.05 \times 30$ slug-ft. Comment on the effect of S_α on wing divergence and flutter.

5.5 For the wing with properties given in Problem **5.4**, the initial conditions are given as $q_1 = 0$, $q_2 = 0$, $\dot{q}_1 = 0$ and $\dot{q}_2 = 0.1$. Use the RK4 method to do the following:

(a) For $q = 0.97q_F$, plot q_1 and q_2.
(b) For $q = 1.03q_F$, plot q_1 and q_2.
Replace k_2 torsional moment with $F(q_2) = 1.3 \times 10^6(1 + 4q_2^2)q_2$ and do the following:
(c) For $q = 0.97q_F$, plot q_1 and q_2.
(d) For $q = 1.03q_F$, plot q_1 and q_2 to observe a limit cycle oscillation.
The source of nonlinearity could be from structural stiffening or from the control input.

5.6 Conduct a literature search on wing flutter at transonic regime and submit a three-page report.

6 VIBRATION ABSORBER

A dynamic system could be subject to a forcing frequency that is at or close to a natural frequency of the system. In this case, we can alter the system by adding a mass and a spring in such a way that the natural frequencies of the modified system are adequately separated from the forcing frequency, resulting in a greatly reduced level of vibration. The added mass and spring constitute a "vibration absorber." A damper can also be added to further mitigate the vibration level. In this chapter, we will examine how a vibration absorber can be introduced to suppress the steady-state vibration of the original, or *primary*, system. For simplicity, we will use a primary system with a single degree of freedom as an example. Specific topics to be discussed are as follows:

6.1 Absorber with a mass and a spring
6.2 Steady-state response of MDOF systems
6.3 Absorber with a mass, a spring, and a damper

6.1 Absorber with a Mass and a Spring

Consider the **steady-state response** of an undamped SDOF system under a sinusoidal loading of frequency Ω as shown below. Damping is neglected for simplicity.

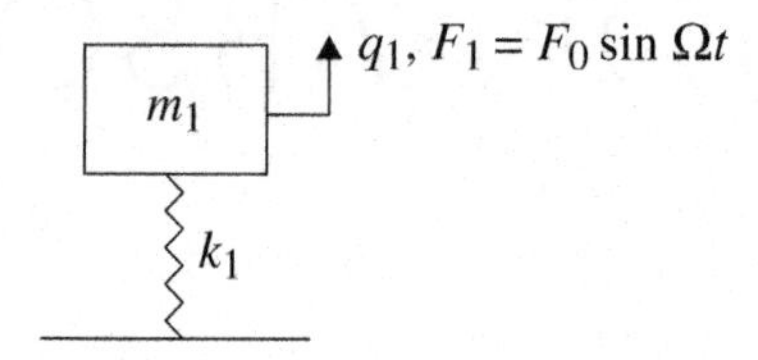

Figure 6.1 SDOF system under sinusoidal loading.

The equation of motion of the system is

$$m_1\ddot{q}_1 + k_1 q_1 = F_0 \sin \Omega t \tag{6.1.1}$$

Suppose that the forcing frequency Ω is close to the natural frequency $\omega_n = \sqrt{k_1/m_1}$ and resonance occurs. To suppress vibration, we can modify the system by adding a mass (m_2) and a spring (k_2) to the original system as shown in the sketch. This modification will result in a system with two natural frequencies placed away from the forcing frequency.

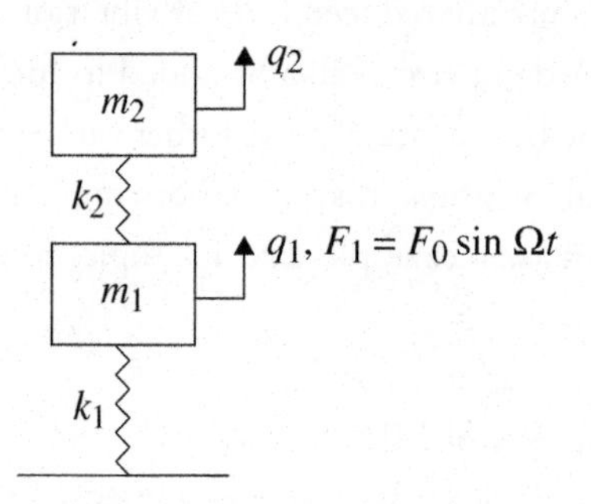

Figure 6.2 System with absorber mass and spring.

We have now a two-DOF system with two natural frequencies that are different from the forcing frequency Ω. But what is the best way to select m_2 and k_2? To answer this question, let's look at the steady-state response of the modified system.

The equation of motion for the system is

$$\begin{bmatrix} m_1 & 0 \\ 0 & m_2 \end{bmatrix} \begin{Bmatrix} \ddot{q}_1 \\ \ddot{q}_2 \end{Bmatrix} + \begin{bmatrix} k_1 + k_2 & -k_2 \\ -k_2 & k_2 \end{bmatrix} \begin{Bmatrix} q_1 \\ q_2 \end{Bmatrix} = \begin{Bmatrix} F_0 \\ 0 \end{Bmatrix} \sin \Omega t \tag{6.1.2}$$

The steady state or particular solution of the above equation can be expressed as

$$\begin{Bmatrix} q_1 \\ q_2 \end{Bmatrix} = \begin{Bmatrix} A_1 \\ A_2 \end{Bmatrix} \sin \Omega t \tag{6.1.3}$$

Placing equation (6.1.3) into equation (6.1.2) and rearranging,

$$\begin{bmatrix} k_1+k_2-\Omega^2 m_1 & -k_2 \\ -k_2 & k_2-\Omega^2 m_2 \end{bmatrix} \begin{Bmatrix} A_1 \\ A_2 \end{Bmatrix} = \begin{Bmatrix} F_0 \\ 0 \end{Bmatrix} \tag{6.1.4}$$

From equation (6.1.4), we can find

$$\begin{aligned} A_1 &= \frac{(k_2-\Omega^2 m_2)F_0}{(k_1+k_2-\Omega^2 m_1)(k_2-\Omega^2 m_2)-k_2^2} \\ A_2 &= \frac{k_2 F_0}{(k_1+k_2-\Omega^2 m_1)(k_2-\Omega^2 m_2)-k_2^2} \end{aligned} \tag{6.1.5}$$

If k_2 and m_2 are chosen such that

$$(k_2-\Omega^2 m_2)=0 \tag{6.1.6}$$

and

$$A_1=0,\ A_2=-\frac{F_0}{k_2}$$

and

$$q_1=0,\ q_2=-\frac{F_0}{k_2}\sin\Omega t \tag{6.1.7}$$

Accordingly, the mass of the original system does not vibrate. From equation (6.1.6),

$$\frac{k_2}{m_2}=\Omega^2 \tag{6.1.8}$$

So, if equation (6.1.8) is satisfied, $q_1=0$. The added mass (m_2) and the spring (k_2) constitute a tuned vibration absorber. It can be shown that, for a system with damping, $q_1 \neq 0$, but q_1 is still small if equation (6.1.8) is satisfied.

Example 6.1.1 Consider the modified system with the following mass ratios:

(a) $\frac{m_2}{m_1}=0.1$, (b) $\frac{m_2}{m_1}=0.2$

From free vibration analysis, we can determine the natural frequencies (or resonance frequencies) as

Case (a) $\omega_1=0.8543\sqrt{k_1/m_1}$, $\omega_2=1.1705\sqrt{k_1/m_1}$

Case (b) $\omega_1=0.8011\sqrt{k_1/m_1}$, $\omega_2=1.2483\sqrt{k_1/m_1}$

So, Case (b), with a higher mass ratio, allows more drift in forcing frequency.

Example 6.1.2 Bending vibration of the vertical tail of a fighter jet at high AOA is modeled as a SDOF system of mass m_1 and spring constant k_1, subject to a harmonic loading of given amplitude F_0 and frequency Ω due to fluctuation of the separated flow. It turns out that the forcing frequency is very close to the first natural frequency of the tail, and it is decided to retrofit an absorber of mass m_2 and spring constant k_2. Due to space limitation, the maximum allowable displacement of the absorber spring is specified. Neglect the effect of damping and do the following:

(a) Determine the absorber spring constant and the absorber mass based on the maximum allowable displacement.

From equation (6.1.7), $(q_2)_{max} = \frac{F_0}{k_2} \rightarrow k_2 = \frac{F_0}{(q_2)_{max}}$ where $(q_2)_{max}$ is a specified value.

From equation (6.1.8), $m_2 = \frac{k_2}{\Omega^2}$

(b) Describe how you would implement the absorber system to the vertical tail.

6.2 Steady-State Response of MDOF Systems

Consider a MDOF system with damping subject to harmonic loading $\mathbf{F} = \mathbf{F}_0 \sin \Omega t$. The equation of motion is then

$$\mathbf{M\ddot{q}} + \mathbf{C\dot{q}} + \mathbf{Kq} = \mathbf{F}_0 \sin \Omega t \tag{6.2.1}$$

For steady-state response,

$$\mathbf{q} = \mathbf{A} \sin \Omega t + \mathbf{B} \cos \Omega t \tag{6.2.2}$$

Then,

$$\begin{aligned} \dot{\mathbf{q}} &= \Omega(\mathbf{A} \cos \Omega t - \mathbf{B} \sin \Omega t) \\ \ddot{\mathbf{q}} &= -\Omega^2(\mathbf{A} \sin \Omega t + \mathbf{B} \cos \Omega t) \end{aligned} \tag{6.2.3}$$

Placing equations (6.2.2) and (6.2.3) to equation (6.2.1),

$$-\Omega^2\mathbf{M}(\mathbf{A} \sin \Omega t + \mathbf{B} \cos \Omega t) + \Omega\mathbf{C}(\mathbf{A} \cos \Omega t - \mathbf{B} \sin \Omega t) + \mathbf{K}(\mathbf{A} \sin \Omega t + \mathbf{B} \cos \Omega t) = \mathbf{F}_0 \sin \Omega t \tag{6.2.4}$$

Collecting $\sin \Omega t$ and $\cos \Omega t$ terms,

$$\sin \Omega t\left[(\mathbf{K} - \Omega^2\mathbf{M})\mathbf{A} - \Omega\mathbf{CB} - \mathbf{F}_0\right] + \cos \Omega t\left[(\mathbf{K} - \Omega^2\mathbf{M})\mathbf{B} + \Omega\mathbf{CA}\right] = \mathbf{0} \tag{6.2.5}$$

From which,

$$\begin{aligned} (\mathbf{K} - \Omega^2\mathbf{M})\mathbf{A} - \Omega\mathbf{CB} &= \mathbf{F}_0 \\ (\mathbf{K} - \Omega^2\mathbf{M})\mathbf{B} + \Omega\mathbf{CA} &= \mathbf{0} \end{aligned} \tag{6.2.6}$$

The above two equations can be combined into a single equation as follows:

$$\begin{bmatrix} K-\Omega^2 M & -\Omega C \\ \Omega C & K-\Omega^2 M \end{bmatrix} \begin{Bmatrix} A \\ B \end{Bmatrix} = \begin{Bmatrix} F_0 \\ 0 \end{Bmatrix} \tag{6.2.7}$$

For given Ω, the above equations can be solved for **A** and **B**. For an N-DOF system, equation (6.2.2) can be expressed in an expanded form as

$$\begin{Bmatrix} q_1 \\ q_2 \\ \cdot\cdot \\ \cdot\cdot \\ \cdot\cdot \\ q_N \end{Bmatrix} = \begin{Bmatrix} A_1 \\ A_2 \\ \cdot\cdot \\ \cdot\cdot \\ \cdot\cdot \\ A_N \end{Bmatrix} \sin\Omega t + \begin{Bmatrix} B_1 \\ B_2 \\ \cdot\cdot \\ \cdot\cdot \\ \cdot\cdot \\ B_N \end{Bmatrix} \cos\Omega t \tag{6.2.8}$$

$$q_i = A_i \sin\Omega t + B_i \cos\Omega t \tag{6.2.9}$$

or

$$q_i = \sqrt{A_i^2 + B_i^2} \sin(\Omega t - \phi) = \bar{q}_i \sin(\Omega t - \phi) \tag{6.2.10}$$

where

$$\bar{q}_i = \sqrt{A_i^2 + B_i^2} \ : \text{amplitude of } q_i \tag{6.2.11}$$

6.3 Absorber with a Mass, a Spring, and a Damper

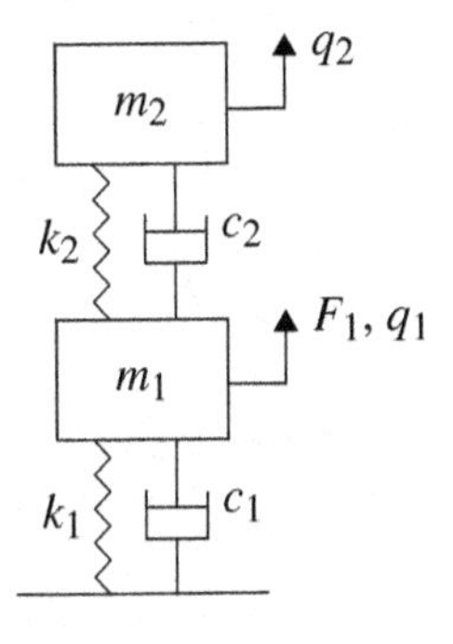

Figure 6.3 System with absorber with damping.

A vibration absorber of mass m_2, spring k_2 and damper c_2 is attached to a primary system with mass m_1, spring k_1 and damper c_1 subject to a force of $F_1 = F_0 \sin\Omega t$. Then,

$$M = \begin{bmatrix} m_1 & 0 \\ 0 & m_2 \end{bmatrix}, \ C = \begin{bmatrix} c_1 + c_2 & -c_2 \\ -c_2 & c_2 \end{bmatrix}, \ K = \begin{bmatrix} k_1 + k_2 & -k_2 \\ -k_2 & k_2 \end{bmatrix}, \ F = \begin{Bmatrix} F_0 \\ 0 \end{Bmatrix} \sin\Omega t \tag{6.3.1}$$

With mass ratio $\beta = \frac{m_2}{m_1}$, $\mathbf{M} = m_1 \begin{bmatrix} 1 & 0 \\ 0 & \beta \end{bmatrix}$ (6.3.2a, b)

Also define

$$\gamma = \frac{\sqrt{\frac{k_2}{m_2}}}{\sqrt{\frac{k_1}{m_1}}} \tag{6.3.3}$$

For $\gamma = 1$ (**Note**: See Section 6.1),

$$k_2 = \frac{m_2}{m_1} k_1 = \beta k_1 \tag{6.3.4}$$

and

$$\mathbf{K} = \begin{bmatrix} k_1 + k_2 & -k_2 \\ -k_2 & k_2 \end{bmatrix} = \begin{bmatrix} k_1 + \beta k_1 & -\beta k_1 \\ -\beta k_1 & \beta k_1 \end{bmatrix} = k_1 \begin{bmatrix} 1+\beta & -\beta \\ -\beta & \beta \end{bmatrix} \tag{6.3.5}$$

Accordingly,

$$\left(\mathbf{K} - \Omega^2 \mathbf{M}\right) = k_1 \begin{bmatrix} 1+\beta & -\beta \\ -\beta & \beta \end{bmatrix} - \Omega^2 m_1 \begin{bmatrix} 1 & 0 \\ 0 & \beta \end{bmatrix} = k_1 \left(\begin{bmatrix} 1+\beta & -\beta \\ -\beta & \beta \end{bmatrix} - \Omega^2 \frac{m_1}{k_1} \begin{bmatrix} 1 & 0 \\ 0 & \beta \end{bmatrix} \right)$$

$$= k_1 \left(\begin{bmatrix} 1+\beta & -\beta \\ -\beta & \beta \end{bmatrix} - \bar{\Omega}^2 \begin{bmatrix} 1 & 0 \\ 0 & \beta \end{bmatrix} \right)$$

and finally

$$\left(\mathbf{K} - \Omega^2 \mathbf{M}\right) = k_1 \begin{bmatrix} 1+\beta-\bar{\Omega}^2 & -\beta \\ -\beta & \beta(1-\bar{\Omega}^2) \end{bmatrix} \tag{6.3.6}$$

where

$$\bar{\Omega} = \frac{\Omega}{\sqrt{\frac{k_1}{m_1}}} \tag{6.3.7}$$

For the $\mathbf{\Omega C}$ matrix, we can proceed as follows:

$$\frac{c_2}{m_2} = 2\varsigma\omega_{n_2} = 2\varsigma\sqrt{\frac{k_2}{m_2}} = 2\varsigma\sqrt{\frac{k_1}{m_1}}$$

$$c_2 = 2\varsigma\sqrt{\frac{k_1}{m_1}} m_2 = 2\varsigma\sqrt{\frac{k_1}{m_1}} \beta m_1 \tag{6.3.8}$$

Then, with $c_1 = \alpha c_2$ (6.3.9)

$$\Omega C = \Omega \begin{bmatrix} c_1 + c_2 & -c_2 \\ -c_2 & c_2 \end{bmatrix} = \Omega c_2 \begin{bmatrix} \alpha+1 & -1 \\ -1 & 1 \end{bmatrix} = \Omega(2\varsigma\sqrt{\frac{k_1}{m_1}}\beta m_1)\begin{bmatrix} \alpha+1 & -1 \\ -1 & 1 \end{bmatrix}$$

$$= (2\varsigma\beta\frac{k_1}{m_1}\frac{\Omega}{\sqrt{\frac{k_1}{m_1}}}m_1)\begin{bmatrix} \alpha+1 & -1 \\ -1 & 1 \end{bmatrix} = k_1(2\varsigma\beta\bar{\Omega})\begin{bmatrix} \alpha+1 & -1 \\ -1 & 1 \end{bmatrix}$$

Finally,

$$\Omega C = k_1(2\varsigma\beta\bar{\Omega})\begin{bmatrix} \alpha+1 & -1 \\ -1 & 1 \end{bmatrix} \tag{6.3.10}$$

Equations (6.3.6) and (6.3.10) can be introduced to equation (6.2.7) in the previous section to solve for **A** and **B**. For convenience, we can introduce a nondimensional displacement as

$$\bar{q}_1 = \frac{|q_1|}{\left(\frac{F_0}{k_1}\right)}, \ |q_1| : \text{amplitude of } q_1$$

Example 6.3.1 Suppose damping of the primary system is small and can be neglected. For $\gamma = 1.0$, plot $\bar{q}_1$ (vertical axis) versus $\bar{\Omega}$ (horizontal axis) for the following parameters:

(a) $\beta = 0.1$ and $\beta = 0.05$ for $\varsigma = 0.01$
(b) $\varsigma = 0.01$ and $\varsigma = 0.1$ for $\beta = 0.1$

(a)

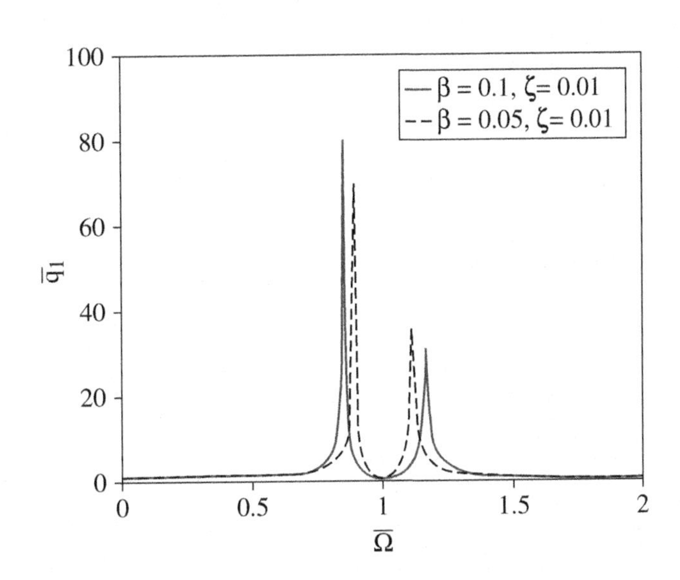

Figure 6.4 Nondimensional displacement of the primary system for different mass ratio.

For a given damping ratio of 0.01, you may observe how mass ratio β affects the system response and the separation of two natural frequencies of the modified system.

(b)

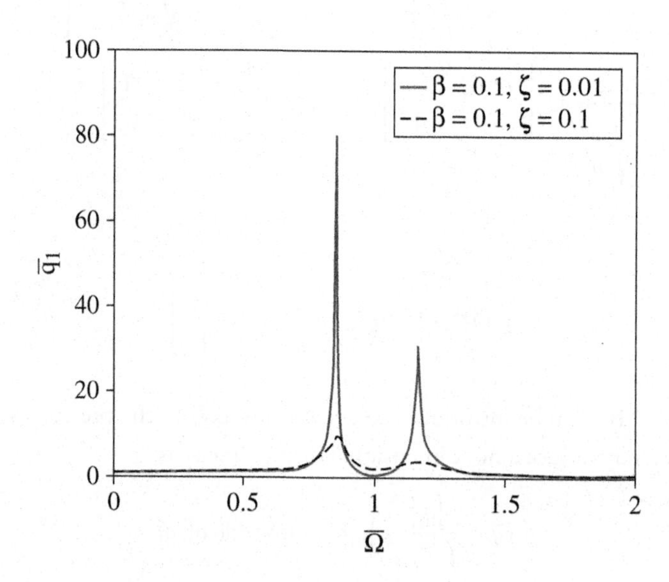

Figure 6.5 Nondimensional displacement of the primary system for different damping ratio.

For a given mass ratio of 0.1, you may observe how the damping ratio affects the system response.

Chapter 6 Problem Sets

6.1 For the problem in Example 6.3.1, determine nondimensional absorber displacement of mass 2 and the force acting on the absorber spring k_2 for each case.

6.2 A vibration absorber of mass m_2, spring k_2 and damper c_2 is attached to a primary system with mass m_1, spring k_1 subject to a force of $F_1 = F_0 \sin \Omega t$. For the primary system, damping is small and can be neglected. The following nondimensional parameters are introduced to simplify the equation of motion.

$$\beta = \frac{m_2}{m_1}, \quad \gamma = \frac{\sqrt{\frac{k_2}{m_2}}}{\sqrt{\frac{k_1}{m_1}}}, \quad \bar{\Omega} = \frac{\Omega}{\sqrt{\frac{k_1}{m_1}}}, \quad \bar{q}_1 = \frac{|q_1|}{\left(\frac{F_0}{k_1}\right)}, \ |q_1| : \text{amplitude of } q_1$$

and $\quad c_2 = 2\varsigma\beta\gamma m_1\sqrt{\frac{k_1}{m_1}}$

For $\gamma \neq 1$, we can show that

$$\mathbf{K} = k_1 \begin{bmatrix} 1+\bar{\beta} & -\bar{\beta} \\ -\bar{\beta} & \bar{\beta} \end{bmatrix}$$

where $\bar{\beta} = \beta\gamma^2$ and

$$\Omega\mathbf{C} = k_1(2\varsigma\beta\gamma\bar{\Omega}) \begin{bmatrix} 1 & -1 \\ -1 & 1 \end{bmatrix}$$

and $\mathbf{M} = m_1 \begin{bmatrix} 1 & 0 \\ 0 & \beta \end{bmatrix}$

(a) For $\gamma = 0.95$ plot $\bar{q}_1$ versus $\bar{\Omega}$ for the following parameters and comment on what you observe: $\beta = 0.1$, $\varsigma = 0.01$ and $\varsigma = 0.1$.

(b) For $\gamma = 1.05$ plot $\bar{q}_1$ versus $\bar{\Omega}$ for the following parameters and comment on what you observe: $\beta = 0.1$, $\varsigma = 0.01$ and $\varsigma = 0.1$.

(c) For $\beta = 0.1$ and $\varsigma = 0.01$, can you find an optimum value of γ?

6.3 For the 3-DOF system shown in the sketch, mass m_3 and spring k_3 constitute an absorber system added to suppress excessive vibration of the primary system.

(a) Set up the equation of motion and determine the steady-state response of the 2-DOF primary system subject a force $F_2 = F_0 \sin \Omega t$. Plot nondimensional displacement amplitudes ($\bar{q}_1$ and $\bar{q}_2$) with respect to $\bar{\Omega}$.

(b) It turns out that Ω is close to the first natural frequency of the primary system. Determine the condition for zero vibration of mass m_1 to select k_3.

(c) To investigate the response of the 3-DOF system with the vibration absorber for different operating speed Ω, plot nondimensional displacement amplitudes ($\bar{q}_1$, $\bar{q}_2$ and $\bar{q}_3$) with respect to $\bar{\Omega}$. Compare with the primary system responses.

(d) For the 3-DOF system, plot spring force amplitude (nondimensionalized with respect to F_0) of each spring with respect to $\bar{\Omega}$. Compare with the spring forces of the primary system.

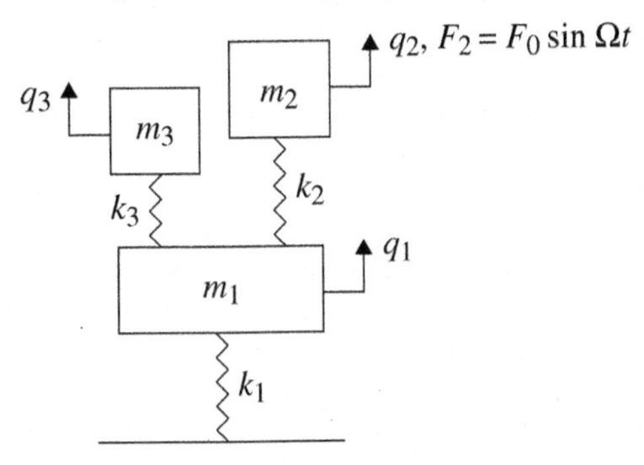

$$m_1 = M_0,\ m_2 = \frac{1}{4}M_0,\ m_3 = \frac{1}{12}M_0,\ k_1 = K_0,\ k_2 = \frac{1}{5}K_0$$

$$\bar{q}_1 = \frac{|q_1|}{(q_1)_{static}},\ \bar{q}_2 = \frac{|q_2|}{(q_1)_{static}},\ \bar{q}_3 = \frac{|q_3|}{(q_1)_{static}},\ \bar{\Omega} = \frac{\Omega}{\omega_1}$$

$(q_1)_{static}$: static displacement of q_1 under F_0

6.4 For the system shown in the sketch, mass m_3 is connected to masses m_A and m_2 via a rigid lever resting on the two fulcrums. The distance between the left fulcrum and the right fulcrum is e and the distance between mass m_A and the left fulcrum is d. Rotation of the lever is assumed small.

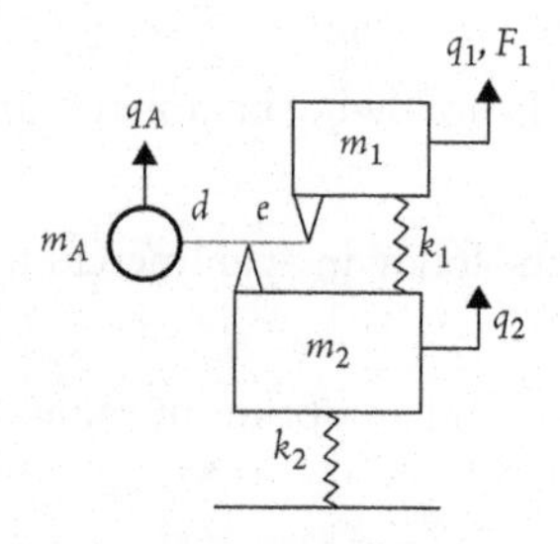

(a) Review problem 2.7 in Chapter 2, and state the condition at which the force transmitted the primary system represented by mass m_2 is equal to zero for $F_1 = F_0 \sin \Omega t$.

(b) Describe how the system in the sketch can be applied to mitigate wing or fuselage vibration of aircraft.

7 VIBRATION OF SLENDER BODIES

In this chapter we consider vibration of slender bodies undergoing longitudinal, torsional and bending vibration. We also consider lateral vibration of taut strings. Equations of motion are constructed using a free body of infinitesimally small length cut out of the body. For slender bodies of uniform cross-section, one can find exact solutions for natural frequencies and natural modes via analytical means.

We note that orthogonality of natural modes observed for discrete systems in the previous chapter also holds for slender bodies. Noteworthy are mathematical equivalence among longitudinal vibration, torsional vibration and vibration of tout strings although they are physically distinct. The last section of this chapter deals with an approximate method in which assumed modes are introduced to find approximate solutions via the Lagrange equation approach.

Finding exact analytical solutions for vibration of slender bodies are important for practical applications. In addition they provide benchmark solutions to an approximate solution method such as the assumed mode method introduced in this chapter or the finite element method which will be discussed in the following chapter. Specific topics covered in this chapter are as follows:

7.1 Longitudinal vibration of a slender body
7.2 Torsional vibration of a slender body
7.3 Vibration of a taut string
7.4 Bending vibration of a slender body
7.5 Assumed mode method for approximate solution

7.1 Longitudinal vibration of a slender body

Consider a slender body undergoing vibration in the longitudinal direction as shown below.

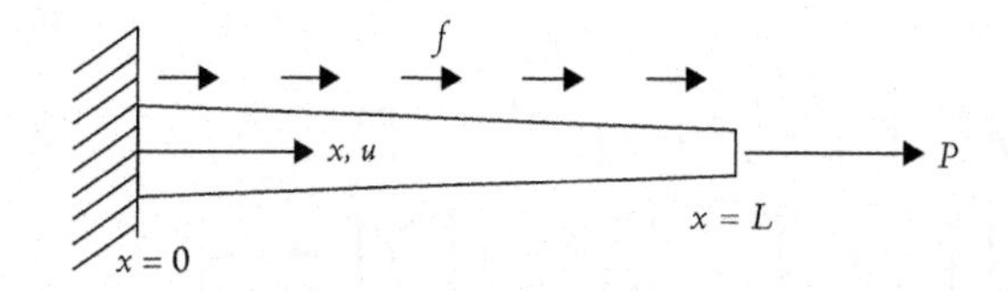

Figure 7.1 Slender body undergoing longitudinal vibration

$f(x,t)$: applied force per unit length
$P(t)$: axial force applied at $x = L$
$A(x)$: cross-sectional area
$u(x,t)$: axial displacement of the cross-section located at x
$m(x) = \rho A(x)$: mass per unit length
ρ : mass per volume

To derive equation of motion, let's create a free body at an instant in time by introducing imaginary cuts at x and $x+dx$.

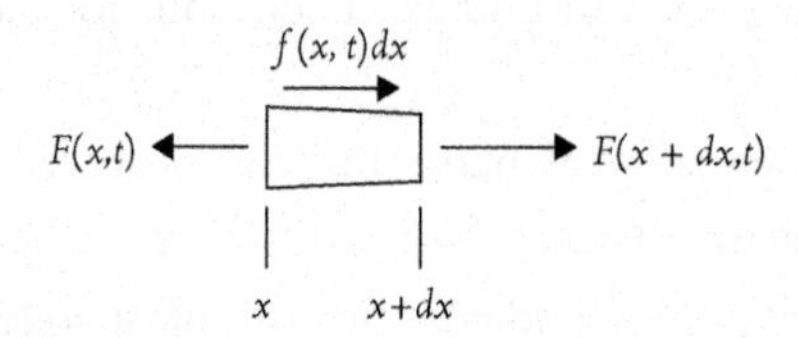

Figure 7.2 Free body diagram of slender body undergoing longitudinal motion.

In Figure 7.2, $F(x,t)$ is axial force acting on the surface located at x. Including the inertia effect,

$$\sum(\text{Axial forces}) = F(x+dx,t) - F(x,t) + f(x,t)dx - (mdx)\ddot{u} = 0 \tag{7.1.1}$$

where

$$F(x+dx,t) = F(x,t) + \frac{\partial F}{\partial x}dx \tag{7.1.2}$$

Substituting equation (7.1.2) into equation (7.1.1),

$$\left(\frac{\partial F}{\partial x} + f - m\ddot{u}\right)dx = 0 \rightarrow \frac{\partial F}{\partial x} + f - m\ddot{u} = 0 \tag{7.1.3}$$

Axial force is related to axial displacement as

$$F = \sigma_{xx}A = E\varepsilon_{xx}A = EA\frac{\partial u}{\partial x} \tag{7.1.4}$$

where σ_{xx} is axial stress, ε_{xx} is axial strain and E is the Young's modulus. Substituting Equation (7.1.4) into equation (7.1.3),

$$m\ddot{u}-\frac{\partial}{\partial x}\left(EA\frac{\partial u}{\partial x}\right)=f \tag{7.1.5}$$

For a slender body fixed at the left end and subjected to an applied force P at the right end as shown in Figure 7.1, the boundary conditions are as follows:

(1) Geometric boundary condition: at $x=0,\ u=0$ (7.1.6)

(2) Force boundary condition: at $x=L,\quad F=P$ (7.1.7)

Free vibration

For free vibration, $f=0$ and $P=0$, and the equation of motion is

$$m\ddot{u}-\frac{\partial}{\partial x}\left(EA\frac{\partial u}{\partial x}\right)=0 \tag{7.1.8}$$

The solution to the above homogeneous equation can be expressed as

$$u=\overline{u}(x)e^{\pm i\omega t} \tag{7.1.9}$$

Placing equation (7.1.9) into equation (7.1.8)

$$-\left[m\omega^2\overline{u}+\frac{\partial}{\partial x}\left(EA\frac{\partial \overline{u}}{\partial x}\right)\right]e^{\pm i\omega t}=0 \tag{7.1.10}$$

and thus

$$m\omega^2\overline{u}+\frac{\partial}{\partial x}\left(EA\frac{\partial \overline{u}}{\partial x}\right)=0 \tag{7.1.11}$$

which is a homogeneous equation for $\overline{u}$. For uniform or constant EA,

$$m\omega^2\overline{u}+EA\frac{\partial^2 \overline{u}}{\partial x^2}=0 \tag{7.1.12}$$

For constant mass per unit length, m, the characteristic solution to equation (7.1.12) is

$$\overline{u}(x)=ce^{\lambda x} \tag{7.1.13}$$

Substituting equation (7.1.13) into equation (7.1.12),

$$\left(\lambda^2+\frac{m\omega^2}{EA}\right)ce^{\lambda x}=0 \tag{7.1.14}$$

For nontrivial solution,

$$\lambda^2+\frac{m\omega^2}{EA}=0\rightarrow\lambda^2+\beta^2=0 \tag{7.1.15}$$

where

$$\beta=\omega\sqrt{\frac{m}{EA}} \tag{7.1.16}$$

From equation (7.1.15),

$$\lambda = \pm i\beta \rightarrow \lambda_1 = i\beta,\ \lambda_2 = -i\beta \tag{7.1.17}$$

The general solution to equation (7.1.12) is

$$\bar{u}(x) = c_1 e^{\lambda_1 x} + c_2 e^{\lambda_2 x} = c_1 e^{i\beta x} + c_2 e^{-i\beta x} \tag{7.1.18}$$

or

$$\bar{u}(x) = B\sin\beta x + D\cos\beta x \tag{7.1.19}$$

where B and D are unknown constants.

Example 7.1.1 A slenderbody of uniform cross-section is fixed at the left end and free at the right end. Determine the natural frequencies and modes of longitudinal free vibration.

For this case the boundary conditions are

$$\text{at } x = 0,\ u = 0 \rightarrow \bar{u} = 0 \tag{7.1.20}$$

$$\text{at } x = L,\ F = EA\frac{\partial u}{\partial x} = 0 \rightarrow \frac{\partial \bar{u}}{\partial x} = 0 \tag{7.1.21}$$

Applying the boundary condition at $x = 0$, one finds that $D = 0$. From the boundary condition at $x = L$,

$$B\beta\cos\beta L = 0 \rightarrow \cos\beta L = 0 \tag{7.1.22}$$

The above equation holds for

$$\beta L = \left(n - \frac{1}{2}\right)\pi \tag{7.1.23}$$

where integer $n\ (=1,2,\cdots\cdots)$ is the mode number. Then from equation (7.1.16), the natural frequency of the mode number n is

$$\omega_n = \beta_n\sqrt{\frac{EA}{m}} \rightarrow \omega_n = \left(n - \frac{1}{2}\right)\pi\sqrt{\frac{EA}{mL^2}} \tag{7.1.24}$$

From equation (7.1.19) with $D = 0$,

$$\bar{u}(x) = B\sin\beta x = B\sin\left(n - \frac{1}{2}\right)\frac{\pi x}{L} = B\phi_n \tag{7.1.25}$$

where

$$\phi_n = \sin\left(n - \frac{1}{2}\right)\frac{\pi x}{L} \tag{7.1.26}$$

is the mode shape of the n-th mode.

Example 7.1.2 A slender body of uniform cross-section is fixed at both ends. Determine the natural frequencies and modes of longitudinal free vibration.

The boundary conditions are $\bar{u}(x)=0$ at $x=0$ and $x=L$. Accordingly, for $\bar{u}(x)$ in equation (7.1.19), $D=0$ and

$$\sin\beta L=0\rightarrow\beta L=n\pi \tag{7.1.27}$$

Then from equation (7.1.16), natural frequency is

$$\omega_n=n\pi\sqrt{\frac{EA}{mL^2}} \tag{7.1.28}$$

where integer n $(=1,2,\cdots\cdots)$ is the mode number, and

$$\bar{u}(x)=B\sin\beta x=B\sin\frac{n\pi x}{L}=B\varphi_n \tag{7.1.29}$$

where

$$\phi_n=\sin\frac{n\pi x}{L} \tag{7.1.30}$$

is the mode shape of the n-th mode.

Orthogonality of natural modes

For mode r and mode s $(r\neq s)$, equation (7.1.11) can be expressed as

$$m\omega_r^2\phi_r+\frac{\partial}{\partial x}\left(EA\frac{\partial\phi_r}{\partial x}\right)=0 \tag{7.1.31}$$

$$m\omega_s^2\phi_s+\frac{\partial}{\partial x}\left(EA\frac{\partial\phi_s}{\partial x}\right)=0 \tag{7.1.32}$$

Multiplying equation (7.1.31) by ϕ_s and integrating over the length,

$$\int_{x=0}^{x=L}\left[m\omega_r^2\phi_r+\frac{\partial}{\partial x}\left(EA\frac{\partial\phi_r}{\partial x}\right)\right]\phi_s dx=0 \tag{7.1.33}$$

Multiplying equation (7.1.32) by ϕ_r and integrating over the length

$$\int_{x=0}^{x=L}\left[m\omega_s^2\phi_s+\frac{\partial}{\partial x}\left(EA\frac{\partial\phi_s}{\partial x}\right)\right]\phi_r dx=0 \tag{7.1.34}$$

Integrating by parts, the second term in equation (7.1.33) can be transformed as follows:

$$\int_{x=0}^{x=L} \phi_s \frac{\partial}{\partial x}\left(EA\frac{\partial \phi_r}{\partial x}\right)dx = \int_{x=0}^{x=L} \phi_s d\left(EA\frac{\partial \phi_r}{\partial x}\right) = \left(\phi_s EA\frac{\partial \phi_r}{\partial x}\right)_{x=0}^{x=L} - \int_{x=0}^{x=L} EA\frac{\partial \phi_r}{\partial x}d\phi_s \tag{7.1.35}$$

For fixed or free boundaries, the first term on the right hand side drops out and

$$\int_{x=0}^{x=L} \phi_s \frac{\partial}{\partial x}\left(EA\frac{\partial \phi_r}{\partial x}\right)dx = -\int_{x=0}^{x=L} EA\frac{\partial \phi_r}{\partial x}\frac{\partial \phi_s}{\partial x}dx \tag{7.1.36}$$

Similarly,

$$\int_{x=0}^{x=L} \phi_r \frac{\partial}{\partial x}\left(EA\frac{\partial \phi_s}{\partial x}\right)dx = -\int_{x=0}^{x=L} EA\frac{\partial \phi_r}{\partial x}\frac{\partial \phi_s}{\partial x}dx \tag{7.1.37}$$

We note that the right hand side of equation (7.1.36) is identical to that of equation (7.1.37). Equations (7.1.33) and (7.1.34) can now be written as

$$\omega_r^2 \int_{x=0}^{x=L} m\phi_r\phi_s\, dx = \int_{x=0}^{x=L} EA\frac{\partial \phi_r}{\partial x}\frac{\partial \phi_s}{\partial x}dx \tag{7.1.38}$$

$$\omega_s^2 \int_{x=0}^{x=L} m\phi_r\phi_s\, dx = \int_{x=0}^{x=L} EA\frac{\partial \phi_r}{\partial x}\frac{\partial \phi_s}{\partial x}dx \tag{7.1.39}$$

Substracting equation (7.1.38) from equation (7.1.39),

$$\left(\omega_r^2 - \omega_s^2\right) \int_{x=0}^{x=L} m\phi_r\phi_s\, dx = 0 \tag{7.1.40}$$

Accordingly, for $\omega_r \neq \omega_s$

$$\int_{x=0}^{x=L} m\phi_r\phi_s\, dx = 0 \tag{7.1.41}$$

Also, from equation (7.1.33) and equation (7.1.37)

$$\int_{x=0}^{x=L} \phi_s \frac{\partial}{\partial x}\left(EA\frac{\partial \phi_r}{\partial x}\right)dx = 0 \rightarrow \int_{x=0}^{x=L} EA\frac{\partial \phi_r}{\partial x}\frac{\partial \phi_s}{\partial x}dx = 0 \tag{7.1.42}$$

Equations (7.1.41) and (7.1.42) are the statements for orthogonality of the natural modes.

Longitudinal vibration response via modal analysis

For analysis of vibration response, one may express displacement as a combination of natural modes as

$$u(x,t) = \alpha_1(t)\phi_1 + \alpha_2(t)\phi_2 + \cdots + \alpha_N(t)\phi_N = \sum_{r=1}^{r=N} \alpha_r\phi_r \tag{7.1.43}$$

where N is the number of natural modes chosen to represent the displacement and α_r are time-dependent unknown modal coefficients. Placing equation (7.1.43) into the equation (7.1.5),

$$m\sum_{r=1}^{r=N}\ddot{\alpha}_r\phi_r - \frac{\partial}{\partial x}\left(EA\sum_{r=1}^{r=N}\alpha_r\frac{\partial\phi_r}{\partial x}\right) = f \tag{7.1.44}$$

Multiplying equation (7.1.44) with natural mode ϕ_s and integrating over the length

$$\int_{x=0}^{x=L}\phi_s\left[m\sum_{r=1}^{r=N}\ddot{\alpha}_r\phi_r - \frac{\partial}{\partial x}\left(EA\sum_{r=1}^{r=N}\alpha_r\frac{\partial\phi_r}{\partial x}\right)\right]dx = \int_{x=0}^{x=L}\phi_s f dx \tag{7.1.45}$$

According to the orthogonality of natural modes in equations (7.1.41) and (7.1.42), the left hand side of the above equation is simplified and thus

$$\left(\int_{x=0}^{x=L}m\phi_s^2 dx\right)\ddot{\alpha}_s + \left(-\int_{x=0}^{x=L}\phi_s\frac{\partial}{\partial x}\left(EA\frac{\partial\phi_s}{\partial x}\right)dx\right)\alpha_s = \int_{x=0}^{x=L}\phi_s f dx \tag{7.1.46}$$

or

$$M_s\ddot{\alpha}_s + K_s\alpha_s = F_s,\ s = 1,2,\cdots,N \tag{7.1.47}$$

where

$$M_s = \int_{x=0}^{x=L}m\phi_s^2 dx \tag{7.1.48}$$

$$K_s = -\int_{x=0}^{x=L}\phi_s\frac{\partial}{\partial x}\left(EA\frac{\partial\phi_s}{\partial x}\right)dx = \omega_s^2\int_{x=0}^{x=L}m\phi_s^2 dx = \omega_s^2 M_s \tag{7.1.49}$$

$$F_s = \int_{x=0}^{x=L}\phi_s f dx \tag{7.1.50}$$

Equation (7.1.47) represents N SDOF systems which can be solved using the techniques discussed in the previous chapters. Dividing equation (7.1.47) by M_s

$$\ddot{\alpha}_s + \omega_s^2\alpha_s = \frac{1}{M_s}F_s \tag{7.1.51}$$

Initial conditions for α_s can be determined using one of the orthogonality of natural modes as follows:

$$\int_{x=0}^{x=L}\phi_s m u(x,t)dx = \int_{x=0}^{x=L}\phi_s m\sum_{r=1}^{r=N}\alpha_r(t)\phi_r dx = \alpha_s(t)\int_{x=0}^{x=L}\phi_s^2 m dx \tag{7.1.52}$$

from which

$$\alpha_s(t) = \frac{1}{M_s}\int_{x=0}^{x=L}\phi_s m u(x,t)dx,\ \dot{\alpha}_s(t) = \frac{1}{M_s}\int_{x=0}^{x=L}\phi_s m\dot{u}(x,t)dx \tag{7.1.53}$$

Accordingly,

$$\alpha_s(0) = \frac{1}{M_s}\int_{x=0}^{x=L}\phi_s m u(x,0)dx,\ \dot{\alpha}_s(0) = \frac{1}{M_s}\int_{x=0}^{x=L}\phi_s m\dot{u}(x,0)dx \tag{7.1.54}$$

Example 7.1.3 Alongitudinal impulse of I_0 is applied at $x = 2L/3$ to a slender body fixed at both ends. The body is of uniform cross-section. Determine the response after the impulse.

There is no applied load after the impulse. Accordingly, the modal equation of motion is

$$\ddot{\alpha}_s + \omega_s^2 \alpha_s = 0$$

The solution to the above equation is in general

$$\alpha_s = c_1 \cos\omega_s t + c_2 \sin\omega_s t$$

in which c_1 and c_1 are determined from the initial conditions. From equation (7.1.54),

$$u(x,0) \rightarrow \alpha_s(0) = 0$$

and

$$\dot{\alpha}_s(0) = \frac{1}{M_s}\int_{x=0}^{x=L} \phi_s m\dot{u}(x,0)dx = \frac{1}{M_s}\int_{x=0}^{x=L} \sin\frac{s\pi x}{L}\cdot m\dot{u}(x,0)dx$$

where

$$M_s = \int_{x=0}^{x=L} m\phi_s^2 dx = m\int_{x=0}^{x=L}\left(\sin\frac{s\pi x}{L}\right)^2 dx = \frac{mL}{2}$$

Noting that the impulse I_o is applied at $x = 2L/3$,

$$\int_{x=0}^{x=L} \sin\frac{s\pi x}{L}\cdot m\dot{u}(x,0)dx = \sin\frac{2s\pi}{3}\cdot I_0$$

where

$$I_0 = (mdx)\dot{u}$$

Accordingly,

$$\dot{\alpha}_s(0) = \frac{2I_o}{mL}\sin\frac{2s\pi}{3}$$

Applying the initial conditions,

$$c_1 = 0, \quad c_2 = \frac{\dot{\alpha}_s(0)}{\omega_s}$$

Accordingly,

$$\alpha_s = \frac{\dot{\alpha}_s(0)}{\omega_s}\sin\omega_s t = b_s \sin\omega_s t$$

where

$$b_s = \frac{\dot{\alpha}_s(0)}{\omega_s} = \frac{1}{\omega_s}\frac{2I_o}{mL}\sin\frac{2s\pi}{3}$$

Thus

$$b_1 = \frac{1}{\omega_1}\frac{2I_o}{mL}\left(\frac{\sqrt{3}}{2}\right), \quad b_2 = \frac{1}{\omega_2}\frac{2I_o}{mL}\left(-\frac{\sqrt{3}}{2}\right), b_3 = 0, \; b_4 = \frac{1}{\omega_4}\frac{2I_o}{mL}\left(\frac{\sqrt{3}}{2}\right)$$

and

$$\left|\frac{b_2}{b_1}\right| = \frac{1}{2}, \quad \left|\frac{b_4}{b_1}\right| = \frac{1}{4}$$

The longitudinal displacement of the slender body is

$$u(x,t) = \alpha_1(t)\phi_1 + \alpha_2(t)\phi_2 + \cdots + \alpha_N(t)\phi_N = \sum_{s=1}^{s=N}\left(\sin\frac{s\pi x}{L}\right)b_s \sin\omega_s t$$

7.2 Torsional vibration of a slender body

Consider a slender body under applied torques as shown below.

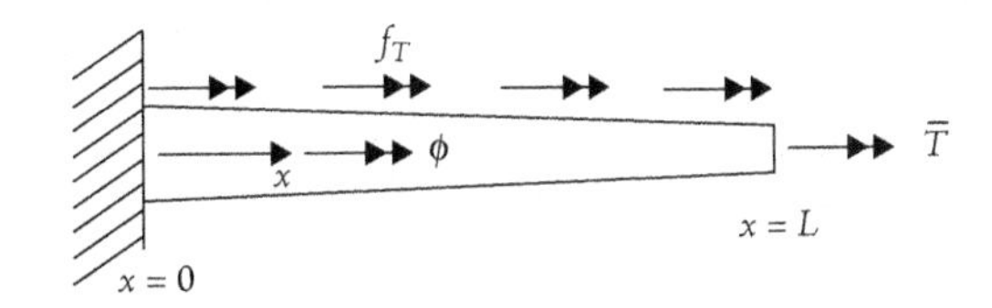

Figure 7.3 Slender body undergoing torsional motion

$\phi(x,t)$: twist angle
$f_T(x,t)$: applied torque per unit length
$\bar{T}(t)$: Torque applied at $x = L$
$I(x)$: mass moment of inertia per unit length

At time t, torques acting on a segment dx are shown below.

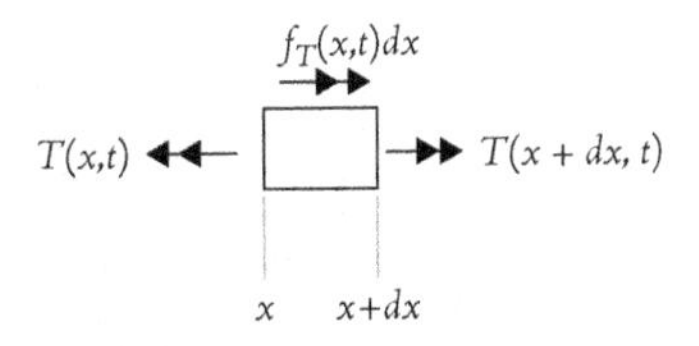

Figure 7.4 Free body diagram of a slender body in torsion.

In Figure 7.4, $T(x,t)$ is torque acting on the cross-section located at position x. Including the inertia effect,

$$\sum(\text{torque}) = T(x+dx,t) - T(x,t) + f_T(x,t)dx - (Idx)\ddot{\phi}(x,t) = 0 \tag{7.2.1}$$

where

$$T(x+dx,t) = T(x,t) + \frac{\partial T}{\partial x}dx \tag{7.2.2}$$

Substituting equation (7.2.2) into equation (7.2.1),

$$\left(\frac{\partial T}{\partial x}+f_T-I\ddot{\phi}\right)dx=0\rightarrow\frac{\partial T}{\partial x}+f_T-I\ddot{\phi}=0 \tag{7.2.3}$$

Also

$$T=GJ\frac{\partial\phi}{\partial x} \tag{7.2.4}$$

where G is the shear modulus and J is the torsion constant of the cross-section. Placing equation (7.2.4) into equation (7.2.3)

$$I\ddot{\phi}-\frac{\partial}{\partial x}\left(GJ\frac{\partial\phi}{\partial x}\right)=f_T \tag{7.2.5}$$

For the slender body shown in Figure7.3, boundary conditions are as follows:

(1) Geometric boundary condition: at $x=0,\ \phi=0$ (7.2.6)

(2) Torque boundary condition: at $x=L,\ T=GJ\frac{\partial\phi}{\partial x}=\bar{T}$ (7.2.7)

We observe that equation (7.2.5) is identical to equation (7.1.5) for longitudinal vibration if ϕ, GJ, I and f_T are replaced with u, EA, m and f. Also, comparing boundary conditions, we observe equivalence between P and $\bar{T}$ applied at $x=L$. Accordingly, analysis of torsional vibration is mathematically identical to that for longitudinal vibration.

7.3 Vibration of a taut string

Consider transverse vibration of a taut string fixed at both ends and under given tension as shown in Figure 7.5, which may representa string in a violin or a piano.

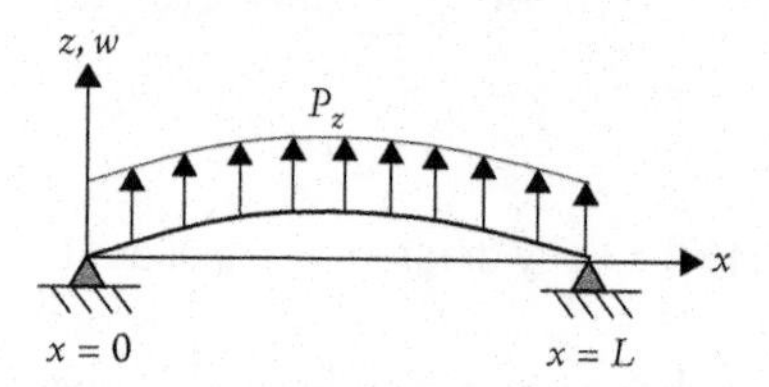

Figure 7.5 Taut string in the displaced configuration

$p_z(x,t)$: applied force per unit length

$w(x,t)$: transverse displacement

For transverse vibration of a taut string under axial tensile force, it is necessary to consider free body diagram in the displaced position in order to capture the effect of tension on transverse displacement. For this, let's create a free body by introducing cuts at x and $x+dx$ in the intial straight configuration and consider equilibrium of the free body in the displaced configuration as shown in Figure 7.6 . We assume that the transverse displacement is small.

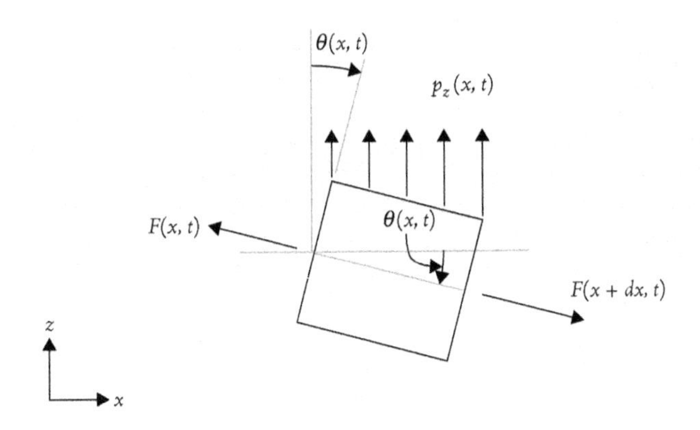

Figure 7.6 Free body diagram of a taut string in the displaced configuration

$F(x,t)$: axial force acting on the cross-section located at x
$\theta(x,t)$: rotational angle of the cross-section located at x

From the free body diagram, $\sum$(forces in the z direction) = 0. Then including the inertia effect,

$$(F\sin\theta)_x - (F\sin\theta)_{x+dx} + p_z dx - (m dx)\ddot{w} = 0 \tag{7.3.1}$$

where
$$(F\sin\theta)_{x+dx} = (F\sin\theta)_x + \frac{\partial}{\partial x}(F\sin\theta)dx \tag{7.3.2}$$

Substituting equation (7.3.2) into equation (7.3.1),

$$\left[-\frac{\partial}{\partial x}(F\sin\theta) + p_z - m\ddot{w}\right]dx = 0 \rightarrow -\frac{\partial}{\partial x}(F\sin\theta) + p_z - m\ddot{w} = 0 \tag{7.3.3}$$

Setting $\sin\theta \approx \theta$ for small θ in equation (7.3.3),

$$-\frac{\partial}{\partial x}(F\theta) + p_z - m\ddot{w} = 0 \tag{7.3.4}$$

Substituting $\theta = -\frac{\partial w}{\partial x}$ into equation (7.3.4),

$$\frac{\partial}{\partial x}\left(F\frac{\partial w}{\partial x}\right) + p_z - m\ddot{w} = 0 \tag{7.3.5}$$

Replacing F in equation (7.3.5) with tensile force T,

$$m\ddot{w} - \frac{\partial}{\partial x}\left(T\frac{\partial w}{\partial x}\right) = p_z \tag{7.3.6}$$

For constant tension, the equation of motion is

$$m\ddot{w} - T\frac{\partial^2 w}{\partial x^2} = p_z \tag{7.3.7}$$

We observe that the above equation is identical to the equation of motion for longitudinal vibration of a slender body with uniform EA if w, T and p_z are replaced with u, EA and f. In the previous section we also observed the mathematical equivalence between torsional vibration and longitudinal vibration. These mathematical equivalences are summarized as follows:

Longitudinal	Torsional	Taut String
u	ϕ	w
EA	GJ	T
m	I	m
f	f_T	p_z

Example 7.4.1 Consider a taut string fixed at both ends and under tension T. The string is now given initial displacement as follows and released.

$$w(x,0)=\frac{3x}{2L} \quad \text{for } 0\le x\le \frac{2}{3}L$$

$$w(x,0)=3\left(1-\frac{x}{L}\right) \quad \text{for } \frac{2}{3}L\le x\le L$$

Determine the amplitude of the first three modes present in the resulting motion. Determine also ratios of the amplitudes of these modes relative the lowest mode?

(a) Utilizing the mathematical equivalence with the longitudinal vibration, the natural frequencies and modes are taken from equations (7.1.28) and (7.1.30) as follows:

$$\omega_n = n\pi\sqrt{\frac{T}{mL^2}}$$

$$\phi_n = \sin\frac{n\pi x}{L}$$

(b) The normal equation of motion is

$$\ddot{\alpha}_s + \omega_s^2\alpha_s = \frac{1}{M_s}F_s$$

where

$$F_s = \int_{x=0}^{x=L} \phi_s p_z dx$$

According to the problem statement, $p_z = 0$ and the normal equation of motion is

$$\ddot{\alpha}_s + \omega_s^2\alpha_s = 0$$

The intial conditions are

$$\alpha_s(0) = \frac{1}{M_s}\int_{x=0}^{x=L} \phi_s m w(x,0)dx = \frac{1}{M_s} m \int_{x=0}^{x=L} \sin\frac{s\pi x}{L} w(x,0)dx,$$

where

$$M_s = \frac{mL}{2}$$

Then

$$\alpha_s(0) = \frac{2}{L}\left[\int_{x=0}^{x=\frac{2L}{3}} \sin\frac{s\pi x}{L}\cdot\left(\frac{3x}{2L}\right)dx + \int_{x=\frac{2L}{3}}^{x=L} \sin\frac{s\pi x}{L}\cdot 3\left(1-\frac{x}{L}\right)dx\right]$$

$$= \frac{9}{s^2\pi^2}\sin\frac{2s\pi}{3}$$

$$\dot{\alpha}_s(0) = \frac{1}{M_s}\int_{x=0}^{x=L} \phi_s m\dot{w}(x,0)dx = 0$$

The solution to the normal equation is now

$$\alpha_s = \alpha_s(0)\cos\omega_s t$$

where $\alpha_1(0) = \frac{9}{\pi^2}\left(\frac{\sqrt{3}}{2}\right)$, $\alpha_2(0) = -\frac{9}{4\pi^2}\left(\frac{\sqrt{3}}{2}\right)$, $\alpha_3(0) = 0$, $\alpha_4(0) = \frac{9}{16\pi^2}\left(\frac{\sqrt{3}}{2}\right)$

and

$$\left|\frac{\alpha_2(0)}{\alpha_1(0)}\right| = \frac{1}{4}, \quad \left|\frac{\alpha_4(0)}{\alpha_1(0)}\right| = \frac{1}{16}$$

The transverse displacement of the string is

$$w(x,t) = \alpha_1(t)\phi_1 + \alpha_2(t)\phi_2 + \cdots + \alpha_N(t)\phi_N = \sum_{s=1}^{s=N}\left(\sin\frac{s\pi x}{L}\right)\alpha_s(0)\cos\omega_s t$$

7.4 Bending vibration of a slender body

For simplicity, consider a slender body undergoing bending vibration in the $x-z$ plane. Example are an aircraft or a launch vehicle in flight modeled as a flying beam, and an aircraft wing modeled as a cantilevered beam. Figure 7.7 shows a cantilevered beam as an example.

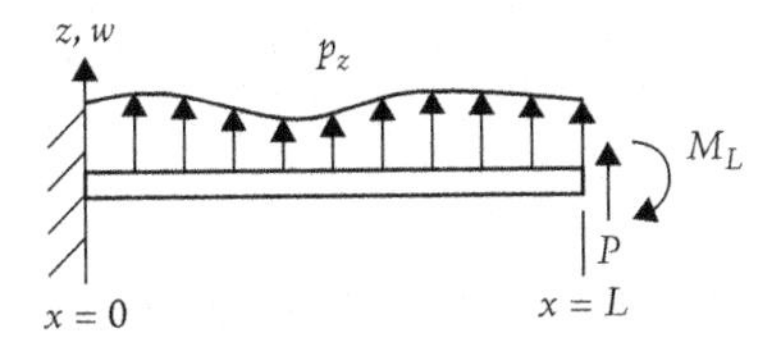

Figure 7.7 Cantilevered slender body under bending load

$p_z(x,t)$: applied force per unit length
$M_L(t)$: moment applied at $x = L$
$P(t)$: force applied at $x = L$
$w(x,t)$: transverse displacement due to bending

Consider a slender body subjected to a lateral load per unit length as shown in the sketch, and introduce cuts at x and $x+dx$ to isolate a free-body.

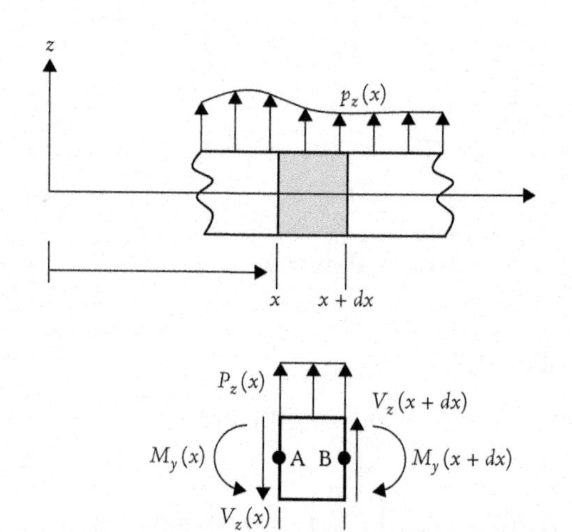

Figure 7.8 Free body diagram of a slender body in bending

$V_z(x)$: shear force acting on cross-section located at x
$M_y(x)$: moment acting on the cross-section located at x
$m(x)$: mass per unit length

Note that, in Figure 7.8, dependence of forces and moments on time is not shown explicitly to avoid cluttering. From the free body diagram, including the inertia effect,

$$\sum(\text{forces in } z) = V_z(x+dx) - V_z(x) + p_z(x)dx - (mdx)\ddot{w} = 0 \tag{7.4.1}$$

Noting that

$$V_z(x+dx) = V_z(x) + \frac{\partial V_z}{\partial x}dx, \tag{7.4.2}$$

equation (7.4.1) becomes

$$\left(\frac{\partial V_z}{\partial x} + p_z - m\ddot{w}\right)dx = 0 \;\rightarrow \frac{\partial V_z}{\partial x} + p_z - m\ddot{w} = 0 \tag{7.4.3}$$

Neglecting the effect of rotary inertia, moment equilibrium about point B is

$$M_y(x+dx) - M_y(x) - V_z(x)dx + \hat{p}_z(x)dx\frac{dx}{2} = 0 \tag{7.4.4}$$

where

$$M_y(x+dx) = M_y(x) + \frac{\partial M_y}{\partial x}dx, \;\; \hat{p}_z = p_z - m\ddot{w} \tag{7.4.5}$$

Introducing the first in equation (7.4.5) into equation (7.4.4),

$$\left(\frac{\partial M_y}{\partial x} - V_z\right)dx + \frac{\hat{p}_z(x)}{2}(dx)^2 = 0 \tag{7.4.6}$$

In the above equation, the second term on the left involving $\hat{p}_z$ is a higher order term and can be dropped as $dx \to 0$. Accordingly,

$$\left(\frac{\partial M_y}{\partial x} - V_z\right)dx = 0 \tag{7.4.7}$$

from which

$$\frac{\partial M_y}{\partial x} = V_z \tag{7.4.8}$$

Combining equation (7.4.3) and (7.4.8),

$$\frac{\partial^2 M_y}{\partial x^2} + p_z - m\ddot{w} = 0 \tag{7.4.9}$$

According to the Bernoulli-Euler beam bending theory, transverse shear strain is assumed zero and thus

$$\theta = -\frac{\partial w}{\partial x} \tag{7.4.10}$$

where θ is the rotational angle of the cross-section, defined positive clockwise in the $x-z$ plane. One may also recall that

$$M_y = -EI_y \frac{\partial^2 w}{\partial x^2} \tag{7.4.11}$$

Placing equation (7.4.11) to equation (7.4.9),

$$m\ddot{w} + \frac{\partial^2}{\partial x^2}\left(EI_y \frac{\partial^2 w}{\partial x^2}\right) = p_z \tag{7.4.12}$$

Boundary conditions: For a beam fixed at $x=0$ and free at $x=L$ as shown in Figure 7.7, boundary conditions are as follows:

(1) at $x=0$, $w=0$ and $\theta = -\frac{\partial w}{\partial x} = 0$ (7.4.13)

(2) at $x=L$,

$$M_y = -EI_y \frac{\partial^2 w}{\partial x^2} = M_L$$
$$V_z = \frac{\partial M_y}{\partial x} = \frac{\partial}{\partial x}\left(-EI_y \frac{\partial^2 w}{\partial x^2}\right) = P \tag{7.4.14}$$

Free vibration

The equation of motion for free vibration is

$$m\ddot{w}+\frac{\partial^2}{\partial x^2}\left(EI_y\frac{\partial^2 w}{\partial x^2}\right)=0 \tag{7.4.15}$$

The solution to the above equation can be expressed as

$$w=\overline{w}(x)e^{\pm i\omega t} \tag{7.4.16}$$

Placing equation (7.4.16) to equation (7.4.15),

$$\left[\frac{\partial^2}{\partial x^2}\left(EI_y\frac{\partial^2 \overline{w}}{\partial x^2}\right)-m\omega^2\overline{w}\right]e^{\pm i\omega t}=0 \tag{7.4.17}$$

from which it follows that

$$\frac{\partial^2}{\partial x^2}\left(EI_y\frac{\partial^2 \overline{w}}{\partial x^2}\right)-m\omega^2\overline{w}=0 \tag{7.4.18}$$

The above equation is a fourth order homogeneous ordinary differential equation for $\overline{w}$. For a beam of uniform cross-section with constant m and EI_y, equation (7.4.18) becomes

$$EI_y\frac{\partial^4 \overline{w}}{\partial x^4}-m\omega^2\overline{w}=0 \tag{7.4.19}$$

The solution to the above homogeneous equation is of the following form:

$$\overline{w}=ce^{\lambda x} \tag{7.4.20}$$

Placing equation (7.4.20) to equation (7.4.19),

$$\left(\lambda^4-\sigma^4\right)ce^{\lambda x}=0 \tag{7.4.21}$$

where

$$\sigma=\sqrt[4]{\frac{m\omega^2}{EI_y}} \tag{7.4.22}$$

For nontrivial solution,

$$\lambda^4-\sigma^4=0\rightarrow\left(\lambda^2+\sigma^2\right)\left(\lambda^2-\sigma^2\right)=0 \tag{7.4.23}$$

from which

$$\lambda^2+\sigma^2=0,\quad \lambda^2-\sigma^2=0 \tag{7.4.24}$$

or

$$\lambda^2=-\sigma^2,\quad \lambda^2=\sigma^2\rightarrow\lambda_{1,2}=\pm i\sigma,\quad \lambda_{3,4}=\pm\sigma \tag{7.4.25}$$

Then

$$\bar{w} = c_1 e^{i\sigma x} + c_2 e^{-i\sigma x} + c_3 e^{\sigma x} + c_4 e^{-\sigma x} \tag{7.4.26}$$

Recalling that

$$\cosh \sigma x = \frac{e^{\sigma x} + e^{-\sigma x}}{2}, \ \sinh \sigma x = \frac{e^{\sigma x} - e^{-\sigma x}}{2} \tag{7.4.27}$$

The right hand side of equation (7.4.26) can be rearranged as

$$\bar{w} = \text{C}\sinh \sigma x + \text{D}\cosh \sigma x + \text{E}\sin \sigma x + \text{F}\cos \sigma x \tag{7.4.28}$$

with unknown coefficients C, D, E and D.

Example 7.4.1 Free vibration of a cantilevered beam of uniform cross-section

For a beam of uniform cross-section fixed at $x = 0$ and free at $x = L$, boundary conditions are as follows:

$$\text{At } x = 0, \ w = 0 \rightarrow \bar{w} = 0, \ \theta = -\frac{\partial w}{\partial x} = 0 \rightarrow \frac{\partial \bar{w}}{\partial x} = 0 \tag{7.4.29}$$

At $x = L$,

$$\begin{aligned} M_y &= -EI_y \frac{\partial^2 w}{\partial x^2} = 0 \rightarrow \frac{\partial^2 \bar{w}}{\partial x^2} = 0 \\ V_z &= \frac{\partial M_y}{\partial x} = \frac{\partial}{\partial x}\left(-EI_y \frac{\partial^2 w}{\partial x^2}\right) = 0 \rightarrow \frac{\partial^3 \bar{w}}{\partial x^3} = 0 \end{aligned} \tag{7.4.30}$$

From equation (7.4.28),

$$\frac{\partial \bar{w}}{\partial x} = \sigma(\text{C}\cosh \sigma x + \text{D}\sinh \sigma x + \text{E}\cos \sigma x - \text{F}\sin \sigma x) \tag{7.4.31}$$

$$\frac{\partial^2 \bar{w}}{\partial x^2} = \sigma^2(\text{C}\sinh \sigma x + \text{D}\cosh \sigma x - \text{E}\sin \sigma x - \text{F}\cos \sigma x) \tag{7.4.32}$$

$$\frac{\partial^3 \bar{w}}{\partial x^3} = \sigma^3(\text{C}\cosh \sigma x + \text{D}\sinh \sigma x - \text{E}\cos \sigma x + \text{F}\sin \sigma x) \tag{7.4.33}$$

Applying the boundary conditions at $x = 0$,

$$\bar{w} = 0 \rightarrow D + F = 0 \rightarrow F = -D \tag{7.4.34}$$

$$\frac{\partial \bar{w}}{\partial x} = 0 \rightarrow \text{C} + \text{E} = 0 \rightarrow \text{E} = -\text{C} \tag{7.4.35}$$

Applying the boundary conditions at $x = L$ and equations (7.4.34) and (7.4.35).

$$\frac{\partial^2 \overline{w}}{\partial x^2} = 0 \rightarrow \mathrm{C}\sinh \sigma L + \mathrm{D}\cosh \sigma L - \mathrm{E}\sin \sigma L - \mathrm{F}\cos \sigma L = 0$$

or

$$\mathrm{C}(\sinh \sigma L + \sin \sigma L) + D(\cosh \sigma L + \cos \sigma L) = 0 \tag{7.4.36}$$

$$\frac{\partial^3 \overline{w}}{\partial x^3} = 0 \rightarrow \mathrm{C}\cosh \sigma L + \mathrm{D}\sinh \sigma L - \mathrm{E}\cos \sigma L + \mathrm{F}\sin \sigma L = 0$$

or

$$\mathrm{C}(\cosh \sigma L + \cos \sigma L) + D(\sinh \sigma L - \sin \sigma L) = 0 \tag{7.4.37}$$

In matrix form equations (7.4.36) and (7.4.37) can be expressed as

$$\begin{bmatrix} \sinh \sigma L + \sin \sigma L & \cosh \sigma L + \cos \sigma L \\ \cosh \sigma L + \cos \sigma L & \sinh \sigma L - \sin \sigma L \end{bmatrix} \begin{Bmatrix} \mathrm{C} \\ \mathrm{D} \end{Bmatrix} = \begin{Bmatrix} 0 \\ 0 \end{Bmatrix} \tag{7.4.38}$$

For nontrivial solution of the above homogeneous equation, the determinant of the coefficient matrix must be equal to zero. Accordingly,

$$(\sinh \sigma L)^2 - (\sin \sigma L)^2 - \left[(\cosh \sigma L)^2 + 2\cosh \sigma L \cdot \cos \sigma L + (\cos \sigma L)^2\right] = 0 \tag{7.4.39}$$

Noting that

$$(\cosh \sigma L)^2 - (\sinh \sigma L)^2 = 1, \;\; (\cos \sigma L)^2 + (\sin \sigma L)^2 = 1 \tag{7.4.40}$$

Equation (7.4.39) is simplified to

$$\cosh \sigma L \cdot \cos \sigma L + 1 = 0 \tag{7.4.41}$$

The solution to the above equation may be expressed as

$$\sigma_n L = a_n \tag{7.4.42}$$

where integer n $(=1, 2, \cdots)$ is a mode number. Solving equation (7.4.41), via a graphical method for example, one can show that $a_1 = 1.8751,\; a_2 = 4.6968,\; a_3 = 7.8851$ etc. Using equation (7.4.22), equation (7.4.42) can then be expressed as

$$\sqrt[4]{\frac{m\omega_n^2}{EI_y}} L = a_n \tag{7.4.43}$$

and

$$\omega_n = a_n^2 \sqrt{\frac{EI_y}{mL^4}} \tag{7.4.44}$$

From the above equation, the three lowest natural frequencies are

$$\omega_1 = 3.516\sqrt{\frac{EI_y}{mL^4}},\quad \omega_2 = 22.06\sqrt{\frac{EI_y}{mL^4}},\quad \omega_3 = 62.17\sqrt{\frac{EI_y}{mL^4}} \tag{7.4.45}$$

Now, using equations (7.4.34) and (7.4.35), and with $\sigma = \sigma_n$, equation (7.4.28) can be expressed as

$$\bar{w} = C(\sinh\sigma_n x - \sin\sigma_n x) + D(\cosh\sigma_n x - \cos\sigma_n x) \tag{7.4.46}$$

and

$$\frac{\bar{w}}{D} = \frac{C}{D}(\sinh\sigma_n x - \sin\sigma_n x) + (\cosh\sigma_n x - \cos\sigma_n x) \tag{7.4.47}$$

With $\sigma = \sigma_n$, equation (7.4.37) can be expressed as

$$C(\cosh\sigma_n L + \cos\sigma_n L) + D(\sinh\sigma_n L - \sin\sigma_n L) = 0 \tag{7.4.48}$$

Then

$$\frac{C}{D} = -\frac{\sinh\sigma_n L - \sin\sigma_n L}{\cosh\sigma_n L + \cos\sigma_n L} \tag{7.4.49}$$

and

$$\phi_n(x) = \frac{\bar{w}}{D} = -\frac{\sinh\sigma_n L - \sin\sigma_n L}{\cosh\sigma_n L + \cos\sigma_n L}(\sinh\sigma_n x - \sin\sigma_n x) + (\cosh\sigma_n x - \cos\sigma_n x) \tag{7.4.50}$$

is the mode shape of the n-th mode.

Orthogonality of natural modes

In general, for mode r and mode s $(r \neq s)$, equation (7.4.18) can be expressed as

$$\frac{\partial^2}{\partial x^2}\left(EI_y\frac{\partial^2\phi_r}{\partial x^2}\right) - m\omega_r^2\phi_r = 0 \tag{7.4.51}$$

$$\frac{\partial^2}{\partial x^2}\left(EI_y\frac{\partial^2\phi_s}{\partial x^2}\right) - m\omega_s^2\phi_s = 0 \tag{7.4.52}$$

Multiplying equation (7.4.51) by ϕ_s and integrating over the length,

$$\int_{x=0}^{x=L}\left(\frac{\partial^2}{\partial x^2}\left(EI_y\frac{\partial^2\phi_r}{\partial x^2}\right) - m\omega_r^2\phi_r\right)\phi_s\,dx = 0 \tag{7.4.53}$$

Multiplying equation (7.4.52) by ϕ_r and integrating over the length

$$\int_{x=0}^{x=L}\left(\frac{\partial^2}{\partial x^2}\left(EI_y\frac{\partial^2\phi_s}{\partial x^2}\right)-m\omega_s^2\phi_s\right)\phi_r\,dx=0 \quad (7.4.54)$$

Integrating by parts twice the first terms in equations (7.4.53) and (7.4.54) and, considering such boundary conditions as clamped, free and hinged for simplicity, one can show that

$$\int_{x=0}^{x=L}\phi_s\frac{\partial^2}{\partial x^2}\left(EI_y\frac{\partial^2\phi_r}{\partial x^2}\right)dx=\int_{x=0}^{x=L}\phi_r\frac{\partial^2}{\partial x^2}\left(EI_y\frac{\partial^2\phi_s}{\partial x^2}\right)dx=\int_{x=0}^{x=L}EI_y\frac{\partial^2\phi_r}{\partial x^2}\frac{\partial^2\phi_s}{\partial x^2}dx \quad (7.4.55)$$

Substracting equation (7.4.54) from equation (7.4.53),

$$\left(\omega_r^2-\omega_s^2\right)\int_{x=0}^{x=L}m\phi_r\phi_s\,dx=0 \quad (7.4.56)$$

Accordingly, for $r\neq s$

$$\int_{x=0}^{x=L}m\phi_r\phi_s\,dx=0 \quad (7.4.57)$$

and

$$\int_{x=0}^{x=L}\phi_s\frac{\partial^2}{\partial x^2}\left(EI_y\frac{\partial^2\phi_r}{\partial x^2}\right)dx=0\rightarrow\int_{x=0}^{x=L}EI_y\frac{\partial^2\phi_r}{\partial x^2}\frac{\partial^2\phi_s}{\partial x^2}dx=0 \quad (7.4.58)$$

Bending vibration response via modal analyis

For analysis of bending vibration response, one may express displacement as a combination of natural modes as

$$w(x,t)=\alpha_1(t)\phi_1+\alpha_2(t)\phi_2+\cdots+\alpha_N(t)\phi_N=\sum_{r=1}^{r=N}\alpha_r\phi_r \quad (7.4.59)$$

where N is the number of natural modes chosen to represents and α_r are time-dependent unknown modal coefficients. Placing equation (7.4.59) into equation (7.4.12),

$$m\sum_{r=1}^{r=N}\ddot{\alpha}_r\phi_r+\frac{\partial^2}{\partial x^2}\left(EI_y\sum_{r=1}^{r=N}\alpha_r\frac{\partial^2\phi_r}{\partial x^2}\right)=p_z \quad (7.4.60)$$

Multiplying the above equation by natural mode ϕ_s and integrating over the length

$$\int_{x=0}^{x=L}\phi_s\left[m\sum_{r=1}^{r=N}\ddot{\alpha}_r\phi_r+\frac{\partial^2}{\partial x^2}\left(EI_y\sum_{r=1}^{r=N}\alpha_r\frac{\partial^2\phi_r}{\partial x^2}\right)\right]dx=\int_{x=0}^{x=L}\phi_s p_z\,dx \quad (7.4.61)$$

According to the orthogonality of natural modes in equations (7.4.57) and (7.4.58), the left hand side of the above equation is simplified and thus

$$\left(\int_{x=0}^{x=L} m\phi_s^2 dx\right)\ddot{\alpha}_s + \left(\int_{x=0}^{x=L} \phi_s \frac{\partial^2}{\partial x^2}\left(EI_y \frac{\partial^2 \phi_s}{\partial x^2}\right)dx\right)\alpha_s = \int_{x=0}^{x=L} \phi_s p_z dx \tag{7.4.62}$$

or

$$M_s\ddot{\alpha}_s + K_s\alpha_s = F_s,\ s = 1,2,\cdots,N \tag{7.4.63}$$

where

$$M_s = \int_{x=0}^{x=L} m\phi_s^2 dx \tag{7.4.64}$$

$$K_s = \int_{x=0}^{x=L} \phi_s \frac{\partial^2}{\partial x^2}\left(EI_y \frac{\partial^2 \phi_s}{\partial x^2}\right)dx = \omega_s^2 \int_{x=0}^{x=L} m\phi_s^2 dx = \omega_s^2 M_s \tag{7.4.65}$$

$$F_s = \int_{x=0}^{x=L} \phi_s p_z dx \tag{7.4.66}$$

Equation (7.4.63) represents N SDOF systems. Initial conditions for the SDOF systems can be determined using the orthogonality of natural modes as follows:

$$\int_{x=0}^{x=L} \phi_s m w(x,t) dx = \int_{x=0}^{x=L} \phi_s m \sum_{r=1}^{r=N} \alpha_r(t)\phi_r dx = \alpha_s(t)\int_{x=0}^{x=L} \phi_s^2 m dx \tag{7.4.67}$$

from which

$$\alpha_s(t) = \frac{1}{M_s}\int_{x=0}^{x=L} \phi_s m w(x,t) dx,\quad \dot{\alpha}_s(t) = \frac{1}{M_s}\int_{x=0}^{x=L} \phi_s m \dot{w}(x,t) dx \tag{7.4.68}$$

Accordingly,

$$\alpha_s(0) = \frac{1}{M_s}\int_{x=0}^{x=L} \phi_s m w(x,0) dx,\quad \dot{\alpha}_s(0) = \frac{1}{M_s}\int_{x=0}^{x=L} \phi_s m \dot{w}(x,0) dx \tag{7.4.69}$$

7.5 Assumed mode method for approximate solution

For a slender body of non-uniform cross-section, one can find an approximation solution via introducing an assumed displacement field into the energy expressions and using the Lagrange equation approach. For example, one may consider a slender body undergoing bending vibration as shown in Figure 7.7.

Kinetic energy:

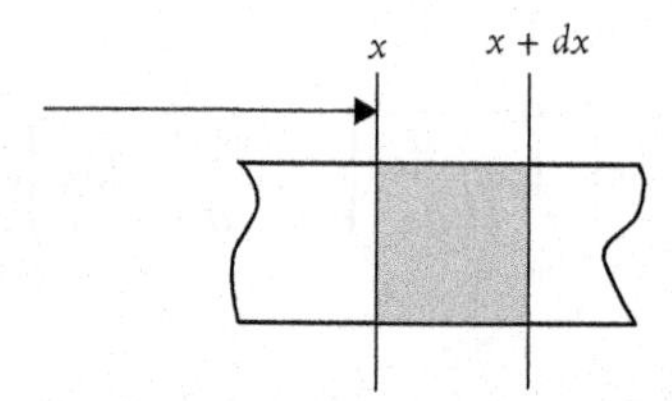

To derive the kinetic energy expression for a slender body in bending vibration, one may first consider a body segment of length dx as shown in the sketch. Neglecting the contribution from rotation around the y axis, the kinetic energy dT of the shaded portion is

$$dT = \frac{1}{2}(mdx)\dot{w}^2 \tag{7.5.1}$$

The kinetic energy for the entire body is then

$$T = \frac{1}{2}\int_{x=0}^{x=L} \dot{w}^2 m dx \tag{7.5.2}$$

Strain energy:

For a slender body in bending, the strain energy can be expressed as

$$U = \frac{1}{2}\int_{x=0}^{x=L} EI_y \left(\frac{\partial^2 w}{\partial x^2}\right)^2 dx \tag{7.5.3}$$

where $$I_y = \int_A z^2\, dy dz : \text{area moment of inertia} \tag{7.5.4}$$

Incremental work done by applied loads

For the applied loads shown in Figure 7.7,

$$\delta W = \int_{x=0}^{x=L} \delta w p_z\, dx + \left(M_L \delta\theta\right)_{x=L} + \left(P\delta w\right)_{x=L} \tag{7.5.5}$$

for incremental displacement δw ($\rightarrow 0$) and rotation $\delta\theta$ ($\rightarrow 0$).

Assumed displacement:

For approximate solution, one may assume w as

$$w = f_1(x)a_1 + f_2(x)a_2 + \cdots f_n(x)a_n \tag{7.5.6}$$

where $f_i(x)$ is an assumed function that satisfies geometric boundary conditions and a_k $(k=1,2,\cdots\cdots)$ is a time-dependent unknown coefficient. For example, for a cantilevered beam fixed at $x=0$, one may assume

$$w = a_1\left(\frac{x}{L}\right)^2 + a_2\left(\frac{x}{L}\right)^3 + \cdots\cdots = a_1 s^2 + a_2 s^3 + \cdots\cdots \tag{7.5.7}$$

where

$$s = \frac{x}{L}. \tag{7.5.8}$$

As an exercise, consider the two-term approximation for a cantilever beam with

$$w = a_1 s^2 + a_2 s^3 \tag{7.5.9}$$

In matrix form

$$w = \lfloor\, s^2 \quad s^3 \,\rfloor \begin{Bmatrix} a_1 \\ a_2 \end{Bmatrix} = \mathbf{Na} \tag{7.5.10}$$

where

$$\mathbf{N} = \lfloor\, s^2 \quad s^3 \,\rfloor, \ \mathbf{a} = \begin{Bmatrix} a_1 \\ a_2 \end{Bmatrix} \tag{7.5.11}$$

or

$$w = \lfloor\, a_1 \quad a_2 \,\rfloor \begin{Bmatrix} s^2 \\ s^3 \end{Bmatrix} = \mathbf{a}^{\mathrm{T}}\mathbf{N}^{\mathrm{T}} \tag{7.5.12}$$

Construction of the mass matrix

From equations (7.5.10) and (7.5.12)

$$\dot{w} = \mathbf{N}\dot{\mathbf{a}}, \ \dot{w} = \dot{\mathbf{a}}^{\mathrm{T}}\mathbf{N}^{\mathrm{T}} \tag{7.5.13}$$

Then

$$\begin{aligned} T &= \frac{1}{2}\int_{x=0}^{x=L} \dot{w}^2 m\,dx = \frac{1}{2}\int_{s=0}^{s=1} \dot{\mathbf{a}}^{\mathrm{T}}\mathbf{N}^{\mathrm{T}}\mathbf{N}\dot{\mathbf{a}} mL\,ds = \frac{1}{2}\dot{\mathbf{a}}^{\mathrm{T}}\left(L\int_{s=0}^{s=1} m\mathbf{N}^{\mathrm{T}}\mathbf{N}\,ds\right)\dot{\mathbf{a}} \\ &= \frac{1}{2}\dot{\mathbf{a}}^{\mathrm{T}}\mathbf{M}\dot{\mathbf{a}} \end{aligned} \tag{7.5.14}$$

where

$$\mathbf{M} = L\int_{s=0}^{s=1} m\mathbf{N}^{\mathrm{T}}\mathbf{N}\,ds : \text{mass matrix} \tag{7.5.15}$$

Construction of the stiffness matrix

$$\begin{aligned} \frac{\partial^2 w}{\partial x^2} &= \frac{\partial}{\partial x}\left(\frac{\partial w}{\partial x}\right) = \frac{\partial}{\partial s}\left(\frac{\partial w}{\partial s}\frac{ds}{dx}\right)\frac{ds}{dx} = \frac{1}{L^2}\frac{\partial^2 w}{\partial s^2} \\ &= \frac{1}{L^2}(2a_1 + 6a_2 s) = \frac{1}{L^2}\lfloor\, 2 \quad 6s \,\rfloor \begin{Bmatrix} a_1 \\ a_2 \end{Bmatrix} = \frac{1}{L^2}\mathbf{Ba} \end{aligned} \tag{7.5.16}$$

where
$$\mathbf{B} = \lfloor\ 2 \quad 6s\ \rfloor \tag{7.5.17}$$

or
$$\frac{\partial^2 w}{\partial x^2} = \lfloor\ a_1 \quad a_2\ \rfloor \frac{1}{L^2} \left\{ \begin{matrix} 2 \\ 6s \end{matrix} \right\} = \frac{1}{L^2} \mathbf{a}^T \mathbf{B}^T \tag{7.5.18}$$

Then, placing equations (7.5.16) and (7.5.18) into equation (7.5.3),

$$\begin{aligned} U &= \frac{1}{2} \int_{x=0}^{x=L} EI_y \left(\frac{\partial^2 w}{\partial x^2} \right)^2 dx = \frac{1}{2} \int_{s=0}^{s=1} \frac{EI_y}{L^4} \mathbf{a}^T \mathbf{B}^T \mathbf{B} \mathbf{a} L\ ds \\ &= \frac{1}{2} \mathbf{a}^T \left(\frac{E}{L^3} \int_{s=0}^{s=1} I_y \mathbf{B}^T \mathbf{B}\ ds \right) \mathbf{a} = \frac{1}{2} \mathbf{a}^T \mathbf{K} \mathbf{a} \end{aligned} \tag{7.5.19}$$

where
$$\mathbf{K} = \frac{E}{L^3} \int_{s=0}^{s=1} I_y \mathbf{B}^T \mathbf{B}\ ds : \text{stiffness matrix} \tag{7.5.20}$$

Construction of the load vector

The load vector is constructed using equation (7.5.5). From equation (7.5.12)

$$\delta w = \lfloor\ \delta a_1 \quad \delta a_2\ \rfloor \left\{ \begin{matrix} s^2 \\ s^3 \end{matrix} \right\} = \delta \mathbf{a}^T \mathbf{N}^T \tag{7.5.21}$$

Incremental work done by applied load per unit length, p_z, is

$$\int_{x=0}^{x=L} \delta w p_z\ dx = \int_{s=0}^{s=1} \delta \mathbf{a}^T \mathbf{N}^T p_z L\, ds = \delta \mathbf{a}^T \left(L \int_{s=0}^{s=1} \mathbf{N}^T p_z\ ds \right) = \delta \mathbf{a}^T \mathbf{A} \tag{7.5.22}$$

where
$$\mathbf{A} = L \int_{s=0}^{s=1} \mathbf{N}^T p_z\ ds \tag{7.5.23}$$

At $x = L$, $s = 1$ and

$$(P\delta w)_{x=L} = P(\delta a_1 + \delta a_2) \tag{7.5.24}$$

Also,
$$\theta = -\frac{\partial w}{\partial x} = -\frac{\partial w}{\partial s}\frac{ds}{dx} = -\frac{1}{L}\left(2a_1 s + 3a_2 s^2\right) \tag{7.5.25}$$

Then at $x = L$, $s = 1$ and

$$(M_L \delta\theta)_{x=L} = -M_L \frac{1}{L}(2\delta a_1 + 3\delta a_2) \tag{7.5.26}$$

Accordingly,

$$\delta W = \lfloor \delta a_1 \quad \delta a_2 \rfloor \begin{Bmatrix} A_1 + P - 2\dfrac{M_L}{L} \\ A_2 + P - 3\dfrac{M_L}{L} \end{Bmatrix} = \delta \mathbf{a}^T \mathbf{F} \tag{7.5.27}$$

where

$$\mathbf{F} = \begin{Bmatrix} A_1 + P - 2\dfrac{M_L}{L} \\ A_2 + P - 3\dfrac{M_L}{L} \end{Bmatrix} : \text{load vector} \tag{7.5.28}$$

Equation of motion

Applying a set of the Lagrange equations,

$$\begin{aligned} \frac{d}{dt}\left(\frac{\partial T}{\partial \dot{a}_1}\right) - \frac{\partial T}{\partial a_1} + \frac{\partial U}{\partial a_1} = F_1 \\ \frac{d}{dt}\left(\frac{\partial T}{\partial \dot{a}_2}\right) - \frac{\partial T}{\partial a_2} + \frac{\partial U}{\partial a_2} = F_2 \end{aligned} \tag{7.5.29}$$

results in the equation of motion as follows:

$$\mathbf{M}\ddot{\mathbf{a}} + \mathbf{K}\mathbf{a} = \mathbf{F} \tag{7.5.30}$$

For free vibration ($\mathbf{F} = 0$),

$$\mathbf{a} = \boldsymbol{\varphi} e^{\pm i\omega t} \tag{7.5.31}$$

where $\boldsymbol{\varphi}$ is the time-independent part of $\mathbf{a}$. Then

$$(\mathbf{K} - \omega^2\mathbf{M})\boldsymbol{\varphi} = 0 \rightarrow \mathbf{K}\boldsymbol{\varphi} = \omega^2\mathbf{M}\boldsymbol{\varphi} \tag{7.5.32}$$

After carrying out an eigenvalue analysis to determine eigenvalues (thus natural frequencies) and eigenvectors, the natural modes are determined as follows:

$$w = \mathbf{N}\mathbf{a} = \mathbf{N}\boldsymbol{\varphi} e^{\pm i\omega t} = \overline{w} e^{\pm i\omega t} \tag{7.5.33}$$

and

$$\overline{w} = \mathbf{N}\boldsymbol{\varphi} \tag{7.5.34}$$

is the time-independent part of w. For the k-th mode with ω_k and $\boldsymbol{\varphi}_k$, one can use equation (7.5.34) to determine natural mode $\overline{w}_k$.

For a beam of uniform cross-section, the two-term approximation results in

$$\omega_1 = 3.5327\sqrt{\frac{EI_y}{mL^4}}, \quad \omega_2 = 33.807\sqrt{\frac{EI_y}{mL^4}} \tag{7.5.35}$$

Comparing the two natural frequencies in equation (7.5.35) with the exact values in equation (7.4.45), we observe that the first natural frequency is quite close to the exact value while the second natural frequency is not as accurate. For improved accuaracy, it is necessary to add more terms in the assumed mode. Eigenvalue analysis also produces two eignvectors as follows:

$$\varphi_1 = \begin{Bmatrix} 1 \\ -0.3837 \end{Bmatrix}, \quad \varphi_2 = \begin{Bmatrix} -0.8221 \\ 1 \end{Bmatrix} \tag{7.5.36}$$

Then from equation (7.5.34), one can obtain the two natural modes as

$$\overline{w}_1 = \mathbf{N}\varphi_1, \quad \overline{w}_2 = \mathbf{N}\varphi_2 \tag{7.5.37}$$

For plotting, each of the natural modes can be scaled such that the maximum value is equal to unity at $s = 1$ (or $x = L$) and compared with the exact natural mode in equation (7.4.50).

Chapter 7 Problem Sets

7.1 A slender body of uniform cross-section is fixed at $x = 0$ and connected to a linear spring of constant k at $x = L$. Find the natural frequencies and modes of longitudinal vibration. The boundary conditions are as follows:

$$u = 0 \text{ at } x = 0, \qquad F\left(= EA\frac{\partial u}{\partial x}\right) = -ku \text{ at } x = L$$

7.2 A slender body of uniform cross-section is fixed at $x = 0$ and free at $x = L$. A concentrated mass of M is now added at $x = L$. Find the natural frequencies and modes of longitudinal vibration. The boundary conditions are as follows:

$$u = 0 \text{ at } x = 0 \qquad F\left(= EA\frac{\partial u}{\partial x}\right) = -M\ddot{u} \text{ at } x = L$$

7.3 A slender body of uniform cross-section is fixed at $x = 0$ and free at $x = L$. The body, initially at rest, is subjected to an axial force P applied suddenly at $x = L$ and held constant. Determine the response using the modal analysis.

7.4 A taut string fixed at both ends and under tension T is given initial displacement as follows and then released.

$$w(x,0) = \frac{2x}{L} \quad \text{for } 0 \le x \le \frac{L}{2}$$

$$w(x,0) = 2\left(1 - \frac{x}{L}\right) \quad \text{for } \frac{L}{2} \le x \le L$$

(a) Sketch the given displacement.
(b) Determine the amplitude of the first three modes present in the resulting motion. What are the amplitude ratios of these modes relative the lowest mode?.
(c) Determine the transvers displacement of the string.

7.5 Repeat problem 7.4 for the initial displacement given as follows:

$$w(x,0) = \sin\frac{3\pi x}{L} \quad \text{for } 0 \le x \le L$$

7.6 For a beam undergoing free bending vibration, prove the orthogonality relations of the natural modes, using integration by parts twice.The beam is either simply supported or cantilevered.

7.7 Consider bending vibration of a slender body of uniform cross-section. The slender body is simply supported at both ends with a fixed hinge at $x = 0$ and a roller hinge at $x = L$. Accordingly, the boundary conditions are

$$w = 0,\ M_y = EI_y \frac{\partial^2 w}{\partial x^2} = 0 \rightarrow \frac{\partial^2 w}{\partial x^2} = 0$$

at both ends. Show that the natural frequencies and modes of free vibration are as follows:

$$\omega_n = n^2 \pi^2 \sqrt{\frac{EI_y}{mL^4}},\ \phi_n = \sin\frac{n\pi x}{L}$$

where integer $n = 1, 2, \cdots\cdots$ is the mode number.

7.8 Consider bending vibration of a slender body of uniform cross-section. The slender body is unconstrained at both ends. Accordingly, the boundary conditions are

$$M_y = -EI_y \frac{\partial^2 w}{\partial x^2} = 0 \rightarrow \frac{\partial^2 w}{\partial x^2} = 0$$

$$V_z = \frac{\partial M_y}{\partial x} = \frac{\partial}{\partial x}\left(-EI_y \frac{\partial^2 w}{\partial x^2}\right) = 0 \rightarrow \frac{\partial^3 w}{\partial x^3} = 0$$

at both $x = 0$ and $x = L$. Determine the natural frequencies and modes of free vibration.

7.9 In order to appreciate effectiveness of the assume mode method, consider a cantilevered beam of uniform cross-section.

(a) Determine natural frequencies and modes for the three-term approximation chosen as follows.

$$w = a_1 s^2 + a_2 s^3 + a_3 s^4$$

where $s = x / L$.

(b) Compare with the exact solutions and the two-term approximation solutions described in the text.

7.10 For a simply supported beam of uniform cross-section, one may consider using the two displacement fieldsassumed as follows:

(1) $w = a_1 \sin \pi s + a_2 \sin 2\pi s + a_3 \sin 3\pi s$

(2) $w = a_1 s(1-s) + a_2 s^2(1-s) + a_3 s(1-s)^2$

where $s = x/L$.

(a) Confirm that each assumed displacement field satisfies geometric boundary conditions.

(b) Determine the natural frequencies and modes for each assumed mode, and compare with the exact solutions.

7.11 Consider a cantilever beam clamped at $x = 0$ and free at $x = L$. The beam is of variable cross-section with m and EI_y given as follows:

$$m = m_0\left(1 - \frac{x}{2L}\right),\ EI_y = EI_0\left(1 - \frac{x}{2L}\right)^3$$

where m_0, E and I_0 are given constant values.

(a) Determine the natural frequencies and modes using a two-term approximation with $w = a_1 s^2 + a_2 s^3$ where $s = x/L$.

(b) Determine the natural frequencies and modes using a three-term approximation with $w = a_1 s^2 + a_2 s^3 + a_3 s^4$.

8 FINITE ELEMENT MODELING

For structures of complicated shape, the finite element method can be used to construct an analytical model of a finite number of degrees of freedom with a mass matrix, a stiffness matrix and a load vector. Then, the techniques described in the previous chapters can be used to conduct free vibration analysis (to determine natural frequencies and natural modes through eigenvalue analysis) and forced vibration analysis. In this chapter, we will consider finite element modeling of slender structures undergoing longitudinal, torsional and bending motions. These exercises will help us appreciate the power of the finite element method.

There are various ways of constructing a finite element model. For structural systems, one may use the "virtual work" principle via the concept of "virtual displacement". However, in this chapter, we will utilize the Lagrange equation approach introduced in a previous chapter. The reader who is familiar with the concept of virtual displacement may consider infinitesimally incremental displacement introduced in this chapter as a virtual displacement. Specific topics covered are as follows:

8.1 Longitudinal vibration of a slender body
8.2 Finite element modeling of longitudinal vibration of a slender body
8.3 Torsional vibration of a slender body
8.4 Bending vibration of a slender body
8.5 Bending vibration under axial force.

8.1 Longitudinal vibration of a slender body

Consider a slender body undergoing vibration in the longitudinal direction as shown below.

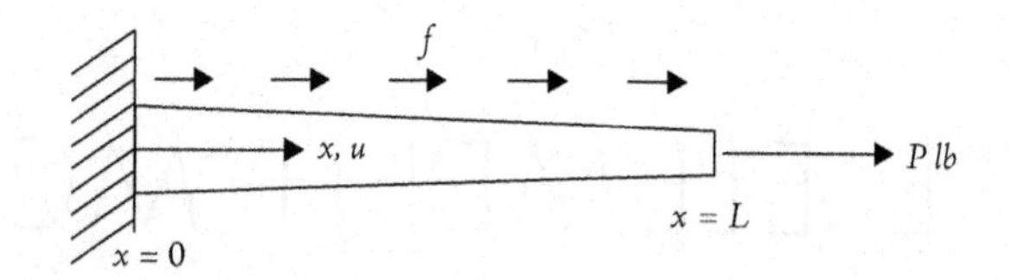

Figure 8.1 Slender body undergoing longitudinal vibration

$f(x,t)$: applied force per unit length
$P(t)$: force applied at $x = L$
$u(x,t)$: axial or longitudinal displacement

Kinetic energy:

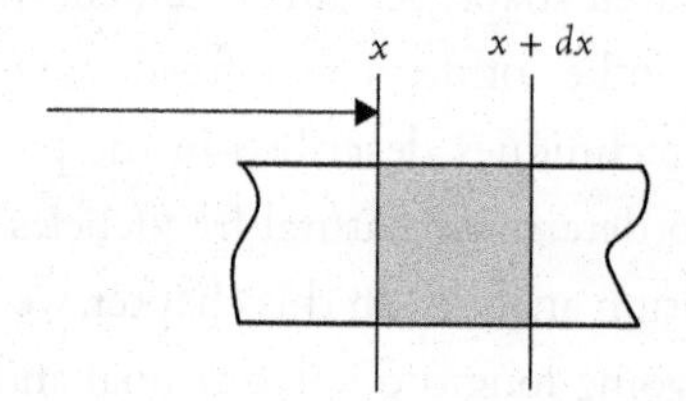

The kinetic energy of the shaded portion is

$$dT = \frac{1}{2}(mdx)\dot{u}^2$$

where $m(x)$: mass per unit length
mdx : mass of the shaded portion
$\dot{u}(x,t)$: axial velocity of the shaded mass

For the entire body,

$$T = \int dT = \frac{1}{2}\int_{x=0}^{x=L} \dot{u}^2 m dx \tag{8.1.1}$$

Strain energy:

One can show that the strain energy is expressed as

$$U = \frac{1}{2}\int_{x=0}^{x=L} EA\left(\frac{\partial u}{\partial x}\right)^2 dx \tag{8.1.2}$$

where E : Young's modulus and $A(x)$: cross-sectional area

Incremental work done:

The incremental work δW done by f and P as they undergo infinitesimally incremental displacement of δu $(\rightarrow 0)$ is expressed as

$$\delta W = \int_{x=0}^{x=L} \delta u f dx + (P\delta u)_{x=L} \tag{8.1.3}$$

Note:
δu is for the change in state while dx is for the change in space.

8.1.1 Construction of a SDOF model

To construct a SDOF model for a slender body fixed at $x=0$, one may assume that axial displacement varies linearly along the body such that

$$u = \frac{x}{L} q = sq \tag{8.1.4}$$

where

$$s = \frac{x}{L} \tag{8.1.5}$$

Note:
$u=0$ at $x=0$, and q is the tip displacement or degree of freedom (DOF).

Placing equation (8.1.4) into equation (8.1.1), the kinetic energy can be expressed as

$$T = \frac{1}{2}\int_{x=0}^{x=L} \dot{u}^2 m dx = \frac{1}{2}\int_{s=0}^{s=1} (s\dot{q})^2 mL ds = \frac{1}{2}\dot{q}^2\left(L\int_{s=0}^{s=1} s^2 m ds\right) = \frac{1}{2}M\dot{q}^2 \tag{8.1.6}$$

where

$$M = L\int_{s=0}^{s=1} s^2 m ds : \text{effective mass} \tag{8.1.7}$$

For constant m,

$$M = \frac{mL}{3} \tag{8.1.8}$$

With the assumed displacement in equation (8.1.4), the strain energy can be expressed as follows:

$$\begin{aligned} U &= \frac{1}{2}\int_{x=0}^{x=L} EA\left(\frac{\partial u}{\partial x}\right)^2 dx = \frac{1}{2}\int_{s=0}^{s=1} EA\left(\frac{\partial u}{\partial s}\frac{ds}{dx}\right)^2 L ds \\ &= \frac{1}{2}\int_{s=0}^{s=1} EA\left(\frac{1}{L}q\right)^2 L ds = \frac{1}{2}q^2\left(\frac{E}{L}\int_{s=0}^{s=1} A ds\right) = \frac{1}{2}Kq^2 \end{aligned} \tag{8.1.9}$$

where $$K=\frac{E}{L}\int_{s=0}^{s=1} A\,ds : \text{effective stiffness or spring constant} \tag{8.1.10}$$

For constant EA, $$K=\frac{EA}{L} \tag{8.1.11}$$

The equation of motion is

$$M\ddot{q}+Kq=F \tag{8.1.12}$$

To determine F, let's introduce the assumed displacement in equation (8.1.4) into equation (8.1.3),

$$\delta W=\int_{s=0}^{s=1}(s\delta q)fL\,ds+P\delta q=\delta q\left(P+L\int_{s=0}^{s=1} sfds\right)=\delta qF \tag{8.1.13}$$

where $$F=P+L\int_{s=0}^{s=1} sfds : \text{applied force corresponding to } q \tag{8.1.14}$$

For free vibration, $\omega=\sqrt{\frac{K}{M}}$: natural frequency (8.1.15)

For constant m and A, $\omega=\sqrt{\frac{3EA}{mL^2}}\simeq 1.732\sqrt{\frac{EA}{mL^2}}$ (8.1.16)

8.1.2 Flying slender body undergoing longitudinal motion: A two-DOF model

Consider a slender body unconstrained at both ends. The body is now modeled as a system with two degrees of freedom as shown below:

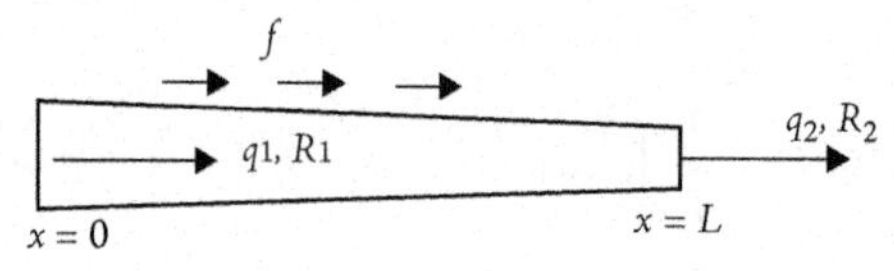

Figure 8.2 Two-DOF model of a slender body undergoing longitudinal vibration

q_1 : displacement or DOF at $x=0$
q_2 : displacement or DOF at $x=L$
R_1 : force applied at $x=0$
R_2 : force applied at $x=L$
f : applied force per unit length

Assumed displacement:

Assuming that axial displacement varies linearly along the body, the displacement u can be expressed as

$$u=a_1+a_2 s \tag{8.1.17}$$

The coefficients a_1 and a_2 can be related to displacements q_1 and q_2 as follows:
At $x=0$ or $s=0$, $u=q_1$ and from equation (8.1.17),

$$q_1 = a_1 \quad \rightarrow \quad a_1 = q_1 \tag{8.1.18}$$

At $x=L$ or $s=1$, $u=q_2$ and from equations (8.1.17) and (8.1.18),

$$q_2 = a_1 + a_2 = q_1 + a_2 \quad \rightarrow \quad a_2 = q_2 - q_1 \tag{8.1.19}$$

Substituting equations (8.1.18) and (8.1.19) into equation (8.1.17), and rearranging

$$u = (1-s)q_1 + sq_2 = \mathrm{N}_1 q_1 + \mathrm{N}_2 q_2 \tag{8.1.20}$$

where

$$\mathrm{N}_1 = 1-s, \quad \mathrm{N}_2 = s \tag{8.1.21}$$

Construction of the mass matrix:

Kinetic energy of the body is

$$T = \frac{1}{2}\int_{x=0}^{x=L} \dot{u}^2 m\,dx \tag{8.1.22}$$

From equation (8.1.20),

$$\dot{u} = \mathrm{N}_1 \dot{q}_1 + \mathrm{N}_2 \dot{q}_2 \tag{8.1.23}$$

Placing equation (8.1.23) into equation (8.1.22),

$$\begin{aligned} T &= \frac{1}{2}\int_{x=0}^{x=L} \left(\mathrm{N}_1\dot{q}_1 + \mathrm{N}_2\dot{q}_2\right)^2 m\,dx = \frac{1}{2}\int_{s=0}^{s=1}\left(\mathrm{N}_1^2\dot{q}_1^2 + 2\mathrm{N}_1\mathrm{N}_2\dot{q}_1\dot{q}_2 + \mathrm{N}_2^2\dot{q}_2^2\right) mL\,ds \\ &= \frac{1}{2}\dot{q}_1^2 L\int_{s=0}^{s=1} \mathrm{N}_1^2 m\,ds + \dot{q}_1\dot{q}_2 L\int_{s=0}^{s=1} \mathrm{N}_1\mathrm{N}_2 m\,ds + \frac{1}{2}\dot{q}_2^2 L\int_{s=0}^{s=1} \mathrm{N}_2^2 m\,ds = \frac{1}{2}a\dot{q}_1^2 + b\dot{q}_1\dot{q}_2 + \frac{1}{2}c\dot{q}_2^2 \end{aligned} \tag{8.1.24}$$

where

$$a = L\int_{s=0}^{s=1} \mathrm{N}_1^2 m\,ds, \quad b = L\int_{s=0}^{s=1} \mathrm{N}_1\mathrm{N}_2 m\,ds, \quad c = L\int_{s=0}^{s=1} \mathrm{N}_2^2 m\,ds \tag{8.1.25}$$

Note:

For constant m, $a = \dfrac{mL}{3}$, $b = \dfrac{mL}{6}$, $c = \dfrac{mL}{3}$ (8.1.26)

Construction of the stiffness matrix:

The strain energy of the body is

$$U = \frac{1}{2}\int_{x=0}^{x=L} \mathrm{EA}\left(\frac{\partial u}{\partial x}\right)^2 dx \tag{8.1.27}$$

From equation (8.1.20),

$$\frac{\partial u}{\partial x} = \frac{\partial u}{\partial s}\frac{ds}{dx} = (-q_1 + q_2)\frac{1}{L} \tag{8.1.28}$$

Placing equation (8.1.28) into equation (8.1.27),

$$\begin{aligned} U &= \frac{1}{2}\int_{x=0}^{x=L} EA\left(\frac{\partial u}{\partial x}\right)^2 dx = \frac{1}{2}\int_{s=0}^{s=1} \frac{EA}{L^2}(q_2 - q_1)^2 L\, ds \\ &= \frac{1}{2}(q_2 - q_1)^2\left(\frac{E}{L}\int_{s=0}^{s=1} A\, ds\right) = \frac{1}{2}K(q_2 - q_1)^2 \end{aligned} \tag{8.1.29}$$

where

$$K = \frac{E}{L}\int_{s=0}^{s=1} A\, ds \tag{8.1.30}$$

Note:

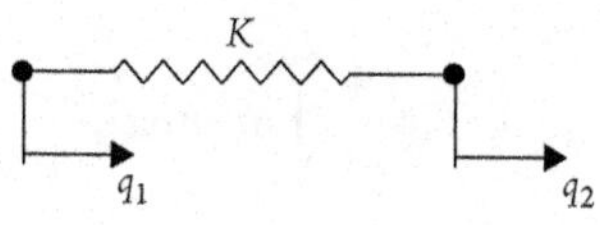

Figure 8.3 Spring analogy of the two-DOF model

For the spring shown in the sketch,

$$U = \frac{1}{2}K(q_2 - q_1)^2 \tag{8.1.31}$$

Comparing equation (8.1.31) with equation (8.1.30),

$$K = \frac{E}{L}\int_{s=0}^{s=1} A\, ds : \text{effective spring constant of the slender body} \tag{8.1.32}$$

For constant EA, $K = \dfrac{EA}{L}$

Construction of load vector:

For the slender body in Figure 8.2, the incremental work done by f, R_1, R_2 is expressed as

$$\delta W = \int_{x=0}^{x=L} \delta u f\, dx + R_1 \delta q_1 + R_2 \delta q_2 \tag{8.1.33}$$

Introducing the assumed displacement in equation(8.1.20) into the first term in equation (8.1.33),

$$\begin{aligned} \int_{x=0}^{x=L} \delta u f\, dx &= \int_{x=0}^{s=1} \left[(1-s)\delta q_1 + s\delta q_2\right] fL\, ds \\ &= \delta q_1 L \int_{s=0}^{s=1} (1-s) f\, ds + \delta q_2 L \int_{s=0}^{s=1} sf\, ds = \delta q_1 A_1 + \delta q_2 A_2 \end{aligned} \tag{8.1.34}$$

where $$A_1 = L\int_{s=0}^{s=1}(1-s)f ds, \quad A_2 = L\int_{s=0}^{s=1} sf ds \tag{8.1.35}$$

Then $$\delta W = \delta q_1(A_1 + R_1) + \delta q_2(A_2 + R_2) = \delta q_1 F_1 + \delta q_2 F_2 \tag{8.1.36}$$

where $$F_1 = A_1 + R_1, \quad F_2 = A_2 + R_2 \tag{8.1.37}$$

Note:

For constant $f = c$,

$$A_1 = cL\int_{s=0}^{s=1}(1-s)ds = \frac{cL}{2}, \quad A_2 = cL\int_{s=0}^{s=1} s ds = \frac{cL}{2} \tag{8.1.38}$$

Equilibrium equation

The Lagrange equations are

$$\begin{aligned} \frac{d}{dt}\left(\frac{\partial T}{\partial \dot{q}_1}\right) - \frac{\partial T}{\partial q_1} + \frac{\partial U}{\partial q_1} = F_1 \\ \frac{d}{dt}\left(\frac{\partial T}{\partial \dot{q}_2}\right) - \frac{\partial T}{\partial q_2} + \frac{\partial U}{\partial q_2} = F_2 \end{aligned} \tag{8.1.39}$$

Applying the Lagrange equation,

$$\begin{aligned} a\ddot{q}_1 + b\ddot{q}_2 + K(q_1 - q_2) = F_1 \\ b\ddot{q}_1 + c\ddot{q}_2 + K(q_2 - q_1) = F_2 \end{aligned} \tag{8.1.40}$$

In matrix form,

$$\begin{bmatrix} a & b \\ b & c \end{bmatrix}\begin{Bmatrix} \ddot{q}_1 \\ \ddot{q}_2 \end{Bmatrix} + K\begin{bmatrix} 1 & -1 \\ -1 & 1 \end{bmatrix}\begin{Bmatrix} q_1 \\ q_2 \end{Bmatrix} = \begin{Bmatrix} F_1 \\ F_2 \end{Bmatrix} \tag{8.1.41}$$

or

$$\begin{bmatrix} M_{11} & M_{12} \\ M_{21} & M_{22} \end{bmatrix}\begin{Bmatrix} \ddot{q}_1 \\ \ddot{q}_2 \end{Bmatrix} + \begin{bmatrix} K_{11} & K_{12} \\ K_{21} & K_{22} \end{bmatrix}\begin{Bmatrix} q_1 \\ q_2 \end{Bmatrix} = \begin{Bmatrix} F_1 \\ F_2 \end{Bmatrix} \tag{8.1.42}$$

where

$$\begin{bmatrix} M_{11} & M_{12} \\ M_{21} & M_{22} \end{bmatrix} = \begin{bmatrix} a & b \\ b & c \end{bmatrix} : \text{mass matrix} \tag{8.1.43}$$

$$\begin{bmatrix} K_{11} & K_{12} \\ K_{21} & K_{22} \end{bmatrix} = K\begin{bmatrix} 1 & -1 \\ -1 & 1 \end{bmatrix} : \text{stiffness matrix} \tag{8.1.44}$$

$$\begin{Bmatrix} F_1 \\ F_2 \end{Bmatrix} : \text{load vector} \tag{8.1.45}$$

8.2 Finite element modeling of longitudinal vibration of a slender body

In general, it is inadequate to assume that displacement is linear along the entire slender body. Accordingly, in the finite element modeling, the slender body is first divided into many segments called 'elements'. Then one may expect the displacement distribution within each element to be very simple. For example, as an approximation one may assume that the displacement varies linearly within each element. Each element then looks like the flying slender body model discussed in the previous section. The equation of motion for the entire structure is then constructed from the equation of motion for individual elements as follows:
For example, consider a three-element model as shown below.

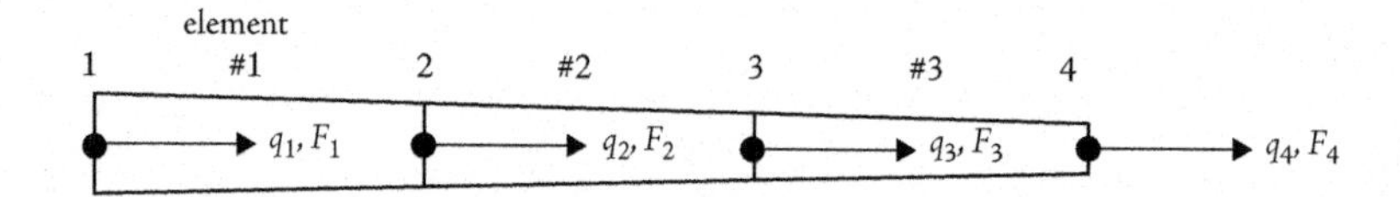

Figure 8.4 Three-element model for longitudinal vibration

$1, 2, 3, 4$: global node numbers
q_1, q_2, q_3, q_4 : global nodal displacements or DOFs
F_1, F_2, F_3, F_4 : global nodal loads

Element # *i*:

The element is a two-DOF system with one DOF placed at each of the element boundaries. For convenience, let's introduce element node and DOF numberings as shown below:

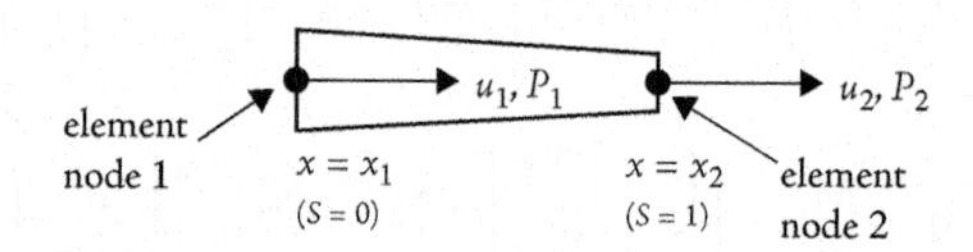

Figure 8.5 Two-node element for longitudinal vibration

u_1, u_2 : element nodal displacements or DOFs
P_1, P_2 : applied and/or reaction forces at element node 1 and 2
x_1, x_2 : element nodal coordinates
$l = x_2 - x_1$: element length

For convenience, one may introduce a non-dimensional coordinate s defined as follows:

$$s = \frac{x - x_1}{x_2 - x_1} = \frac{x - x_1}{l} \rightarrow x = x_1 + ls \tag{8.2.1}$$

such that $s=0$ at node 1 and $s=1$ at node 2. The assumed displacement is then expressed as

$$u=(1-s)u_1+su_2=N_1u_1+N_2u_2 \tag{8.2.2}$$

where

$$N_1=1-s,\quad N_2=s \tag{8.2.3}$$

One can then utilize the results for a flying slender body discussed in the previous section to construct the equation of motion for the element expressed as follows:

$$\begin{bmatrix} m_{11}^i & m_{12}^i \\ m_{21}^i & m_{22}^i \end{bmatrix}\begin{Bmatrix} \ddot{u}_1 \\ \ddot{u}_2 \end{Bmatrix}_i+\begin{bmatrix} k_{11}^i & k_{12}^i \\ k_{21}^i & k_{22}^i \end{bmatrix}\begin{Bmatrix} u_1 \\ u_2 \end{Bmatrix}_i=\begin{Bmatrix} P_1 \\ P_2 \end{Bmatrix}_i \tag{8.2.4}$$

Superscripts or subscripts i in equation (8.2.4) indicate the element number. Note that

$$\begin{bmatrix} m_{11}^i & m_{12}^i \\ m_{21}^i & m_{22}^i \end{bmatrix}=\begin{bmatrix} a^{(i)} & b^{(i)} \\ b^{(i)} & c^{(i)} \end{bmatrix}\text{: element mass matrix} \tag{8.2.5}$$

where
$$a^{(i)}=l\int_{s=0}^{s=1} N_1^2 m\,ds,\quad b^{(i)}=l\int_{s=0}^{s=1} N_1N_2 m\,ds,\quad c^{(i)}=l\int_{s=0}^{s=1} N_2^2 m\,ds \tag{8.2.6}$$

and

$$\begin{bmatrix} k_{11}^i & k_{12}^i \\ k_{21}^i & k_{22}^i \end{bmatrix}=K^{(i)}\begin{bmatrix} 1 & -1 \\ -1 & 1 \end{bmatrix}\text{: element stiffness matrix} \tag{8.2.7}$$

where
$$K^{(i)}=\frac{E}{l}\int_{s=0}^{s=1} A\,ds \tag{8.2.8}$$

Recall that for constant m,

$$\begin{bmatrix} m_{11}^i & m_{12}^i \\ m_{21}^i & m_{22}^i \end{bmatrix}=\frac{ml}{6}\begin{bmatrix} 2 & 1 \\ 1 & 2 \end{bmatrix} \tag{8.2.9}$$

and for constant EA, $K^{(i)}=\dfrac{EA}{l}$ (8.2.10)

For the entire structure, the equation of motion can be expressed as

$$\mathbf{M}\ddot{\mathbf{q}}+\mathbf{K}\mathbf{q}=\mathbf{F} \tag{8.2.11}$$

For the three-element model,

$$\mathbf{q} = \begin{Bmatrix} q_1 \\ q_2 \\ q_3 \\ q_4 \end{Bmatrix} : \text{global DOF vector, } \mathbf{F} = \begin{Bmatrix} F_1 \\ F_2 \\ F_3 \\ F_4 \end{Bmatrix} : \text{global load vector} \tag{8.2.12}$$

and the equation of motion is

$$\begin{bmatrix} M_{11} & M_{12} & M_{13} & M_{14} \\ M_{21} & M_{22} & M_{23} & M_{24} \\ M_{31} & M_{32} & M_{33} & M_{34} \\ M_{41} & M_{42} & M_{43} & M_{44} \end{bmatrix} \begin{Bmatrix} \ddot{q}_1 \\ \ddot{q}_2 \\ \ddot{q}_3 \\ \ddot{q}_4 \end{Bmatrix} + \begin{bmatrix} K_{11} & K_{12} & K_{13} & K_{14} \\ K_{21} & K_{22} & K_{23} & K_{24} \\ K_{31} & K_{32} & K_{33} & K_{34} \\ K_{41} & K_{42} & K_{43} & K_{44} \end{bmatrix} \begin{Bmatrix} q_1 \\ q_2 \\ q_3 \\ q_4 \end{Bmatrix} = \begin{Bmatrix} F_1 \\ F_2 \\ F_3 \\ F_4 \end{Bmatrix} \tag{8.2.13}$$

The equation of motion for the entire structure can be constructed from the equation of motion for individual elements. This can be done by noting that, for the entire body, the incremental work done can be expressed as

$$\delta W = \lfloor \delta q_1 \quad \delta q_2 \quad \delta q_3 \quad \delta q_4 \rfloor \begin{Bmatrix} F_1 \\ F_2 \\ F_3 \\ F_4 \end{Bmatrix} \tag{8.2.14}$$

and using the relationship between element DOF and global DOF as follows.

Assembly of global mass matrix, stiffness matrix and load vector.

For element i, the equation of motion can be rewritten as

$$\begin{Bmatrix} P_1 \\ P_2 \end{Bmatrix}_i = \begin{bmatrix} m_{11}^i & m_{12}^i \\ m_{21}^i & m_{22}^i \end{bmatrix} \begin{Bmatrix} \ddot{u}_1 \\ \ddot{u}_2 \end{Bmatrix}_i + \begin{bmatrix} k_{11}^i & k_{12}^i \\ k_{21}^i & k_{22}^i \end{bmatrix} \begin{Bmatrix} u_1 \\ u_2 \end{Bmatrix}_i \tag{8.2.15}$$

and the incremental work done is

$$\delta W_i = \lfloor \delta u_1 \quad \delta u_2 \rfloor_i \begin{Bmatrix} P_1 \\ P_2 \end{Bmatrix}_i \tag{8.2.16}$$

and

$$\delta W = \sum_{i=1}^{i=3} \delta W_i \tag{8.2.17}$$

For element 1,

$$\begin{Bmatrix} P_1 \\ P_2 \end{Bmatrix}_1 = \begin{bmatrix} m_{11}^1 & m_{12}^1 \\ m_{21}^1 & m_{22}^1 \end{bmatrix} \begin{Bmatrix} \ddot{u}_1 \\ \ddot{u}_2 \end{Bmatrix}_1 + \begin{bmatrix} k_{11}^1 & k_{12}^1 \\ k_{21}^1 & k_{22}^1 \end{bmatrix} \begin{Bmatrix} u_1 \\ u_2 \end{Bmatrix}_1 \tag{8.2.18}$$

For element 1, $u_1 = q_1$, $u_2 = q_2$. Then P_1 sums to F_1 and P_2 sums to F_2. Accordingly, one can express equation (8.2.18) in an expanded form including all nodal loads and nodal displacements as follows:

$$\begin{Bmatrix} P_1 \\ P_2 \\ 0 \\ 0 \end{Bmatrix}_1 = \begin{bmatrix} m_{11}^1 & m_{12}^1 & 0 & 0 \\ m_{21}^1 & m_{22}^1 & 0 & 0 \\ 0 & 0 & 0 & 0 \\ 0 & 0 & 0 & 0 \end{bmatrix} \begin{Bmatrix} \ddot{q}_1 \\ \ddot{q}_2 \\ \ddot{q}_3 \\ \ddot{q}_4 \end{Bmatrix} + \begin{bmatrix} k_{11}^1 & k_{12}^1 & 0 & 0 \\ k_{21}^1 & k_{22}^1 & 0 & 0 \\ 0 & 0 & 0 & 0 \\ 0 & 0 & 0 & 0 \end{bmatrix} \begin{Bmatrix} q_1 \\ q_2 \\ q_3 \\ q_4 \end{Bmatrix} \tag{8.2.19}$$

For element 2,

$$\begin{Bmatrix} P_1 \\ P_2 \end{Bmatrix}_2 = \begin{bmatrix} m_{11}^2 & m_{12}^2 \\ m_{21}^2 & m_{22}^2 \end{bmatrix} \begin{Bmatrix} \ddot{u}_1 \\ \ddot{u}_2 \end{Bmatrix}_2 + \begin{bmatrix} k_{11}^2 & k_{12}^2 \\ k_{21}^2 & k_{22}^2 \end{bmatrix} \begin{Bmatrix} u_1 \\ u_2 \end{Bmatrix}_2 \tag{8.2.20}$$

For element 2, $u_1 = q_2$, $u_2 = q_3$. Then P_1 sums to F_2 and P_2 sums to F_3. Accordingly, equation (8.2.20) can be expressed in an expanded form including all nodal loads and nodal displacements as follows:

$$\begin{Bmatrix} 0 \\ P_1 \\ P_2 \\ 0 \end{Bmatrix}_2 = \begin{bmatrix} 0 & 0 & 0 & 0 \\ 0 & m_{11}^2 & m_{12}^2 & 0 \\ 0 & m_{21}^2 & m_{22}^2 & 0 \\ 0 & 0 & 0 & 0 \end{bmatrix} \begin{Bmatrix} \ddot{q}_1 \\ \ddot{q}_2 \\ \ddot{q}_3 \\ \ddot{q}_4 \end{Bmatrix} + \begin{bmatrix} 0 & 0 & 0 & 0 \\ 0 & k_{11}^2 & k_{12}^2 & 0 \\ 0 & k_{21}^2 & k_{22}^2 & 0 \\ 0 & 0 & 0 & 0 \end{bmatrix} \begin{Bmatrix} q_1 \\ q_2 \\ q_3 \\ q_4 \end{Bmatrix} \tag{8.2.21}$$

For element 3,

$$\begin{Bmatrix} P_1 \\ P_2 \end{Bmatrix}_3 = \begin{bmatrix} m_{11}^3 & m_{12}^3 \\ m_{21}^3 & m_{22}^3 \end{bmatrix} \begin{Bmatrix} \ddot{u}_1 \\ \ddot{u}_2 \end{Bmatrix}_3 + \begin{bmatrix} k_{11}^3 & k_{12}^3 \\ k_{21}^3 & k_{22}^3 \end{bmatrix} \begin{Bmatrix} u_1 \\ u_2 \end{Bmatrix}_3 \tag{8.2.22}$$

For element 3, $u_1 = q_3$, $u_2 = q_4$. Then P_1 sums to F_3 and P_2 sums to F_4. Accordingly, equation (8.2.22) can be expressed in an expanded form including all nodal loads and nodal displacements as follows:

$$\begin{Bmatrix} 0 \\ 0 \\ P_1 \\ P_2 \end{Bmatrix}_3 = \begin{bmatrix} 0 & 0 & 0 & 0 \\ 0 & 0 & 0 & 0 \\ 0 & 0 & m_{11}^3 & m_{12}^3 \\ 0 & 0 & m_{21}^3 & m_{22}^3 \end{bmatrix} \begin{Bmatrix} \ddot{q}_1 \\ \ddot{q}_2 \\ \ddot{q}_3 \\ \ddot{q}_4 \end{Bmatrix} + \begin{bmatrix} 0 & 0 & 0 & 0 \\ 0 & 0 & 0 & 0 \\ 0 & 0 & k_{11}^3 & k_{12}^3 \\ 0 & 0 & k_{21}^3 & k_{22}^3 \end{bmatrix} \begin{Bmatrix} q_1 \\ q_2 \\ q_3 \\ q_4 \end{Bmatrix} \tag{8.2.23}$$

For the entire structure,

$$\begin{Bmatrix} F_1 \\ F_2 \\ F_3 \\ F_4 \end{Bmatrix} = \begin{Bmatrix} P_1 \\ P_2 \\ 0 \\ 0 \end{Bmatrix}_1 + \begin{Bmatrix} 0 \\ P_1 \\ P_2 \\ 0 \end{Bmatrix}_2 + \begin{Bmatrix} 0 \\ 0 \\ P_1 \\ P_2 \end{Bmatrix}_3 \tag{8.2.24}$$

Summing the right hand sides of equations (8.2.19), (8.2.21) and (8.2.23),

$$\begin{Bmatrix} F_1 \\ F_2 \\ F_3 \\ F_4 \end{Bmatrix} = \begin{bmatrix} m_{11}^1 & m_{12}^1 & 0 & 0 \\ m_{21}^1 & m_{22}^1 + m_{11}^2 & m_{12}^2 & 0 \\ 0 & m_{21}^2 & m_{22}^2 + m_{11}^3 & m_{12}^3 \\ 0 & 0 & m_{21}^3 & m_{22}^3 \end{bmatrix} \begin{Bmatrix} \ddot{q}_1 \\ \ddot{q}_2 \\ \ddot{q}_3 \\ \ddot{q}_4 \end{Bmatrix} + \begin{bmatrix} k_{11}^1 & k_{12}^1 & 0 & 0 \\ k_{21}^1 & k_{22}^1 + k_{11}^2 & k_{12}^2 & 0 \\ 0 & k_{21}^2 & k_{22}^2 + k_{11}^3 & k_{12}^3 \\ 0 & 0 & k_{21}^3 & k_{22}^3 \end{bmatrix} \begin{Bmatrix} q_1 \\ q_2 \\ q_3 \\ q_4 \end{Bmatrix} \tag{8.2.25}$$

Note that, when the force vector is summed, reaction forces disappear at the nodes at which elements are joined. Comparing the above equation with equation (8.2.13),

$$\mathbf{M} = \begin{bmatrix} m_{11}^1 & m_{12}^1 & 0 & 0 \\ m_{21}^1 & m_{22}^1 + m_{11}^2 & m_{12}^2 & 0 \\ 0 & m_{21}^2 & m_{22}^2 + m_{11}^3 & m_{12}^3 \\ 0 & 0 & m_{21}^3 & m_{22}^3 \end{bmatrix} = \begin{bmatrix} M_{11} & M_{12} & M_{13} & M_{14} \\ M_{21} & M_{22} & M_{23} & M_{24} \\ M_{31} & M_{32} & M_{33} & M_{34} \\ M_{41} & M_{42} & M_{43} & M_{44} \end{bmatrix} \tag{8.2.26}$$

is the 4×4 global mass matrix,

$$\mathbf{K} = \begin{bmatrix} k_{11}^1 & k_{12}^1 & 0 & 0 \\ k_{21}^1 & k_{22}^1 + k_{11}^2 & k_{12}^2 & 0 \\ 0 & k_{21}^2 & k_{22}^2 + k_{11}^3 & k_{12}^3 \\ 0 & 0 & k_{21}^3 & k_{22}^3 \end{bmatrix} = \begin{bmatrix} K_{11} & K_{12} & K_{13} & K_{14} \\ K_{21} & K_{22} & K_{23} & K_{24} \\ K_{31} & K_{32} & K_{33} & K_{34} \\ K_{41} & K_{42} & K_{43} & K_{44} \end{bmatrix} \tag{8.2.27}$$

is the 4×4 global stiffness matrix.

Note:

1) The process of constructing the global mass matrix **M**, the global stiffness matrix **K** and the global load vector **F** is called '**assembly**' of **M**, **K** and **F**.
2) The global mass matrix and the global stiffness matrix are assembled in a similar manner.

Equation of motion in reduced form

Suppose the left end of the slender body is fixed against axial motion, then applying $q_1 = 0$ and $\ddot{q}_1 = 0$ conditions to the equation of motion,

$$\begin{bmatrix} M_{12} & M_{13} & M_{14} \\ M_{22} & M_{23} & M_{24} \\ M_{32} & M_{33} & M_{34} \\ M_{42} & M_{43} & M_{44} \end{bmatrix} \begin{Bmatrix} \ddot{q}_2 \\ \ddot{q}_3 \\ \ddot{q}_4 \end{Bmatrix} + \begin{bmatrix} K_{12} & K_{13} & K_{14} \\ K_{22} & K_{23} & K_{24} \\ K_{32} & K_{33} & K_{34} \\ K_{42} & K_{43} & K_{44} \end{bmatrix} \begin{Bmatrix} q_2 \\ q_3 \\ q_4 \end{Bmatrix} = \begin{Bmatrix} F_1 \\ F_2 \\ F_3 \\ F_4 \end{Bmatrix} \tag{8.2.28}$$

The above matrix equation represents four equations for three unknowns. Deleting the first equation with F_1 which contains unknown reaction force at the fixed boundary, the equation of motion reduces to

$$\begin{bmatrix} M_{22} & M_{23} & M_{24} \\ M_{32} & M_{33} & M_{34} \\ M_{42} & M_{43} & M_{44} \end{bmatrix} \begin{Bmatrix} \ddot{q}_2 \\ \ddot{q}_3 \\ \ddot{q}_4 \end{Bmatrix} + \begin{bmatrix} K_{22} & K_{23} & K_{24} \\ K_{32} & K_{33} & K_{34} \\ K_{42} & K_{43} & K_{44} \end{bmatrix} \begin{Bmatrix} q_2 \\ q_3 \\ q_4 \end{Bmatrix} = \begin{Bmatrix} F_2 \\ F_3 \\ F_4 \end{Bmatrix} \tag{8.2.29}$$

Example 8.2.1: A slender body of constant m and EA is fixed at the left end as shown in the sketch. The body is modeled with three element of equal length.

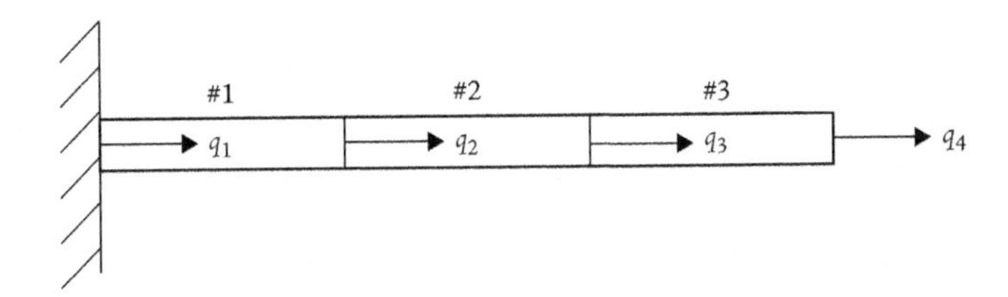

Figure 8.6 Three-element model with the left end fixed

For constant m, EA and $l = \dfrac{L}{3}$,

$$\mathbf{m}^i = \begin{bmatrix} m_{11}^i & m_{12}^i \\ m_{21}^i & m_{22}^i \end{bmatrix} = \frac{ml}{6}\begin{bmatrix} 2 & 1 \\ 1 & 2 \end{bmatrix}, \quad \mathbf{k}^i = \begin{bmatrix} k_{11}^i & k_{12}^i \\ k_{21}^i & k_{22}^i \end{bmatrix} = \frac{EA}{l}\begin{bmatrix} 1 & -1 \\ -1 & 1 \end{bmatrix} \tag{8.2.30}$$

Assembling all elements,

$$\mathbf{M} = \frac{ml}{6}\begin{bmatrix} 2 & 1 & 0 & 0 \\ 1 & 2+2 & 1 & 0 \\ 0 & 1 & 2+2 & 1 \\ 0 & 0 & 1 & 2 \end{bmatrix} = \frac{ml}{6}\begin{bmatrix} 2 & 1 & 0 & 0 \\ 1 & 4 & 1 & 0 \\ 0 & 1 & 4 & 1 \\ 0 & 0 & 1 & 2 \end{bmatrix} \tag{8.2.31}$$

$$\mathbf{K} = \frac{EA}{l}\begin{bmatrix} 1 & -1 & 0 & 0 \\ -1 & 1+1 & -1 & 0 \\ 0 & -1 & 1+1 & -1 \\ 0 & 0 & -1 & 1 \end{bmatrix} = \frac{EA}{l}\begin{bmatrix} 1 & -1 & 0 & 0 \\ -1 & 2 & -1 & 0 \\ 0 & -1 & 2 & -1 \\ 0 & 0 & -1 & 1 \end{bmatrix} \tag{8.2.32}$$

Applying $q_1 = 0$ and $\ddot{q}_1 = 0$ conditions, and deleting the equation with unknown reaction force in the load vector, the equation of motion is

$$\mathbf{M}\ddot{\mathbf{q}} + \mathbf{K}\mathbf{q} = \mathbf{F} \tag{8.2.33}$$

where

$$\mathbf{M} = \frac{ml}{6}\begin{bmatrix} 4 & 1 & 0 \\ 1 & 4 & 1 \\ 0 & 1 & 2 \end{bmatrix} = \frac{mL}{18}\begin{bmatrix} 4 & 1 & 0 \\ 1 & 4 & 1 \\ 0 & 1 & 2 \end{bmatrix} \tag{8.2.34}$$

$$\mathbf{K} = \frac{EA}{l}\begin{bmatrix} 2 & -1 & 0 \\ -1 & 2 & -1 \\ 0 & -1 & 1 \end{bmatrix} = \frac{3EA}{L}\begin{bmatrix} 2 & -1 & 0 \\ -1 & 2 & -1 \\ 0 & -1 & 1 \end{bmatrix} \tag{8.2.35}$$

$$\mathbf{F} = \begin{Bmatrix} F_2 \\ F_3 \\ F_4 \end{Bmatrix} \tag{8.2.36}$$

For free vibration ($\mathbf{F} = \mathbf{0}$), the equation of motion is

$$\mathbf{M}\ddot{\mathbf{q}} + \mathbf{K}\mathbf{q} = \mathbf{0} \tag{8.2.37}$$

A solution to equation (8.2.37) is of the following form:

$$\mathbf{q} = \boldsymbol{\varphi} e^{\pm i\omega t} \tag{8.2.38}$$

where $\boldsymbol{\varphi}$ is the time-independent part of $\mathbf{q}$. Placing equation (8.2.38) into equation (8.2.37),

$$(\mathbf{K} - \omega^2\mathbf{M})\boldsymbol{\varphi} = \mathbf{0} \tag{8.2.39}$$

or

$$\mathbf{K}\boldsymbol{\varphi} = \omega^2\mathbf{M}\boldsymbol{\varphi} \tag{8.2.40}$$

$$\rightarrow \begin{bmatrix} 2 & -1 & 0 \\ -1 & 2 & -1 \\ 0 & -1 & 1 \end{bmatrix}\begin{Bmatrix} \phi_2 \\ \phi_3 \\ \phi_4 \end{Bmatrix} = \overline{p}\left(\frac{1}{54}\right)\begin{bmatrix} 4 & 1 & 0 \\ 1 & 4 & 1 \\ 0 & 1 & 2 \end{bmatrix}\begin{Bmatrix} \phi_2 \\ \phi_3 \\ \phi_4 \end{Bmatrix} \tag{8.2.41}$$

where

$$\overline{p} = \omega^2 \frac{mL^2}{EA} \tag{8.2.42}$$

From eigenvalue analysis,

$$\overline{p}_1 = 2.5243, \ \overline{p}_2 = 27.0000, \ \overline{p}_3 = 88.8603 \tag{8.2.43}$$

$$\boldsymbol{\varphi}_1 = \begin{Bmatrix} 0.5 \\ 0.866 \\ 1 \end{Bmatrix}, \ \boldsymbol{\varphi}_2 = \begin{Bmatrix} -1 \\ 0 \\ 1 \end{Bmatrix}, \ \boldsymbol{\varphi}_3 = \begin{Bmatrix} 0.5 \\ -0.866 \\ 1 \end{Bmatrix} \tag{8.2.44}$$

Note that each eigenvector is scaled such that the largest (in magnitude) entry is equal to unity. The natural frequencies obtained by the 3-element model are as follows:

$$\omega_1 = \sqrt{p_1}\sqrt{\frac{EA}{mL^2}} = 1.5888\sqrt{\frac{EA}{mL^2}}, \quad \omega_2 = \sqrt{p_2}\sqrt{\frac{EA}{mL^2}} = 5.1962\sqrt{\frac{EA}{mL^2}}$$

$$\omega_3 = \sqrt{p_3}\sqrt{\frac{EA}{mL^2}} = 9.4266\sqrt{\frac{EA}{mL^2}} \tag{8.2.45}$$

<u>The natural modes are determined using the eigenvectors in equation (8.2.44) as follows:</u>

Recall that, for element # k, the assumed axial displacement is

$$u = N_1 u_1 + N_2 u_2 = \begin{bmatrix} N_1 & N_2 \end{bmatrix}\begin{Bmatrix} u_1 \\ u_2 \end{Bmatrix} = \mathbf{Nd} \tag{8.2.46}$$

where $N_1 = 1 - s, \quad N_2 = s$

$$\mathbf{N} = \begin{bmatrix} N_1 & N_2 \end{bmatrix}, \ \mathbf{d} = \begin{Bmatrix} u_1 \\ u_2 \end{Bmatrix} \tag{8.2.47}$$

For free vibration of the global model,

$$\mathbf{q} = \boldsymbol{\varphi} e^{\pm i\omega t} \tag{8.2.48}$$

or

$$\begin{Bmatrix} q_2 \\ q_3 \\ q_4 \end{Bmatrix} = \begin{Bmatrix} \phi_2 \\ \phi_3 \\ \phi_4 \end{Bmatrix} e^{\pm i\omega t} \tag{8.2.49}$$

Including q_1,

$$\begin{Bmatrix} q_1 = 0 \\ q_2 \\ q_3 \\ q_4 \end{Bmatrix} = \begin{Bmatrix} \phi_1 = 0 \\ \phi_2 \\ \phi_3 \\ \phi_4 \end{Bmatrix} e^{\pm i\omega t} \tag{8.2.50}$$

Then, for element #k,

$$\mathbf{d} = \boldsymbol{\varphi}^k e^{\pm i\omega t} \tag{8.2.51}$$

Note that $\boldsymbol{\varphi}^k$ for element #k can be found from equation (8.2.50). Substituting equation (8.2.51) into equation (8.2.46),

$$u = \mathbf{Nd} = \mathbf{N}\boldsymbol{\varphi}^k e^{\pm i\omega t} = \bar{u} e^{\pm i\omega t} \tag{8.2.52}$$

where

$$\bar{u} = \mathbf{N}\boldsymbol{\varphi}^k \tag{8.2.53}$$

is the time-independent part of the displacement for element #k. To determine the first natural mode, we use the first eigenvector in equation (8.2.44) expanded as

$$\boldsymbol{\varphi}_1 = \begin{Bmatrix} 0 \\ 0.5 \\ 0.866 \\ 1 \end{Bmatrix} \tag{8.2.54}$$

For element #1,

$$\bar{u} = \mathbf{N}\boldsymbol{\varphi}^1 = \begin{bmatrix} 1-s & s \end{bmatrix} \begin{Bmatrix} 0 \\ 0.5 \end{Bmatrix} = 0.5s \tag{8.2.55}$$

For element #2,

$$\bar{u} = \mathbf{N}\boldsymbol{\varphi}^2 = \begin{bmatrix} 1-s & s \end{bmatrix} \begin{Bmatrix} 0.5 \\ 0.866 \end{Bmatrix} = 0.5 + 0.366s \tag{8.2.56}$$

For element #3,

$$\bar{u} = \mathbf{N}\boldsymbol{\varphi}^3 = \begin{bmatrix} 1-s & s \end{bmatrix} \begin{Bmatrix} 0.866 \\ 1 \end{Bmatrix} = 0.866 + 0.134s \tag{8.2.57}$$

One can plot the first natural mode by combining the time-independent displacement of three elements. The second and third modes can be determined in a similar manner.

For this simple example, there exist analytical solutions for exact natural frequencies and natural modes given as follows:

$$\omega_n = (n - \frac{1}{2})\pi\sqrt{\frac{EA}{mL^2}}, \quad \phi_n(x) = \sin\left[(n - \frac{1}{2})\frac{\pi x}{L}\right] \tag{8.2.58}$$

where $n = 1, 2, \cdots$ are called "mode numbers". Exact natural frequencies for the first three modes are then as follows:

$$\omega_1 = \frac{\pi}{2}\sqrt{\frac{EA}{mL^2}} = 1.5708\sqrt{\frac{EA}{mL^2}}, \quad \omega_2 = \frac{3\pi}{2}\sqrt{\frac{EA}{mL^2}} = 4.7124\sqrt{\frac{EA}{mL^2}},$$

$$\omega_3 = \frac{5\pi}{2}\sqrt{\frac{EA}{mL^2}} = 7.8540\sqrt{\frac{EA}{mL^2}} \tag{8.2.59}$$

Corresponding exact natural modes are

$$\phi_1 = \sin\frac{\pi x}{2L}, \quad \phi_2 = \sin\frac{3\pi x}{2L}, \quad \phi_3 = \sin\frac{5\pi x}{2L} \tag{8.2.60}$$

or any constant multiple of the sine functions shown above. Figure 8.7 plots the natural modes obtained by the finite element model in comparison with the exact modes. Note that the signs of modes are chosen such that the maximum values are equal to unity at $x = L$. We observe that accuracy of the finite element solutions deteriorates as the frequency number increases and more elements are needed to improve accuracy.

(a) The 1st natural mode:

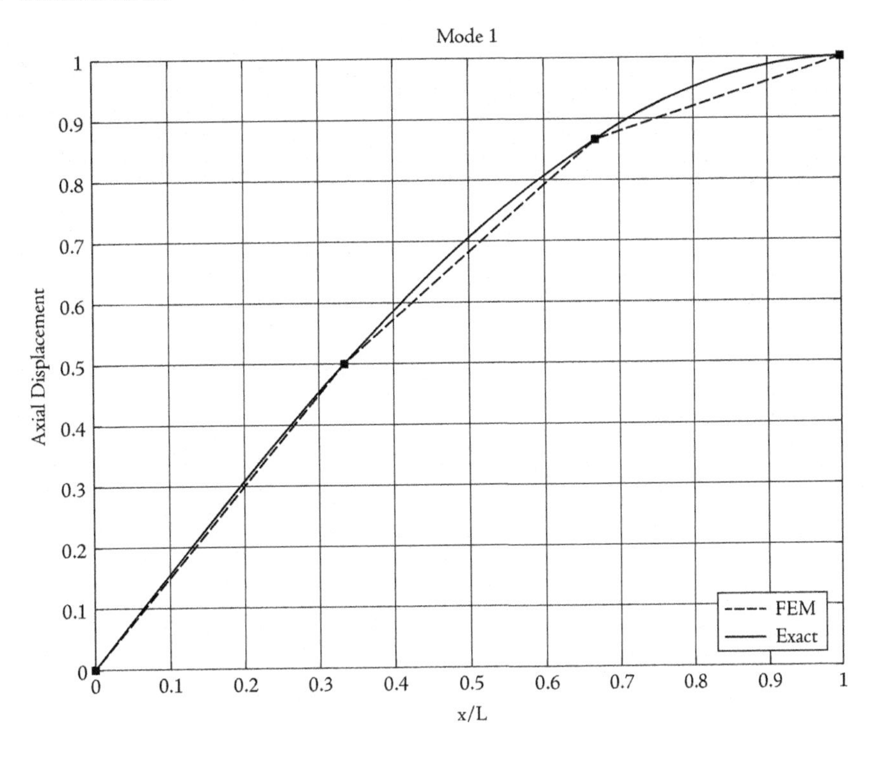

(b) The 2nd natural mode:

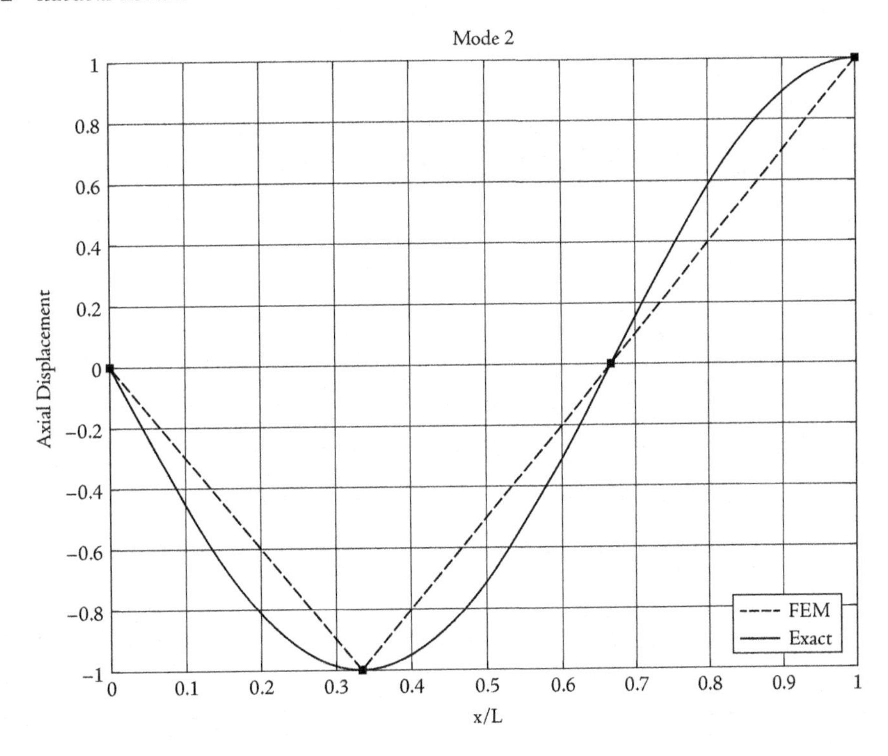

(c) The 3rd natural mode:

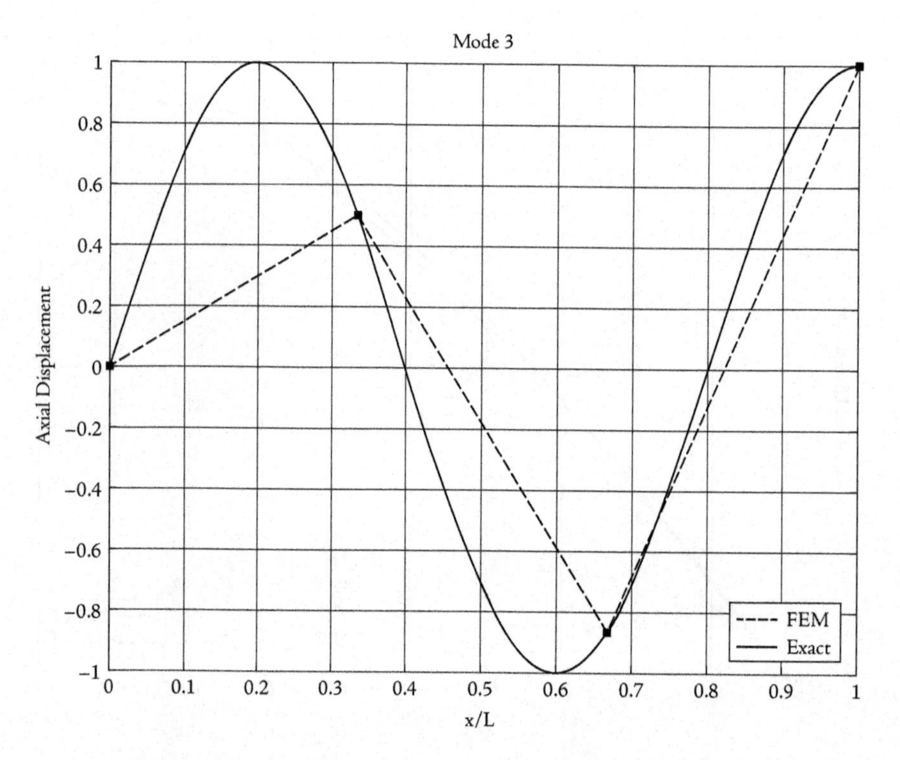

Figure 8.7 Natural modes obtained by the three-element model

8.3 Torsional vibration of a slender body

Consider a slender body under applied torques as shown in Figure 8.8.

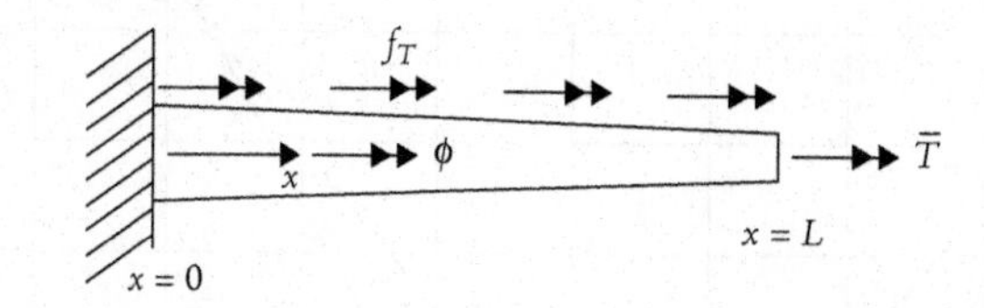

Figure 8.8 Slender body undergoing torsional motion

$f_T(x,t)$: applied torque per unit length
$\bar{T}(t)$: torque applied at the tip $x = L$
$\phi(x,t)$: twist angle

Kinetic energy:

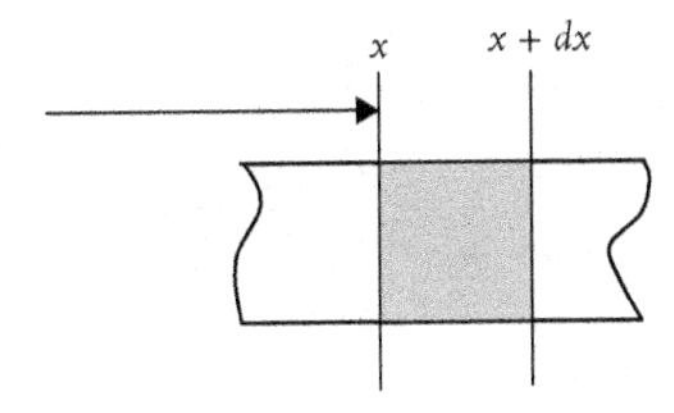

The kinetic energy of the shaded portion is

$$dT = \frac{1}{2}(Idx)\dot{\phi}^2$$

where $I(x)$: mass moment of inertia per unit length with respect to the axis of rotation
Idx : mass moment of inertia of the shaded portion
$\dot{\phi}(x,t)$: rotational velocity of the shaded portion

For the entire body, the kinetic energy is expressed as

$$T = \int dT = \frac{1}{2}\int_{x=0}^{x=L} \dot{\phi}^2 I\, dx \tag{8.3.1}$$

Strain energy:

It can be shown that the strain energy is expressed as

$$U = \frac{1}{2}\int_{x=0}^{x=L} GJ\left(\frac{\partial \phi}{\partial x}\right)^2 dx \tag{8.3.2}$$

where G: shear modulus, J: torsional constant

The incremental work done:

The incremental work done by applied torque is expressed as

$$\delta W = \int_{x=0}^{x=L} \delta\phi f_T\, dx + \left(\overline{T}\delta\phi\right)_{x=L} \tag{8.3.3}$$

where $\delta\phi$ $(\rightarrow 0)$ is incremental twist angle.

Mathematical equivalence between the longitudinal vibration and torsional vibration

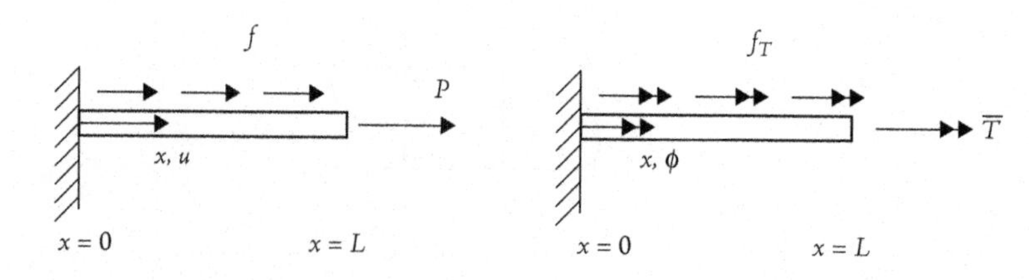

Figure 8.9 Slender body undergoing longitudinal motion and torsional motion

Longitudinal vibration	Torsional vibration
$T = \frac{1}{2}\int_{x=0}^{x=L} \dot{u}^2 m dx$	$T = \frac{1}{2}\int_{x=0}^{x=L} \dot{\phi}^2 I dx$
$U = \frac{1}{2}\int_{x=0}^{x=L} EA\left(\frac{\partial u}{\partial x}\right)^2 dx$	$U = \frac{1}{2}\int_{x=0}^{x=L} GJ\left(\frac{\partial \phi}{\partial x}\right)^2 dx$
$\delta W = \int_{x=0}^{x=L} \delta u f dx + (P\delta u)_{x=L}$	$\delta W = \int_{x=0}^{x=L} \delta\phi f_T dx + (\overline{T}\delta\phi)_{x=L}$

Accordingly, mathematical equivalence exists between the longitudinal vibration and torsional vibration as follows:

$$u \leftrightarrow \phi$$
$$EA \leftrightarrow GJ$$
$$m \leftrightarrow I$$
$$f \leftrightarrow f_T$$
$$P \leftrightarrow \overline{T}$$

Accordingly, finite element modeling of a slender body undergoing torsional vibration is mathmatically equivalent to that for the slender body undergoing axial or longitudinal vibration. For a two-node element for torsion, the nodal DOF are ϕ_1 and ϕ_2. For constant I and GJ, the element mass matrix and the element stiffness matrix are then as follows:

$$\mathbf{m}^i = \frac{Il}{6}\begin{bmatrix} 2 & 1 \\ 1 & 2 \end{bmatrix}, \quad \mathbf{k}^i = \frac{GJ}{l}\begin{bmatrix} 1 & -1 \\ -1 & 1 \end{bmatrix} \tag{8.3.4}$$

8.4 Bending vibration of a slender body

Consider a slender body undergoing bending vibration in the x-z plane. Examples are a launch vehicle in flight modeled as a flying beam and an aircraft wing modeled as a cantilevered beam.

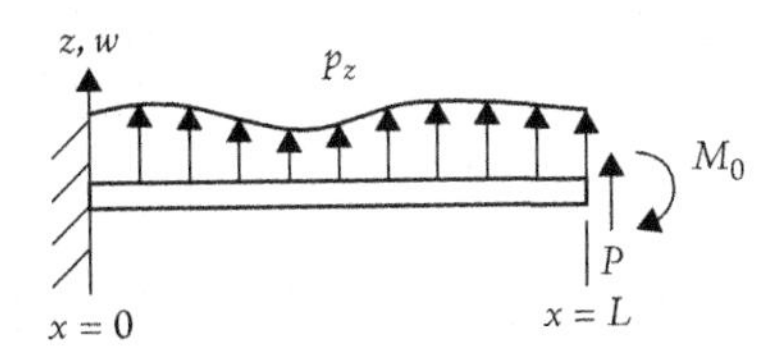

Figure 8.10 Cantilevered slender body under bending loads

$m(x)$: mass per unit length
$w(x,t)$: transverse displacement due to bending.
$p_z(x,t)$: applied force per unit length
$P(t)$: applied force at $x = L$
$M_0(t)$: applied moment at $x = L$

Kinetic energy:

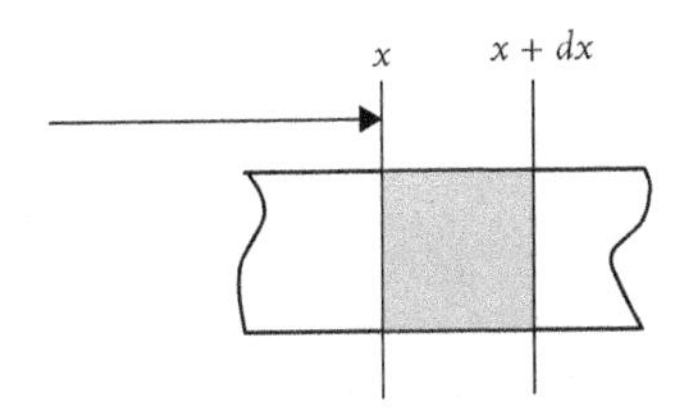

The kinetic energy dT of the shaded portion is

$$dT = \frac{1}{2}(mdx)\dot{w}^2 \tag{8.4.1}$$

neglecting the contribution from rotation around the y axis. The kinetic energy for the entire body is

$$T = \frac{1}{2}\int_{x=0}^{x=L} \dot{w}^2 m dx \tag{8.4.2}$$

Strain energy:

For a slender body in bending it can be shown that

$$U = \frac{1}{2}\int_{x=0}^{x=L} EI_y \left(\frac{\partial^2 w}{\partial x^2}\right)^2 dx \tag{8.4.3}$$

where $$I_y = \int_A z^2\, dydz: \text{area moment of inertia} \tag{8.4.4}$$

Incremental work done by applied loads

For the applied loads shown in Figure 8.10,

$$\delta W = \int_{x=0}^{x=L} \delta w p_z dx + \left(M_0 \delta\theta\right)_{x=L} + \left(P\delta w\right)_{x=L} \tag{8.4.5}$$

For incremental displacement δw ($\rightarrow 0$) and rotation $\delta\theta$ ($\rightarrow 0$). Note that angle θ for cross-sectional rotation is defined positive clockwise.

8.4.1 Formulation for beam bending element

For finite element modeling, the slender body is divided into many elements. Consider now a four DOF model with w_1, θ_1, w_2, θ_2 as the nodal degrees of freedom as shown below.

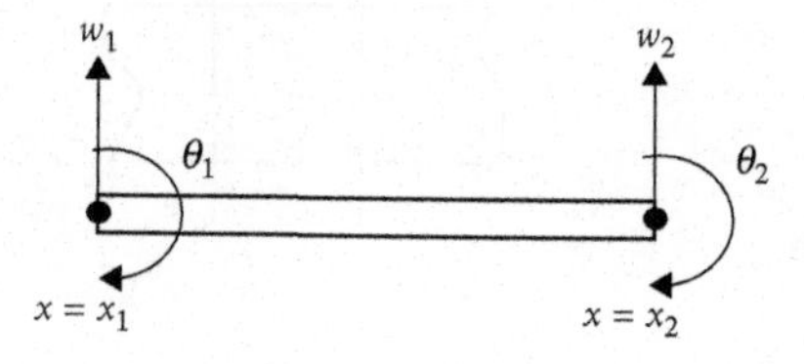

Figure 8.11 Two-node bending element

Assumed displacement:

For the element with four DOFs as shown in Figure 8.11, we may assume w to be a cubic function as

$$w = a_1 + a_2 s + a_3 s^2 + a_4 s^3 \tag{8.4.6}$$

where $$s = \frac{x - x_1}{l},\ l = x_2 - x_1 \rightarrow x = x_1 + ls \tag{8.4.7}$$

Not that non-dimensional coordinate s is equal to zero at node 1 ($x = x_1$) and equal to one at node 2 ($x = x_2$). Then, based on the Bernoulli-Euler beam bending theory,

$$\theta = -\frac{\partial w}{\partial x} = -\frac{\partial w}{\partial s}\frac{ds}{dx} = -\frac{1}{l}(a_2 + 2a_3 s + 3a_4 s^2) \tag{8.4.8}$$

Using equations (8.4.6) and (8.4.8), coefficients a_1, a_2, a_3 and a_4 can be expressed in terms of w_1, θ_1, w_2, and θ_2 as follows:

At node 1, $s=0$ and then from equations (8.4.6) and (8.4.8),

$$w_1 = a_1 \tag{8.4.9}$$

$$\theta_1 = -\frac{1}{l}a_2 \tag{8.4.10}$$

At node 2, $s=1$ and then from equations (8.4.6) and (8.4.8),

$$w_2 = a_1 + a_2 + a_3 + a_4 \tag{8.4.11}$$

$$\theta_2 = -\frac{1}{l}(a_2 + 2a_3 + 3a_4) \tag{8.4.12}$$

From equations (8.4.9) to (8.4.12),

$$\begin{aligned} a_1 &= w_1,\ a_2 = -l\theta_1 \\ a_3 &= -3w_1 + 3w_2 + 2l\theta_1 + l\theta_2 \\ a_4 &= 2w_1 - 2w_2 - l\theta_1 - l\theta_2 \end{aligned} \tag{8.4.13}$$

Substituting equation (8.4.13) into equation (8.4.6) and rearranging,

$$w = N_1 w_1 + N_2 \theta_1 + N_3 w_2 + N_4 \theta_2 \tag{8.4.14}$$

where $$N_1 = 1 - 3s^2 + 2s^3, \quad N_2 = (-s + 2s^2 - s^3)l$$

$$N_3 = 3s^2 - 2s^3, \quad N_4 = (s^2 - s^3)l \tag{8.4.15}$$

For convenience, one may now introduce alternate symbols for element degrees of freedom defined as follows and shown also in Figure 8.12:

$$d_1 = w_1,\ d_2 = \theta_1,\ d_3 = w_2,\ d_4 = \theta_2 \tag{8.4.16}$$

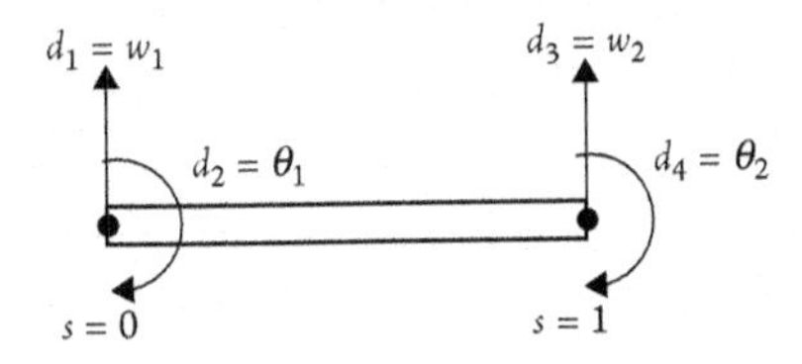

Figure 8.12 New notations for element DOFs

Then $$w = N_1 d_1 + N_2 d_2 + N_3 d_3 + N_4 d_4 \tag{8.4.17}$$

In matrix form,

$$w = \lfloor N_1 \quad N_2 \quad N_3 \quad N_4 \rfloor \begin{Bmatrix} d_1 \\ d_2 \\ d_3 \\ d_4 \end{Bmatrix} = \mathbf{Nd} \tag{8.4.18}$$

where

$$\mathbf{N} = \lfloor N_1 \quad N_2 \quad N_3 \quad N_4 \rfloor \tag{8.4.19}$$

$$\mathbf{d} = \begin{Bmatrix} d_1 \\ d_2 \\ d_3 \\ d_4 \end{Bmatrix} \tag{8.4.20}$$

or

$$w = \lfloor d_1 \quad d_2 \quad d_3 \quad d_4 \rfloor \begin{Bmatrix} N_1 \\ N_2 \\ N_3 \\ N_4 \end{Bmatrix} = \mathbf{d}^T \mathbf{N}^\mathrm{T} \tag{8.4.21}$$

Construction of the element mass matrix

For element i, the kinetic energy is

$$T_i = \frac{1}{2} \int_{x=x_1}^{x=x_2} \dot{w}^2 m dx \tag{8.4.22}$$

From the assumed displacement,

$$\dot{w} = \dot{\mathbf{d}}^T \mathbf{N}^\mathrm{T} \tag{8.4.23}$$

or

$$\dot{w} = \mathbf{N}\dot{\mathbf{d}} \tag{8.4.24}$$

Placing equations (8.4.23) and (8.4.24) into the kinetic energy expression in equation (8.4.22),

$$\begin{aligned} T_i &= \frac{1}{2} \int_{x=x_1}^{x=x_2} \dot{w}^2 m dx = \frac{1}{2} \int_{s=0}^{s=1} \dot{\mathbf{d}}^T \mathbf{N}^\mathrm{T} \mathbf{N} \dot{\mathbf{d}} mlds \\ &= \frac{1}{2} \dot{\mathbf{d}}^T \left(l \int_{s=0}^{s=1} m \mathbf{N}^\mathrm{T} \mathbf{N} ds \right) \dot{\mathbf{d}} = \frac{1}{2} \dot{\mathbf{d}}^T \mathbf{m}^i \dot{\mathbf{d}} \end{aligned} \tag{8.4.25}$$

where

$$\mathbf{m}^i = l \int_{s=0}^{s=1} \mathbf{N}^\mathrm{T} \mathbf{N} m ds \tag{8.4.26}$$

is the 4×4 element mass matrix. For constant m, it can be shown that

$$\mathbf{m}^i = \frac{ml}{420}\begin{bmatrix} 156 & -22l & 54 & 13l \\ -22l & 4l^2 & -13l & -3l^2 \\ 54 & -13l & 156 & 22l \\ 13l & -3l^2 & 22l & 4l^2 \end{bmatrix} \tag{8.4.27}$$

Construction of the element stiffness matrix

For element i,

$$U_i = \frac{1}{2}\int_{x=x_1}^{x=x_2} EI_y \left(\frac{\partial^2 w}{\partial x^2}\right)^2 dx \tag{8.4.28}$$

From the assumed displacement,

$$\begin{aligned} \frac{\partial^2 w}{\partial x^2} &= \frac{\partial}{\partial x}\left(\frac{\partial w}{\partial x}\right) = \frac{\partial}{\partial s}\left(\frac{\partial w}{\partial s}\frac{\partial s}{\partial x}\right)\frac{\partial s}{\partial x} = \frac{1}{l^2}\frac{\partial^2 w}{\partial s^2} \\ &= \frac{1}{l^2}\left(\frac{\partial^2 N_1}{\partial s^2}d_1 + \frac{\partial^2 N_2}{\partial s^2}d_2 + \frac{\partial^2 N_3}{\partial s^2}d_3 + \frac{\partial^2 N_4}{\partial s^2}d_4\right) \\ &= \frac{1}{l^2}\lfloor -6+12s \quad (4-6s)l \quad 6-12s \quad (2-6s)l \rfloor \begin{Bmatrix} d_1 \\ d_2 \\ d_3 \\ d_4 \end{Bmatrix} = \frac{1}{l^2}\mathbf{Bd} \end{aligned} \tag{8.4.29}$$

where

$$\mathbf{B} = \frac{1}{l^2}\lfloor -6+12s \quad (4-6s)l \quad 6-12s \quad (2-6s)l \rfloor \tag{8.4.30}$$

or

$$\frac{\partial^2 w}{\partial x^2} = \lfloor d_1 \quad d_2 \quad d_3 \quad d_4 \rfloor \frac{1}{l^2}\begin{Bmatrix} -6+12s \\ (4-6s)l \\ 6-12s \\ (2-6s)l \end{Bmatrix} = \frac{1}{l^2}\mathbf{d}^T\mathbf{B}^T \tag{8.4.31}$$

Then, placing equations (8.4.29) and (8.4.31) into the strain energy expression in equation (8.4.28),

$$U_i = \frac{1}{2}\int_{s=0}^{s=1}\frac{1}{l^4}EI_y\mathbf{d}^T\mathbf{B}^T\mathbf{B}\mathbf{d}l\,ds = \frac{1}{2}\mathbf{d}^T\left(\frac{1}{l^3}\int_{s=0}^{s=1}EI_y\mathbf{B}^T\mathbf{B}\,ds\right)\mathbf{d} = \frac{1}{2}\mathbf{d}^T\mathbf{k}^i\mathbf{d} \tag{8.4.32}$$

where

$$\mathbf{k}^i = \frac{1}{l^3}\int_{s=0}^{s=1} EI_y\mathbf{B}^T\mathbf{B}\,ds \tag{8.4.33}$$

is the 4×4 element stiffness matrix. For constant EI_y, it can be shown that

$$\mathbf{k}^i = \frac{2EI_y}{l^3}\begin{bmatrix} 6 & -3l & -6 & -3l \\ -3l & 2l^2 & 3l & l^2 \\ -6 & 3l & 6 & 3l \\ -3l & l^2 & 3l & 2l^2 \end{bmatrix} \tag{8.4.34}$$

Construction of the element load vector

For the applied loads shown in Figure 8.13,

$$\delta W_i = \int_{x=x_1}^{x=x_2} \delta w p_z dx + R_1\delta d_1 + R_2\delta d_2 + R_3\delta d_3 + R_4\delta d_4 \tag{8.4.35}$$

where R_1, R_2, R_3, R_4 are reaction or applied forces or moments at the element boundaries.

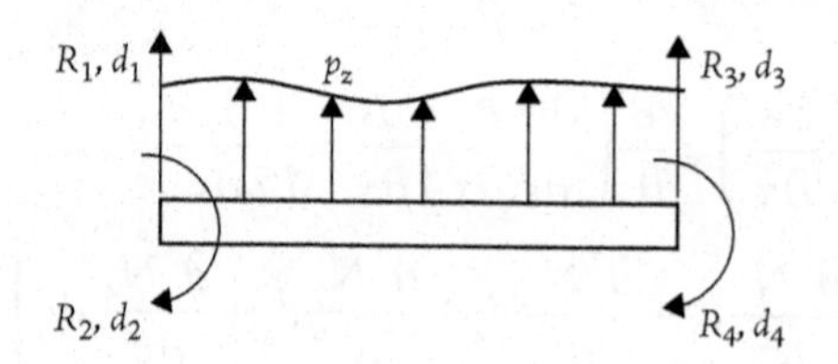

Figure 8.13 Loads acting on a bending element

Introducing the assumed displacement field in the first term on the right hand side of equation (8.4.35),

$$\begin{aligned} \int_{x=x_1}^{x=x_2} \delta w p_z dx &= \int_{s=0}^{s=1} (N_1\,\delta d_1 + N_2\,\delta d_2 + N_3\,\delta d_3 + N_4\,\delta d_4) p_z l\, ds \\ &= \delta d_1 A_1 + \delta d_2 A_2 + \delta d_3 A_3 + \delta d_4 A_4 \end{aligned} \tag{8.4.36}$$

where

$$\begin{aligned} A_1 &= l\int_{s=0}^{s=1} N_1 p_z\, ds, & A_2 &= l\int_{s=0}^{s=1} N_2 p_z\, ds \\ A_3 &= l\int_{s=0}^{s=1} N_3 p_z\, ds, & A_4 &= l\int_{s=0}^{s=1} N_4 p_z\, ds \end{aligned} \tag{8.4.37}$$

For example, for constant $p_z = c$,

$$A_1 = \frac{cl}{2}, \quad A_2 = -\frac{cl^2}{12}, \quad A_3 = \frac{cl}{2}, \quad A_4 = \frac{cl^2}{12} \tag{8.4.38}$$

Introducing equation (8.4.36) into equation (8.4.35),

$$\delta W_i = \delta d_1 P_1 + \delta d_2 P_2 + \delta d_3 P_3 + \delta d_4 P_4 \tag{8.4.39}$$

where $$P_1 = A_1 + R_1,\quad P_2 = A_2 + R_1,\quad P_3 = A_3 + R_3,\quad P_4 = A_4 + R_4 \tag{8.4.40}$$

In matrix form,

$$\delta W_i = \begin{bmatrix} \delta d_1 & \delta d_2 & \delta d_3 & \delta d_4 \end{bmatrix} \begin{Bmatrix} P_1 \\ P_2 \\ P_3 \\ P_4 \end{Bmatrix} = \delta \mathbf{d}^T \mathbf{P} \tag{8.4.41}$$

where

$$\mathbf{P} = \begin{Bmatrix} P_1 \\ P_2 \\ P_3 \\ P_4 \end{Bmatrix} \tag{8.4.42}$$

is the element load vector including reaction forces and moments at the nodes.

Equation of motion for element

Applying the Lagrange equation approach, the equation of motion for the element can be expressed as

$$\begin{Bmatrix} P_1 \\ P_2 \\ P_3 \\ P_4 \end{Bmatrix}_i = \begin{bmatrix} m_{11}^i & m_{12}^i & m_{13}^i & m_{14}^i \\ m_{21}^i & m_{22}^i & m_{23}^i & m_{24}^i \\ m_{31}^i & m_{32}^i & m_{33}^i & m_{34}^i \\ m_{41}^i & m_{42}^i & m_{43}^i & m_{44}^i \end{bmatrix} \begin{Bmatrix} \ddot{d}_1 \\ \ddot{d}_2 \\ \ddot{d}_3 \\ \ddot{d}_4 \end{Bmatrix}_i + \begin{bmatrix} k_{11}^i & k_{12}^i & k_{13}^i & k_{14}^i \\ k_{21}^i & k_{22}^i & k_{23}^i & k_{24}^i \\ k_{31}^i & k_{32}^i & k_{33}^i & k_{34}^i \\ k_{41}^i & k_{42}^i & k_{43}^i & k_{44}^i \end{bmatrix} \begin{Bmatrix} d_1 \\ d_2 \\ d_3 \\ d_4 \end{Bmatrix}_i \tag{8.4.43}$$

8.4.2 Equation of motion for the global model

The equation of motion for the global model can be constructed by using the relationship between the element DOFs and the global DOFs. The procedure is similar to that for finite element modeling of a slender body undergoing longitudinal vibration. For example, consider a 3-element model shown below.

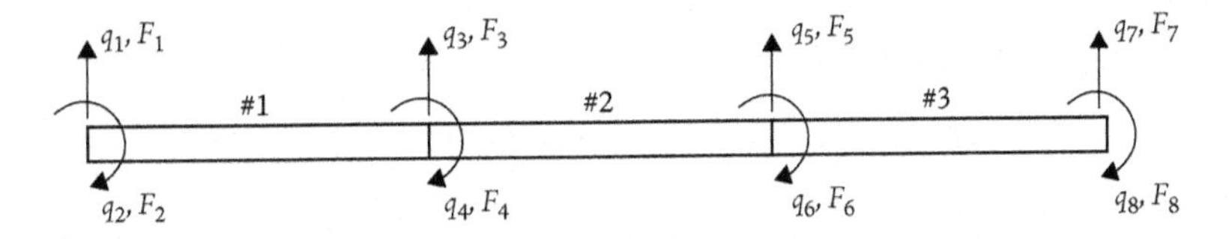

Figure 8.14 Three-element model for bending vibration analysis

For element #3,

$$d_1 = q_5,\quad d_2 = q_6,\quad d_3 = q_7,\quad d_4 = q_8 \tag{8.4.44}$$

and the element stiffness matrix is summed into the global stiffness matrix as shown below.

$$\begin{array}{c} \\ 5 \\ 6 \\ 7 \\ 8 \end{array}\begin{array}{c} \begin{array}{cccc} 5 & 6 & 7 & 8 \end{array} \\ \begin{bmatrix} k_{11}^3 & k_{12}^3 & k_{13}^3 & k_{14}^3 \\ k_{21}^3 & k_{22}^3 & k_{23}^3 & k_{24}^3 \\ k_{31}^3 & k_{32}^3 & k_{33}^3 & k_{34}^3 \\ k_{41}^3 & k_{42}^3 & k_{43}^3 & k_{44}^3 \end{bmatrix} \end{array} \tag{8.4.45}$$

Note that numbers 5, 6, 7 and 8 in equation (8.4.45) indicate the row number and the column number of each entry in the global stiffness matrix. For example, k_{24}^3 sums to K_{68}.

The element mass matrix is assembled into the global mass matrix following a similar procedure such that:

$$\begin{array}{c} \\ 5 \\ 6 \\ 7 \\ 8 \end{array}\begin{array}{c} \begin{array}{cccc} 5 & 6 & 7 & 8 \end{array} \\ \begin{bmatrix} m_{11}^3 & m_{12}^3 & m_{13}^3 & m_{14}^3 \\ m_{21}^3 & m_{22}^3 & m_{23}^3 & m_{24}^3 \\ m_{31}^3 & m_{32}^3 & m_{33}^3 & m_{34}^3 \\ m_{41}^3 & m_{42}^3 & m_{43}^3 & m_{44}^3 \end{bmatrix} \end{array} \tag{8.4.46}$$

Also, the element load vector is assembled into the global load vector using the relationship between the element DOFs and global DOFs.

The equation of motion for the entire structure is expressed symbolically as

$$\mathbf{M}\ddot{\mathbf{q}} + \mathbf{K}\mathbf{q} = \mathbf{F} \tag{8.4.47}$$

where $\mathbf{M}$: 8×8 global stiffness matrix
$\mathbf{K}$: 8×8 global stiffness matrix
$\mathbf{q}$: 8×1 global DOF vector
$\mathbf{F}$: 8×1 global load vector

Free vibration

For free vibration ($\mathbf{F} = \mathbf{0}$), the equation of motion is

$$\mathbf{M}\ddot{\mathbf{q}} + \mathbf{K}\mathbf{q} = \mathbf{0} \tag{8.4.48}$$

A solution to equation (8.4.48) is of the following form:

$$\mathbf{q} = \boldsymbol{\varphi} e^{\pm i\omega t} \tag{8.4.49}$$

where $\boldsymbol{\varphi}$ is the time-independent part of $\mathbf{q}$. Placing equation (8.4.49) into equation (8.4.48),

$$(\mathbf{K} - \omega^2 \mathbf{M})\boldsymbol{\varphi} = \mathbf{0} \tag{8.4.50}$$

or
$$\mathbf{K\varphi} = \omega^2 \mathbf{M\varphi} \tag{8.4.51}$$

After carrying out an eigenvalue analysis to determine eigenvalues (thus natural frequencies) and eigenvectors, the natural modes are determined as follows:

For element # k,

$$w = \mathbf{Nd} = \mathbf{Nq}^k = \mathbf{N\varphi}^k e^{\pm i\omega t} = \bar{w} e^{\pm i\omega t} \tag{8.4.52}$$

where $\mathbf{d} = \mathbf{q}^k$: part of $\mathbf{q}$ that belongs to element # k

$\boldsymbol{\varphi}^k$: part of $\boldsymbol{\varphi}$ that belongs to element # k

and
$$\bar{w} = \mathbf{N\varphi}^k \tag{8.4.53}$$

is the time-independent part of w for element # k. For mode n with ω_n and $\boldsymbol{\varphi}_n$, one can use equation (8.4.53) to determine $\bar{w}$ for each element and plot the natural mode.

8.4.3 Alternate finite element formulation for bending vibration

Assumed displacement:

If elements of equal length are used to model a slender body in bending, one may introduce for convenience a new variable $\hat{\theta}$ defined as follows:

$$\hat{\theta} = l\theta \tag{8.4.54}$$

Then, the assumed displacement can be expressed as

$$w = N_1 w_1 + N_2 \hat{\theta}_1 + N_3 w_2 + N_4 \hat{\theta}_2 \tag{8.4.55}$$

where
$$N_1 = 1 - 3s^2 + 2s^3, \quad N_2 = -s + 2s^2 - s^3$$

$$N_3 = 3s^2 - 2s^3, \quad N_4 = s^2 - s^3 \tag{8.4.56}$$

and w_1, $\hat{\theta}_1$, w_2, $\hat{\theta}_2$ are the nodal degrees of freedom as shown in Figure 8.15.

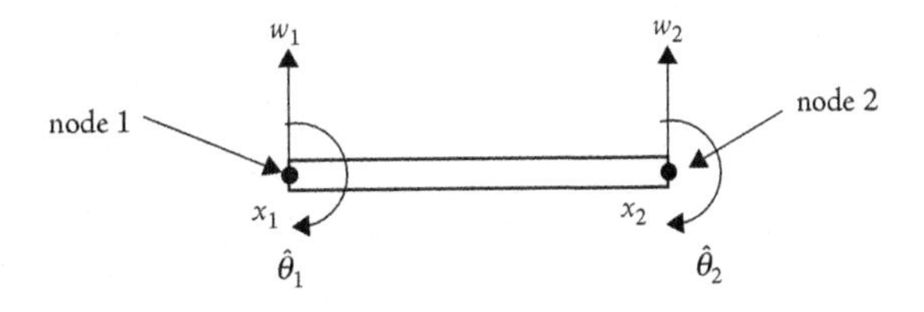

Figure 8.15 Two-node bending element with alternate DOFs

The assumed displacement can then be expressed in matrix form as follows:

$$w = \mathbf{N}\mathbf{d} \tag{8.4.57}$$

where

$$\mathbf{N} = \lfloor N_1 \quad N_2 \quad N_3 \quad N_4 \rfloor \tag{8.4.58}$$

$$\mathbf{d} = \begin{Bmatrix} d_1 \\ d_2 \\ d_3 \\ d_4 \end{Bmatrix} = \begin{Bmatrix} w_1 \\ \hat{\theta}_1 \\ w_2 \\ \hat{\theta}_2 \end{Bmatrix} \tag{8.4.59}$$

or

$$w = \mathbf{d}^{\mathrm{T}}\mathbf{N}^{\mathrm{T}} \tag{8.4.60}$$

Construction of the element mass matrix

For element #i,

$$\begin{aligned} T &= \frac{1}{2}\int_{x=x_1}^{x=x_2} \dot{w}^2 m\,dx = \frac{1}{2}\int_{s=0}^{s=1} \dot{\mathbf{d}}^T\mathbf{N}^{\mathrm{T}}\mathbf{N}\dot{\mathbf{d}}ml\,ds \\ &= \frac{1}{2}\dot{\mathbf{d}}^T\left(l\int_{s=0}^{s=1} m\mathbf{N}^{\mathrm{T}}\mathbf{N}ds \right)\dot{\mathbf{d}} = \frac{1}{2}\dot{\mathbf{d}}^T\mathbf{m}^i\dot{\mathbf{d}} \end{aligned} \tag{8.4.61}$$

where

$$\mathbf{m}^i = l\int_{s=0}^{s=1} \mathbf{N}^T\mathbf{N}m\,ds \tag{8.4.62}$$

is the element mass matrix. For constant m, it can be shown that

$$\mathbf{m}^i = \frac{ml}{420}\begin{bmatrix} 156 & -22 & 54 & 13 \\ -22 & 4 & -13 & -3 \\ 54 & -13 & 156 & 22 \\ 13 & -3 & 22 & 4 \end{bmatrix} \tag{8.4.63}$$

Construction of the element stiffness matrix

For element i, from the assumed displacement,

$$\frac{\partial^2 w}{\partial x^2} = \frac{1}{l^2}\lfloor -6+12s \quad 4-6s \quad 6-12s \quad 2-6s \rfloor\begin{Bmatrix} w_1 \\ \hat{\theta}_1 \\ w_2 \\ \hat{\theta}_2 \end{Bmatrix} \tag{8.4.64}$$

Symbolically,

$$\frac{\partial^2 w}{\partial x^2} = \frac{1}{l^2}\mathbf{B}\mathbf{d} \tag{8.4.65}$$

where

$$\mathbf{B} = \lfloor \ -6+12s \quad 4-6s \quad 6-12s \quad 2-6s \ \rfloor \tag{8.4.66}$$

or

$$\frac{\partial^2 w}{\partial x^2} = \frac{1}{l^2}\mathbf{d}^T\mathbf{B}^T \tag{8.4.67}$$

Then, placing equations (8.4.65) and (8.4.67) into the strain energy expression

$$\begin{aligned} U_i &= \frac{1}{2}\int_{x=x_1}^{x=x_2} EI_y \left(\frac{\partial^2 w}{\partial x^2}\right)^2 dx = \frac{1}{2}\frac{1}{l^4}\int_{s=0}^{s=1} EI_y \mathbf{d}^T\mathbf{B}^T\mathbf{B}\mathbf{d} l \, ds \\ &= \frac{1}{2}\mathbf{d}^T\left(\frac{1}{l^3}\int_{s=0}^{s=1} EI_y \mathbf{B}^T\mathbf{B}\, ds\right)\mathbf{d} = \frac{1}{2}\mathbf{d}^T\mathbf{k}^i\mathbf{d} \end{aligned} \tag{8.4.68}$$

where

$$\mathbf{k}^i = \frac{1}{l^3}\int_{s=0}^{s=1} EI_y \mathbf{B}^T\mathbf{B}\, ds \tag{8.4.69}$$

is the element stiffness matrix. For constant EI_y,

$$\mathbf{k}^i = \frac{2EI_y}{l^3}\begin{bmatrix} 6 & -3 & -6 & -3 \\ -3 & 2 & 3 & 1 \\ -6 & 3 & 6 & 3 \\ -3 & 1 & 3 & 2 \end{bmatrix} \tag{8.4.70}$$

Example 8.4.1: Consider free bending vibration of a cantilever beam clamped at $x = 0$ and free at $x = L$. For simplicity assume that the beam is of uniform cross-section with constant m and EI_y. Determine the natural frequencies and the natural modes using a model with two elements of equal length.

Note:

Introduce variable $\hat{\theta} = l\theta$ and $\lambda = \omega^2 \dfrac{mL^4}{EI_y}$.

Carrying out eigenvalue analysis using the two-element model, one can obtain the first three natural frequencies as follows:

$$\omega_1 = 3.519\sqrt{\frac{EI_y}{mL^4}}, \quad \omega_2 = 22.22\sqrt{\frac{EI_y}{mL^4}}, \quad \omega_3 = 75.16\sqrt{\frac{EI_y}{mL^4}}$$

Comparing these frequencies with the values listed in equation (7.4.45), one can observe that the first two frequencies are quite accurate while the third frequency is not so accurate. Accordingly, a model with more elements are needed for improved accuracy. Details are left for exercise in Problem set 8.4 at the end of this chapter.

8.5 Bending vibration under axial force

Consider now bending vibration of a slender body subjected to a static axial force $F(x)$. Axial stress due to bending is linear through thickness and does not affect total axial force. One can also neglect the inertia force effect in the axial direction. As the slender body bends, the cross-section of segment dx rotates by angle θ. The net axial translation Δ due to the rotation is then

$$\Delta = dx - dx\cos\theta = dx(1-\cos\theta) \tag{8.5.1}$$

For small rotation,

$$\cos\theta \simeq 1 - \frac{1}{2}\theta^2 \tag{8.5.2}$$

and thus

$$\Delta = dx(1-\cos\theta) = \frac{1}{2}\theta^2 dx = \frac{1}{2}\left(-\frac{\partial w}{\partial x}\right)^2 dx \tag{8.5.3}$$

The work done by axial force F is then

$$W_F = -\frac{1}{2}\int_{x=0}^{x=L} F\left(\frac{\partial w}{\partial x}\right)^2 dx \tag{8.5.4}$$

For the two-node bending element with four degrees of freedom described in the previous sections,

$$w = \mathbf{N}\mathbf{d} \tag{8.5.5}$$

Then

$$\frac{\partial w}{\partial x} = \frac{\partial w}{\partial s}\frac{ds}{dx} = \frac{1}{l}\frac{\partial w}{\partial s} = \frac{1}{l}\frac{\partial}{\partial s}(\mathbf{N}\mathbf{d}) = \frac{1}{l}\mathbf{A}\mathbf{d} = \frac{1}{l}\mathbf{d}^T\mathbf{A}^T \tag{8.5.6}$$

where

$$\mathbf{A} = \frac{\partial}{\partial s}(\mathbf{N}) \tag{8.5.7}$$

Then for the element,

$$\begin{aligned} W_F^i &= -\frac{1}{2}\int_{x=x_1}^{x=x_2} F\left(\frac{\partial w}{\partial x}\right)^2 dx = -\frac{1}{2}\int_{s=0}^{s=1} F\frac{1}{l^2}\mathbf{d}^T\mathbf{A}^T\mathbf{A}\mathbf{d}\, l\, ds \\ &= -\frac{1}{2}\mathbf{d}^T\left(\frac{1}{l}\int_{s=0}^{s=1} F\mathbf{A}^T\mathbf{A}\, ds\right)\mathbf{d} = -\frac{1}{2}\mathbf{d}^T\mathbf{k}_F^i\mathbf{d} \end{aligned} \tag{8.5.8}$$

where

$$\mathbf{k}_F^i = \frac{1}{l}\int_{s=0}^{s=1} F\mathbf{A}^T\mathbf{A}\, ds \tag{8.5.9}$$

is a symmetric matrix. For the entire body,

$$W_F = -\frac{1}{2}\mathbf{q}^T\mathbf{K}_F\mathbf{q} \tag{8.5.10}$$

where $\mathbf{K}_F$ is assembled from $\mathbf{k}_F^i$. Infinitesimal increment of W_F can be expressed as

$$\delta W_F = -\delta\mathbf{q}^T\mathbf{K}_F\mathbf{q} = \delta\mathbf{q}^T\mathbf{F}_F \tag{8.5.11}$$

where

$$\mathbf{F}_F = -\mathbf{K}_F\mathbf{q} \tag{8.5.12}$$

Then equation of the motion for the entire body is

$$\mathbf{M}\ddot{\mathbf{q}} + \mathbf{K}\mathbf{q} = \mathbf{F} = \mathbf{F}_F + \mathbf{F}_{app} = -\mathbf{K}_F\mathbf{q} + \mathbf{F}_{app} \tag{8.5.13}$$

or

$$\mathbf{M}\ddot{\mathbf{q}} + \mathbf{K}_{eff}\mathbf{q} = \mathbf{F}_{app} \tag{8.5.14}$$

where

$$\mathbf{K}_{eff} = \mathbf{K} + \mathbf{K}_F \tag{8.5.15}$$

Note that $\mathbf{K}$ is the global bending stiffness matrix assembled from the element stiffness matrix in equation (8.4.70), and $\mathbf{F}_{app}$ is the global load vector due to applied loads excluding the axial force.

Alternatively, one may derive from equation (8.5.4) infinitesimally incremental work as

$$\delta W_F = -\int_{x=0}^{x=L} F\frac{\partial \delta w}{\partial x}\frac{\partial w}{\partial x}dx \tag{8.5.16}$$

Introducing assumed displacement into an element,

$$\delta W_F^i = -\int_{x=x_1}^{x=x_2} F\frac{\partial \delta w}{\partial x}\frac{\partial w}{\partial x}dx = -\int_{s=0}^{s=1} F\frac{1}{l^2}\delta\mathbf{d}^T\mathbf{A}^T\mathbf{A}\mathbf{d}l\,ds = -\delta\mathbf{d}^T\mathbf{k}_F^i\mathbf{d} \tag{8.5.17}$$

For the entire body, one can then obtain the expressions in equations (8.5.11) and (8.5.12)

Consider now a body clamped at $x = 0$ and free at $x = L$ or simply supported with a fixed hinge at $x = 0$ and a roller hinge at $x = L$, and subjected to a compressive axial force P at $x = L$. In these cases axial force is $F(x) = -P$ and

$$\mathbf{k}_F^i = -P\left(\frac{1}{l}\int_{s=0}^{s=1}\mathbf{A}^T\mathbf{A}ds\right) = -P\mathbf{k}_P^i \tag{8.5.18}$$

where

$$\mathbf{k}_P^i = \frac{1}{l}\int_{s=0}^{s=1}\mathbf{A}^T\mathbf{A}ds \tag{8.5.19}$$

and

$$\mathbf{K}_F = -P\mathbf{K}_P \tag{8.5.20}$$

where $\mathbf{K}_P$ is assembled from $\mathbf{k}_P^i$. The equation of motion is then

$$\mathbf{M}\ddot{\mathbf{q}} + \mathbf{K}_{eff}\mathbf{q} = \mathbf{F}_{app} \tag{8.5.21}$$

where

$$\mathbf{K}_{eff} = \mathbf{K} - P\mathbf{K}_P \tag{8.5.22}$$

Note that introducing $\hat{\theta} = l\theta$,

$$\mathbf{A} = \begin{bmatrix} -6s+6s^2 & -1+4s-3s^2 & 6s-6s^2 & 2s-3s^2 \end{bmatrix} \tag{8.5.23}$$

$$\mathbf{k}_P^i = \frac{1}{l}\int_{s=0}^{s=1} \mathbf{A}^T\mathbf{A}\,ds = \frac{1}{10l}\begin{bmatrix} 12 & -1 & -12 & -1 \\ -1 & \frac{4}{3} & 1 & -\frac{1}{3} \\ -12 & 1 & 12 & 1 \\ -1 & -\frac{1}{3} & 1 & \frac{4}{3} \end{bmatrix} \tag{8.5.24}$$

Example 8.5.1: A slender body supported by a fixed hinge at $x = 0$ and a roller hinge at $x = L$ is subjected to a compressive axial force P applied at $x = L$. For simplicity assume the body is of uniform cross-section with constant m, EI_y. The body is modeled with two elements of equal length.

Note:
Introduce $\hat{\theta} = l\theta$ and $\lambda = \omega^2 \dfrac{mL^4}{EI_y}$.

(a) Determine the natural frequencies of free bending vibration, and plot $\bar{\omega}$ vs. $\bar{P}$ defined as follows for $\bar{P} = 0,\ 0.25,\ 0.5,\ 0.75$.

$$\bar{\omega} = \frac{\omega}{\sqrt{\dfrac{EI_y}{mL^4}}},\quad \bar{P} = \frac{P}{\left(\dfrac{\pi^2 EI_y}{L^2}\right)} \tag{8.5.25}$$

(b) Plot the natural modes. Scale each mode such that maximum displacement is equal to unity.

(c) Compare the results of finite element analysis with the analytical solution given as follows:

$$\omega_r = (r\pi)^2 \sqrt{\frac{EI_y}{mL^4}} \sqrt{1 - \frac{PL^2}{EI_y \pi^2 r^2}} \tag{8.5.26}$$

$$\phi_r(x) = \sin\frac{r\pi x}{L} \tag{8.5.27}$$

where integer r is the mode number. Note that the natural frequency is dependent on the axial force while the natural mode is independent of the axial force.

Constructing the mass matrix and the effective stiffness matrix for the two-element model, and carrying out eigenvalue analysis for free vibration, one can find that

$$\bar{\omega}_1 = 9.9086,\ 8.5917,\ 7.0325,\ 5.0095 \tag{8.5.28}$$

corresponding to $\overline{P}=0,\ 0.25,\ 0.5,\ 0.75$. The first natural frequency obtained by the two-element model is very close to the exact frequency. However, one can observe that, as the mode number increases, the finite element results become less accurate, indicating more elements are needed for improved accuracy. The details are left for exercise by the reader.

Example 8.5.2 A cantilevered beam, clamped at $x = 0$ and free at $x = L$, is rotating around the z axis at constant rotating speed of Ω (rad/sec). For simplicity assume that the beam is of uniform cross-section with constant m and EI_y. Carry out free bending vibration analysis using elements of equal length.

For a uniform cross-section, the axial force is

$$F=\frac{1}{2}m\Omega^2\left(L^2-x^2\right)=\frac{1}{2}m\Omega^2L^2\left[1-\left(\frac{x}{L}\right)^2\right] \tag{8.5.29}$$

According to equation (8.4.7), $x=x_1+ls$ and then from equation (8.5.9),

$$\begin{aligned}\mathbf{k}_F^i&=\frac{1}{l}\int_{s=0}^{s=1}F\mathbf{A}^T\mathbf{A}ds=\frac{1}{2l}m\Omega^2L^2\int_{s=0}^{s=1}\left[1-\left(\frac{x}{L}\right)^2\right]\mathbf{A}^T\mathbf{A}ds\\&=\frac{1}{2l}m\Omega^2L^2\int_{s=0}^{s=1}\left[1-\left(\frac{x_1+ls}{L}\right)^2\right]\mathbf{A}^T\mathbf{A}ds\end{aligned} \tag{8.5.30}$$

The global $\mathbf{K}_F$ matrix can be then assembled to construct the $\mathbf{K}_{eff}$ matrix shown in equation (8.5.15). The details are left for exercise in Problem set 8.8 at the end of this chapter.

Chapter 8 Problem Sets

8.1 A slender body of uniform cross-section is undergoing free vibration in the longitudinal direction. The body is fixed at $x=0$ and free at $x=L$. Do the following using a model of six elements of equal length.

(a) Determine the natural frequencies and modes.
(b) Plot the natural modes. Scale each mode such that max displacement is equal to unity.
(c) Compare the results with the analytical solutions.

8.2 For a tapered slender body, mass per unit length and cross-sectional area are distributed as follows:

$$m(x)=m_0\left(1-\frac{x}{2L}\right),\ A(x)=A_0\left(1-\frac{x}{2L}\right)$$

where m_0 and A_0 are given constant values The body is clamped at $x=0$ and free at $x=L$.

(a) Use a finite element model with three elements of equal length to determine the natural frequencies and modes of longitudinal vibration. Plot the natural modes. Scale each mode such that max displacement is equal to unity.

(b) Repeat using a finite element model with six elements of equal length.

8.3 A slender body of uniform cross-section is fixed at both $x = 0$ and $x = L$. Use a finite element model with three elements of equal lengths to determine the natural frequencies and modes of torsional free vibration.

8.4 Consider a cantilever beam clamped at $x = 0$ and free at $x = L$. For simplicity assume that the beam is of uniform cross-section with constant m and EI_y. Do the following using the models with two elements of equal length and three elements of equal length.

(a) Determine the natural frequencies and modes.

(b) Plot the natural modes. Scale each mode such that max displacement is equal to unity.

(c) Compare with the analytical solutions given in Chapter 7.

Note:

Introduce variable $\hat{\theta} = l\theta$ and $\lambda = \omega^2 \dfrac{mL^4}{EI_y}$

8.5 Consider a cantilever beam clamped at $x = 0$ and free at $x = L$. The beam is of variable cross-section with m and EI_y given as follows:

$$m = m_0\left(1 - \frac{x}{2L}\right),\ EI_y = EI_0\left(1 - \frac{x}{2L}\right)^3$$

where m_0, E and I_0 are given constant values. Do the following using the models with two elements of equal length and three elements of equal length.

(a) Determine the natural frequencies and modes.

(b) Plot the natural modes. Scale each mode such that max displacement is equal to unity.

Note:

Introduce variable $\hat{\theta} = l\theta$ and $\lambda = \omega^2 \dfrac{m_0L^4}{EI_0}$

8.6 Consider bending vibration of an unconstrained slender body modeled as a beam free at both $x = 0$ and $x = L$. For simplicity assume that the beam is of uniform cross-section with constant m and EI_y. Do the following using models with two elements of equal length and three elements of equal length.

(a) Determine the natural frequencies and modes.

(b) Plot the natural modes. Scale each mode such that max displacement is equal to unity.

(c) Compare the results with the exact solutions.

8.7 For the problem described in Example 8.5.1, carry out free vibration analysis using a model with three elements of equal length.

(a) Determine the natural frequencies and modes.
(b) Plot the natural modes. Scale each mode such that max displacement is equal to unity.

8.8 For the rotating beam problem described in Example 8.5.2, carry out free vibration analysis using models of two elements of equal length, three elements of equal length and four elements of equal length.

(a) Determine the natural frequencies and modes of free bending vibration.
(b) Plot $\omega_1 / \omega_{1,NR}$ vs. $\Omega / \omega_{1,NR}$ for $0 \leq \Omega / \omega_{1,NR} \leq 2$. Note that $\omega_{1,NR}$ is the first frequency of the non-rotating $(\Omega = 0)$ beam.
(c) Plot the first three natural modes for $\Omega / \omega_{1,NR} = 1$. Scale each mode such that max displacement is equal to unity.

APPENDICES

A.1: Nomenclature

Chapter 1

m: mass of a SDOF system
k: spring constant of a SDOF system
c: damping constant of a SDOF system
F: force applied to a SDOF system
t: time
y, $\dot{y}$, $\ddot{y}$: displacement, velocity, and acceleration of a SDOF system
y_0, $\dot{y}_0$: initial displacement and initial velocity at the start of vibration
g: gravity constant

$\omega_n = \sqrt{\dfrac{k}{m}}$: natural frequency (in rad/sec) of a SDOF system

$f = \dfrac{1}{T}$: natural frequency in Hertz or cycles per second C: amplitude
T: period
C: amplitude
ϕ: phase angle
ς: damping ratio
I: impulse
θ: rotational angle

Chapter 2

F_0: amplitude of applied force, which is sinusoidal in time
Ω: frequency of applied force
y_p: particular solution or steady-state response
Y_0: amplitude of steady-state response
MF: magnification factor
ϕ: phase angle
TR: force transmissibility
m_0: unbalanced mass
e: offset distance of unbalanced mass from the axis of rotation
d: displacement of a moving base
y_R: displacement of a SDOF mass relative to a moving base

Chapter 3

q: Column vector of degrees of freedom of a MDOF system
M: mass matrix of a MDOF system
C: damping matrix of a MDOF system
K: stiffness matrix of a MDOF system
F: applied load vector of a MDOF system
φ: eigenvector, or natural mode, independent of time

ω: natural frequency in rad/sec
α_i: time-dependent coefficient in the modal analysis of forced vibration

Chapter 4
T: kinetic energy
V: potential energy, including gravity potential and strain energy
U: strain energy
L: length
x, y: Cartesian coordinate in a plane
I: mass moment of inertia
M: concentrated mass
k: linear spring constant
k_θ: torsional spring constant
D: dissipation function

Chapter 5
M_1, M_2, M_0: concentrated masses
K_1, K_2, K: torsional spring constants
θ, ϕ: rotational angles
L: length of rigid massless bar
P: thrust
dW: infinitesimally incremental work done by applied load
$\bar{P}$: nondimensional thrust parameter
$\mathbf{K}_{eff}$: effective stiffness matrix
τ: nondimensional scaled time
U: flight speed or upstream velocity
q_1: vertical displacement
q_2: rotation angle
k_1: linear spring constant representing bending stiffness of the wing
k_2: torsional spring constant representing torsional stiffness of the wing
e: distance between the aerodynamic center and the elastic axis
M: total mass of the wing
S_α: wing static moment of mass about the elatic axis
I_α: wing mass moment of inertia about the elastic axis
q: dynamic pressure
L: lift
M_{ac}: aerodynamic moment about the aerodynamic center
M_{ea}: aerodynamic moment about the elastic axis
α: angle of attack
S: wing planform area
c: chord length
$\frac{\partial C_L}{\partial \alpha}$: lift slope

$\frac{\partial C_M}{\partial \dot{\alpha}}$: moment slope per wing angular velocity

Chapter 6
m_1, k_1, c_1: mass, spring constant, and damping of the primary system
m_2, k_2, c_2: mass, spring constant, and damping of the vibration absorber
Ω: frequency of applied load

$\beta = \frac{m_2}{m_1}$: mass ratio

$\gamma = \frac{\sqrt{\frac{k_2}{m_2}}}{\sqrt{\frac{k_1}{m_1}}}$: frequency ratio

$\bar{\Omega} = \frac{\Omega}{\sqrt{\frac{k_1}{m_1}}}$: nondimensional frequency of applied load

ς: absorber damping ratio

Chapter 7
$u(x,t)$: axial or longitudinal displacement of a slender body
m: mass per unit length
L: length of the slender body
A: cross-sectional area of the slender body
f: applied force per unit length in the longitudinal direction
F: axial force acting on the cross-section
ω_n: natural frequency of the n-th mode
$\phi_n(x)$: n-th natural mode

α_r: modal coefficient for the r-th mode
T: torquein a slender bodyor tension in a taut string or kinetic energy
ϕ: twist angle of the cross-section in torsion
I:mass moment of inertia per length
f_T: applied torque per unit length
$w(x,t)$: transverse displacement
$p_z(x,t)$: applied transverse force per unit length
I_y : area moment of inertia for beam bending
θ: rotational angle of the cross-section in bending
M_y: moment acting on the cross-section
V_z: shear force acting on the cross-section
U: strain energy
M: mass matrix
K: stiffness matrix
F: load vector
δw: infinitesimally incremental transverse displacement in bending
$\delta\theta$: infinitesimally incremental rotation angle of cross-section in bending

Chapter 8
$u(x,t)$: axial or longitudinal displacement of a slender body
m: mass per unit length
L: length of the slender body
A: cross-sectional area of the slender body
δu: infinitesimally incremental axial displacement
δW: infinitesimally incremental work done by applied force
q_i: nodal displacement at node i
R_i: applied force or reaction for at node$i$
x_1, x_2 : element nodal coordinates
l: element length
q: global DOF vector
M: global mass matrix
K: global stiffness matrix
F: global load vector
ϕ: torsional twist angle
$w(x,t)$: transverse displacement of beam bending
I_y: area moment of inertia for beam bending
θ: rotational angle of the cross-section in bending
$p_z(x,t)$: applied transverse per unit length
δw: infinitesimally incremental transverse displacement in bending
F: axial force acting on the cross-section
Ω : rotational velocity

A.2: List of Figures

Chapter 8

A.3: References

Abramson, H. Norman. 1958. *An Introduction to the Dynamics of Airplanes.* New York: Ronald Press Company.

Bismarck-Nasr, Maher N. 1999. *Structural Dynamics in Aeronautical Engineering.* AIAA Education Series.

Bisplinghoff, Raymond L., Holt Ashley, and Robert L. Halfman. 1955. *Aeroelasticity.* Addison-Wesley.

Dugundji, John. 1974. MIT Courses, 16.91 *Structural Dynamics* and 16.92 *Advanced Aeroelasticity.*

Flomenhoft, Hubert I. 1997. *The Revolution in Structural Dynamics.* Palm Beach Gardens, FL: Dynaflo Press.

Greenwood, Donald T. 1965. *Principles of Dynamics.* Englewood Cliffs, NJ: Prentice-Hall.

Inman, Daniel J. 2008. *Engineering Vibration*, 3rd ed. Englewood Cliffs, NJ: Prentice-Hall.

Meirovitch, Leonard. 1985. *Elements of Vibration Analysis*, 2nd ed. New York: McGraw-Hill.

Rivlin, Eugene I. 2003. *Passive Vibration Isolation.* New York: ASME Press.

Thomson, William T., and Marie D. Dahleh. 1997. *Theory of Vibration with Applications*, 5th ed. Englewood Cliffs, NJ: Prentice-Hall.

CPSIA information can be obtained
at www.ICGtesting.com
Printed in the USA
LVOW04s2055050917
547639LV00014B/186/P

9 781634 879941